Sex and Destiny

Francisco Candido Xavier
and Waldo Vieira

Sex and Destiny

By the Spirit
Andre Luiz

Translated by Darrel W. Kimble and Marcia M. Saiz

ISBN 978-1-936547-65-4

Original title in Portuguese:
Sexo e Destino
(Brazil, 1963)

Translated by Darrel W. Kimble and Marcia M. Saiz
Cover design by: Luciano Carneiro Holanda
Photo: www.istockphoto.com/aldomurillo

Edition of
EDICEI OF AMERICA
8425 Biscayne Blvd. - Suite 104
Miami, FL 33138 USA
www.ediceiofamerica.com
info@ediceiofamerica.com
Phone: (305) 758-7444
Fax: (305) 758-7449

Authorized edition by Brazilian Spiritist Federation

INTERNATIONAL DATA FOR CATALOGING IN PUBLICATION (ICP)

L979   Luiz, Andre (Spirit).
            Sex and Destiny / dictated by the spirit Andre Luiz ; [received by] Francisco Candido Xavier and Waldo Vieira ; translated by Darrel W. Kimble and Marcia M. Saiz. – Miami (FL), USA : Edicei of America, 2014.
            384 p. ; 21 cm

            Original title: Sexo e Destino
            ISBN 978-1-936547-65-4

            1. Spiritualism. 2. Spirit writings. I. Xavier, Francisco Candido, 1910-2002. II. Title.
                                                    CDD 133.9
                                                    CDU 133.7

Contents

A prayer before starting

Father of Infinite Goodness!

This is a book in which you have allowed our dear Andre Luiz to use this thrilling account to inform us about some of the concepts of Higher Spirituality with regard to sex and destiny. It is a verbal "photograph" of our harsh reality, which you have filled with eternal hope.

By offering it to our incarnate friends in the world, we want to remember Jesus – the Messenger of your Unlimited Mercy – on that sunny day in Jerusalem…

In the square crowded with accusers, some scribes and Pharisees brought him a suffering woman and said that she had been caught sinning. Actually, they were testing him to see what he would do:

"Master, this woman was caught in adultery … The law says that she is to be stoned. But what do you say?"

The Master contemplated these zealous followers of Moses at length, and because it would be useless to explain anything to their prejudice-filled minds, he said to them, and to all the moralists of the centuries to come:

"Let him who is without sin cast the first stone!"

In present times, Jerusalem represents the whole world!

In the enormous "square" of human conventions and in patent disregard for human dignity, materialism tries hard to do away with moral values, whilst venerable religions fight against nature in a vain attempt to block life, as if they wanted to fool themselves. Due to the tremendous conflict between the gigantic forces that fight for the moral control of earth, you have sent us the Spiritist Doctrine in the name of Christ's Gospel to reassure souls and tell them that love is the essence of the universe; that all people were born from the Divine Breath in order to love one another; that sex is a sublime legacy and the home a sanctifying shelter, clarifying, however, that love and sex create natural responsibilities in each person's conscience, and that no one hurts another person in the treasures of love without paying a high price for it.

This book is also meant to affirm that if you cannot keep the guilty from suffering the consequences of their wrongs, neither do you allow the defeated to be left without assistance, provided they accept your redemptive light on their path. This book also shows that, with your blessing, the moral delinquents of yesterday, but redeemed today, have become your messengers of redemption for those who fell into the traps of darkness in the past.

Therefore, bless this true and hope-filled account, and as we entrust it to our brothers and sisters in the world, may we remind them that physical existence, whether in childhood or youth, in adulthood or old age, is an ineffable gift, which we must always honor, and that even if imprisoned within a crawling or shapeless, deformed or infirm body, we must repeat before Your Immeasurable Wisdom:

"Thank you, dear God!"

EMMANUEL
Uberaba, July 4, 1963
(Psychographed by the medium Francisco Candido Xavier)

Sex and Destiny

Sex and destiny, love and conscience, freedom and commitment, guilt and redemption, home and reincarnation are the themes of this book, born in the forge of everyday reality.

Nevertheless, dear reader, after our benefactor's prayer in the previous two pages, there is nothing left for us to do but offer you the account that Divine Providence has allowed us to write, not for the exclusive purpose of exposing the truth, but with the objective of learning from the library of experience.

We do not think it necessary to explain that the names of the characters in this true-life story have been changed for obvious reasons, and that this group biography is theirs exclusively, as they were kind enough to give us permission to write it for our own edification after having been consulted.

We would also like to say that not one iota has been removed from the truths that compose it – truths of the truth, which is thrilling chapter after chapter, bringing with it, in these many passages, the light of our hopes and the bitter taste of our tears.

ANDRE LUIZ
Uberaba, July 4, 1963
(Psychographed by the medium Waldo Vieira)

Part One

(Medium: Waldo Vieira)

1

As happens among incarnate men and women, in the Spirit World that surrounds them, suffering and hope sculpt the soul, disciplining, improving and reconstructing it...

While we wear the physical garment, we usually imagine the heaven taught by religions to be situated somewhere beyond death. We dream of the total appeasement of the senses, the access to an ineffable bliss that anaesthetizes every memory that has become a mental wound. However, after crossing the ashen boundary of discarnation, we find ourselves standing before the unavoidable responsibility of having to confront our own conscience.

A human life, continuing naturally in the Afterlife, thus assumes the form of departure at two distinct times. The arenas and garments may differ, but the struggle of the personality from one reincarnation to the next is like a fierce battle composed of two phases: the obverse and the reverse of the experience. The cradle begins; the grave continues. With extremely rare exceptions to the rule, only reincarnation can transform us in a fundamental way.

We leave our withered cocoons in the coffin and take with us, recorded on the same I.D card, the spiritual elements that we have cultivated and attracted.

Intelligences evolving in the eternity of space and time, the spirits presently living in the terrestrial dwelling place may figuratively be compared to insects when they abandon their envelopes of dense matter. There are larvae that, upon leaving the egg, become parasites, whereas others immediately become butterflies of prodigious beauty, winging their way to the heights.

There are individuals who leave behind their corporeal shell only to begin lengthy obsessions, in which they live at the cost of others' energies, while at the same time there are others who immediately ascend, more perfected and beautiful, to the higher realms of evolution. And between those who are too deeply attached to the sensations of their physical natures and those who have won the sublime ascent to edifying stays in the Great Beyond, there is an infinite gamut of levels at which all the others may be placed.

Emerging in the Spirit World after discarnation, at first we suffer the disenchantment of all those who were anticipating the easy-to-reach heaven taught by theology.

The truth appears as a lever of renewal.

Still suffering from heavy amnesia concerning our remote past, which lies resting in the basement of our memory, we are confronted by old prejudices that clash with each other within us, toppling over in pieces. We sigh for an idleness that does not exist. We demand an affirmative explanation from the absurdities of the dogmatic, conventionalist faith that claims that only it possesses the full knowledge of God, pretentiously excluding from the Divine Parenthood those who do not share in its narrow vision.

From such exhaustive, terrible conflicts in the recesses of our mind, many of us emerge, smitten or rebellious, for lengthy incursions into vampirism or despair. Most discarnates, however, adjust to the circumstances little by little, accepting the continuity of the work of self-reeducation as they wait for another reincarnation that makes renewal and a fresh start possible.

*****

These considerations sered my mind as I pondered the sadness and exhaustion on the face of my friend Pedro Neves, a devoted servant in the Ministry of Assistance[1]. As he took part in bold and valorous expeditions involving meritorious activities, we had never seen him falter even once. As a veteran of assistance endeavors, he had never shown discouragement or weakness, no matter how heavy his share of the duties and commitments were.

Pedro had been a lawyer in his last existence; consequently, he was extremely lucid when examining the problems and eventualities that would often come up.

He had always been valiant and humble, but now he was displaying perceptible changes of behavior.

I knew that he had made brief trips to the physical realm to more directly attend to family matters, the nature and extent of which I had no idea.

Ever since then, he had become reticent and disenchanted, behaving more like a spirit that had just arrived from earth. He isolated himself in deep thought. He avoided fraternal conversation. He complained about this or that. And from time to time, even when he was at work, I saw tears that never quite fell.

---

1   An organization in Nosso Lar – Spirit Auth. (See the book *Nosso Lar*, International Spiritist Council, 3rd ed. 2010) – Tr.

But nobody dared ask him what the problem was, such was the moral fiber expressed in his attitudes.

Nevertheless, when we took a few hours off to sit on a bench in the garden, I tried to get him to talk, alleging personal problems that were bothering me. I referred to family members that I had left behind in the world and the concerns they were causing me.

I could tell from his sadness that he, too, was faced with some family struggles that were tormenting his soul like wounds that had been reopened. And I was not mistaken.

My friend took the loving bait and began pouring out his heart.

At first, he talked vaguely about the worries that were assailing his agonized mind. He wanted to forget, to isolate himself; but ... the family he had left behind inflicted him with pain-filled memories that were difficult to root out.

"Is it your wife who is causing you so much pain?" I risked, trying to locate the tumor of sorrow that provoked his silent weeping.

Pedro looked at me with the grief-stricken posture of a beaten dog and answered:

"There are times, Andre, when we have to take stock of ourselves, even if superficially, to stir up the past and extract the truth from it – just the truth."

He thought for a moment, a bit choked up, and then continued:

"I'm not someone who is overly sentimental although I do give my emotions their just due. Moreover, experience taught me a long time ago to use my head. I have lived here for forty years and for forty years now I have been completely uninterested in my Enedina. I left her when she was in her prime, and understandably, she was unable to deny her needs as a woman."

He explained that she had married another man, giving him three stepchildren. This new husband, however, had taken her completely away from her spiritual life. Being an ambitious man, he took full control of their assets and increased them greatly by means of risky business deals. He acted with such thoughtlessness that the formerly unassuming Enedina fell in love with too many amenities and wasted her time on fopperies until she fell over the cliff of uncontrolled sex. Upon seeing her husband constantly involved with other women, enjoying his status as a rich, carefree gentleman, she decided to get back at him and fully indulged herself in the wanton worship of pleasure, not knowing that she was only harming herself in regrettable imbalances.

"And my two sons, Jorge and Ernesto, were blinded by the lust for wealth, with which their stepfather bought their subservience. They went mad with the delirium of easy money and lowered themselves to the point that now they do not even remember me, even though they are wealthy middle-aged businessmen.

"What about your wife now? Is she still in the physical world?" I risked, interrupting the long pause in order to keep him talking.

"My poor Enedina came back ten years ago. She abandoned her material body due to jaundice, which attacked as an invisible tormenter brought on by alcoholic drink. I was alarmed at seeing her swollen and defeated, and I tried everything I could to help her ... I was terrified at the prospect of seeing her enslaved to the debasing forces she was yoked to without even realizing it. I was anxious to keep her in her physical body, like someone hiding an unconscious child in a disguised refuge. But alas! She was taken by unfortunate spirits, with whom she had thoughtlessly consorted. I have tried in vain to offer her some consolation because, ever since her discarnation, she has been seeking pleasure in vice in the futile effort of escaping from herself. There is nothing to do but wait and wait."

"And your sons?"

"Jorge and Ernesto are hypnotized by material wealth and I cannot even approach them. They have no memory of me whatsoever. With the intention of gaining their cooperation and sympathy, their stepfather even insinuated that they were not really my sons but his instead as the result of an affair between him and their mother while I was still alive. Sadly, Enedina didn't even try to deny it."

He grinned and continued:

"Can you believe it?! Incarnates are normally afraid of discarnates, but in my case, I was the one who fled my home in unspeakable horror ... Even so, God's goodness did not relegate me to loneliness regarding my family's love. I have a daughter Beatriz, from whom I have never been apart in spirit ... I left her in the flower of early childhood. She has patiently borne every offense and has remained faithful to my name. So, we are two souls on the same wavelength of understanding."

Pedro wiped his tears and added:

"Now, after nearly half a century in the material world, and in spite of being bound by her love for her husband and her only child, Beatriz is being prepared to return ... She is in her final days, her body tortured by cancer."

"Are you sad because of that? Shouldn't you be overjoyed at the idea of seeing her again?"

"But what about the problems, my friend? The problems of my blood group? I have been away from all the intrigues of the family ship for many years now ... I set sail on the vast ocean of life ... Now, because of my love for my unforgettable daughter, I have had to confront thoughtlessness and effrontery with the spirit of charity. I feel incapable, out of place ... Ever since I took my place at my beloved daughter's bedside, I have felt like a student who has become self-doubting after having committed too many errors."

Pedro was about to continue, but an urgent call to service made us go our separate ways. In an effort to set his mind at ease, I said goodbye and promised to help him more closely with Beatriz, starting the very next day.

2

Beatriz displayed extreme fatigue as she lay in a comfortable bed.

It was obvious that the disease had been consuming her body for a long time, because at only forty-seven years of age, her face was particularly shriveled and she was emaciated.

She was self-absorbed and sad as she reflected on her situation ... It was easy to see that she was preoccupied with her imminent crisis. Lofty, lively ideas flowed freely, indicating that she had gotten used to the certainty of her impending discarnation. Her mind was set with the conviction of a traveler that has finally reached the end of a thorn-strewn trail, which she can now leave.

Although tranquil, she was worried about the bonds that held her to the earth. Nevertheless, she could foresee the gates to the Spirit World, forming lovely images in her mind as if she were daydreaming. She was thinking about Pedro, the father she had lost in childhood, as if she were about to see him again, finally, so intense was their love for each another.

However, it was also easy to see that her loving soul was more strongly divided between her husband and son, from whom she was gradually and unavoidably slipping away.

In the warm, tastefully decorated room, everything suggested cleanliness, comfort, assistance, caring...

Beside her bed stood a serious-looking discarnate male caregiver, whom Pedro embraced in a display of immense esteem.

He introduced me:

"Amaro, this is Andre Luiz, a friend and doctor who will be assisting us from here on out."

We greeted each other cordially.

Pedro asked attentively:

"Has brother Felix been here yet today?"

"As always."

I was told that for many years brother Felix had been the overseer of an important outpost connected with the Ministry of Regeneration in Nosso Lar[2]. He was famous for his goodness and patience, and was known as an apostle of selflessness and common sense.

However, we did not have any time for personal matters.

Beatriz was experiencing acute pain and Pedro decided to give her some relief by means of comforting passes[3] while she was seemingly by herself in the room. In her state of extreme prostration, she displayed profound mediumistic sensitivity.

Oh! The sublime thoughts born on the bed of pain! ... Although she could not see her father, whom she thought to be far away and inaccessible at the time, she recalled his loving

---

2 Organizations on the spirit plane. – Spirit Auth. (The Ministry of Regeneration is one of several ministries in the spirit colony Nosso Lar. See *Nosso Lar,* 3rd ed., International Spiritist Council, 2010) – Tr.

3 Passes are a transfusion of energy, altering the cellular field... In magnetic assistance, spiritual resources are blended between emission and reception, helping the individual in need to help him or herself."
(Andre Luiz, *In the Realms of Mediumship,* p. 157 – International Spiritist Council, 2011). – Tr.

tenderness. She recalled once more her innocence as a child ...
In the acoustics of her memory, she was listening to the songs
of home; enchanted, she was a little girl again, reconstructing
relics from her early childhood in her memory. She felt as if she
were back in her father's lap, like a bird that had returned to the
downy feathers of its nest!

Beatriz wept. Tears of inexpressible love streamed down
her face. And even if her mouth did not make a single sound,
deep down she cried out with all her soul: "Father, oh father!"

Think it over, you who in the world believe that the
deceased are nothing but dust! Know that for those of us beyond
the grave, love and longing very often become ardent tears in the
vessel of our hearts!

Pedro stumbled in agony ... I embraced him and asked
him to be brave. Fortunately, the gale of anxiety that blew
over the spirit of my troubled friend lasted for only a few
moments. The composure returned to his face, which suffering
had transformed, and placing his right hand on his daughter's
forehead, he prayed asking for the help of Divine Goodness.

Sparks of light, like small bluish flames, came from his
chest area and were projected upon that wasted body, filling it
with calming energies.

Moved, I noticed that Beatriz had fallen into a light torpor.
Before I could remark about it, a young woman who looked to be
around twenty cautiously entered the room. She quickly passed
by us without perceiving us and checked the patient's pulse.

She made a gesture indicating that everything was in
order; then she walked over to a small cabinet nearby, took out
some objects, returned to the bed and gave the patient a shot
of painkillers.

Beatriz did not react in the least but continued to rest
without falling asleep.

The magnetic passes of a few minutes earlier had dulled her nerve centers.

Looking perfectly relaxed, the girl, her supposed nurse, walked to a corner of the room and sat down in a comfortable wicker chair. Then, she got up and opened the window a crack to let in some fresh air.

She took a few deep breaths, and then to my surprise, she lit up a cigarette and began smoking with a distracted look, as if she were trying to escape from her own thoughts.

Pedro looked at her with an expression that was a mixture of pity and repulsiveness. He nodded to her discreetly and said:

"That's Marina, my son-in-law's accountant. He works in commercial real estate ... Now, at his request, she is working as his assistant."

It was easy to detect the sarcasm in his reticent voice.

"I don't believe it!" he continued. "Smoking in a room of suffering where death is about to put in its appearance!"

I looked at Marina. Her eyes denoted recondite restlessness.

But she did display a bit of respect for the woman lying in bed by blowing the smoke out the window.

Dividing his attention between Marina and Amaro – our friend from the spirit plane – Pedro, although quiet and constrained, looked as if he wanted to talk some more.

But first, I tried to learn more about the problem.

I respectfully approached the girl with the intention of reading her innermost vibrations, but I retreated in alarm.

Strange thought-forms, portraying her habits and anxieties, clashed with our efforts to help Beatriz. I could tell that Marina was there against her will. Her mind was far away...

Living pictures of boiling agitation filled her mind ... With an empty look, she was recalling the lively music of the festive night before, and she still felt in her throat the flavor and taste of the gin that she had gulped down.

Despite having the appearance of a young woman, behind the dense smoke she displayed complex mental screens that kept flashing in her blurred aura.

Although I had been asked to help out with Beatriz, I began to study Marina's behavior indirectly, without any unworthy intentions. In order to assist patients better, earthly medicine in the future will also examine in detail the spiritual aspect of all those who make up the medical team.

I respectfully tried to get a fuller psychological anamnesis.

To start with, Marina produced the image of a middle-aged man, who repeatedly appeared above her forehead.

He and she were together ... One could immediately sense the intimacy between them and tell they were romantically involved ... Physically, they looked like father and daughter; however, considering their sentimental attitudes, they could not hide the burning passion they felt for each other. On the subtle panels that came and went, one could see that both were ecstatic and drunk with pleasure, whether inside an expensive car, lying in each other's arms on the warm sands of the beach, resting in the shade of a peaceful tree, or smiling in noise-filled nightclubs. The marvelous scenery from Copacabana to Leblon provided the backdrop.

To my surprise, the girl, with her eyes half-closed to more securely control the memories that thrilled her senses, visualized another man, as young as she was, giving me the impression that she was recalling scenes from a different, inner movie ... She constructed a new kind of backdrop to exhibit her adventures in the company of this other man, as if she were accustomed to the same places, yet enjoying the company of different people ... Both of them together, in the same car or as happy pedestrians, enjoying soft drinks or having joyful conversations in public gardens, suggesting the behavior of two teenagers in love, with their aspirations and desires...

During those brief moments of spiritual perception, moments in which Marina exteriorized her true self, she revealed the double personality of a woman torn between the love of two men. She was beset with thoughts of fear, anxiety, restlessness and remorse.

Pedro had somehow been sharing my inspection. He broke the silence by expressing his discouragement:

"See that? Do you think it's easy for me, the patient's father, to put up with such a creature?"

I tried to console him, and following his suggestion, we went into a small, adjacent reading room where we could think and talk.

3

In the isolated room, my friend looked at me with his lucid eyes and began:

"After discarnation, we find ourselves in the second phase of our existence, and no one on earth can imagine the new conditions we are faced with all of a sudden ... At the start, our lives are renewed: assistance teams, support through prayer, the study of vibrations, the school of charity. We happily practice the veneration of the major human sentiments ... Then, as in my case, when we go back to do closer work in the domestic arena, which we thought we had buried forever in our memories, the didactic is otherwise ... We have to wring the blood from our heart to confirm what we teach with our mind ... Consider the fact that I have been working here in this place for only twenty days, but my soul has already been stabbed so many times that, if it were not for my daughter's needs, I would have fled forthwith ... If I had not seen it with my own eyes, I would have never believed my son-in-law could be so thoughtless ... A crooked, boastful, shameless creature."

"Yes, yes…" I said, trying to get him to stop such painful accusations.

I mentioned the excellence of forgetting about every wrong committed against us. I argued about the merit of receiving silent help through prayer.

Pedro smiled, half-disconsolate, and added:

"I realize that you are referring to the importance of positive thinking for establishing the Good. And believe you me, I shall do all I can not to forget it. But I'm asking you to please tolerate my possibly inappropriate comments … Medicine is a luminous science filled with pure reasoning; still, sometimes it has to come down from the heights in order to dissect corpses."

He looked at me like a person who longed to pour out his soul to someone, and continued:

"You should know that on the fifth night of my stay here, Beatriz was suffering excruciating pain; I went in search of my son-in-law so that he would come and help her personally … Do you know where I found him? Not in his office, according to the deceitful information he had left at home. I was disgusted to find him, in the dead of night, in a sleazy bar with the girl you just met. The two of them together, as if they were husband and wife. Champagne flowing. Lascivious music. Disturbed and disturbing entities glued to the bodies of the dancers, while others came and went, bending over glasses whose contents bored lips had not emptied completely. In a multicolored corner, where some young women were showing off their half-naked forms and wriggling strangely, vampirizers made disgustingly suggestive gestures, complementing the paintings that human bad taste tried to call art. Everything shameful, improper, inappropriate … I caught sight of my son-in-law and his collaborator in each other's arms, thought of my sick daughter and felt repulsed. I was assailed by sudden despair. My darkened mind wavered because I suddenly understood the deplorable attitude of discarnates who become merciless avengers. The 'old man' I used to be and the 'new man' I longed to be fought deep inside my soul."

He paused to gather his thoughts and continued:

"In the past, I was horrified at seeing spirits, who had become animal-like after death, violently attacking loved ones who had deserted their affection ... I had worked enthusiastically on several assistance expeditions trying to enlighten them and change them for the Good. I tried to help them see that moral struggles after discarnation would result in a painful heritage for all those with whom they were in conflict. I also warned them that the grave was waiting for all those incapable of loyalty and tenderness ... and I often succeeded in getting them calmed down enough to be taken to a better place. But there ... imprudently angered by the insensitiveness of the man who had married my daughter, I realized I was being forced to practice the good advice I had been giving others."

My friend paused again, dried the tears that were streaming down his face as he recalled his rebelliousness, and completed his thought:

"But I couldn't do it. Dominated by rage, I advanced on him like an unchained beast, and blinded by fury, I punched him right in the face. His head fell on his companion's shoulder and he felt dreadfully sick, as if he were under the impact of sudden lipothymy ... I wanted to twist his body in my muscular arms, but couldn't. Then, a discarnate woman with a serene, stately face approached and completely disarmed me. She didn't show any outward signs of her lofty status. In fact, she looked as completely human as you and I. The only difference was a small, faintly luminous badge she was wearing on her chest, and which shone like a precious jewel emitting a subtle radiation. She stroked my head lightly and restored my serenity. I was ashamed of myself and was embarrassed as I looked at her, but she didn't scold me, nor did she make any allusion to my unfortunate attitude. On the contrary, she spoke to me kindly about Beatriz. She seemed to know her as well as I did. She ended up inviting me to leave and accompany her to my daughter's bedroom. I gladly accepted. And on the way, because the kindly woman talked only about the merits of understanding and tolerance, without any mention of the awful place we had just left, I got a grip on myself and thought only of helping my daughter. The anonymous messenger saw me to the door and delicately said goodbye. That was the last time I saw her and ever since then, whenever I recall her, I am positively intrigued."

Remembering my own personal experiences, I was trying to think of something comforting to say to Pedro, when he seemed to read my thoughts and asked after another pause:

"And you, Andre? Have you ever been through a situation as unpleasant as this one?"

I emotionally recalled my first pain-filled impressions after my discarnation. In my mind I reconstructed all the screens on which I saw myself discouraged, exasperated, torn, defeated...

The changes at home, family problems, the impositions inherent to the human struggle, and the suggestions of a physical nature that had affected my children when they realized I was gone: all came to mind. I felt closer to Pedro than ever. I understood his tormented mind completely.

"Yes, my friend, I did face enormous problems when I first crossed the great barrier."

However, I was not able to tell him about them because, at that moment, a handsome, middle-aged gentleman entered the room. Of course, he did not know we were there.

Pedro looked very uncomfortable and told me:

"That's Nemesio, my son-in-law."

The newcomer looked carefully at himself in a mirror, wiped the sweat off his forehead with a white handkerchief, and as he straightened his tie, he heard a long groan. He went immediately to the bedroom and we followed him.

Marina met him at the door with a smile and led him over to Beatriz, who gazed at him between comfort and weakness.

Beatriz raised her bony hand and Nemesio kissed it. He sat on the bed, leaned on the pillows and started talking to her in a tender voice while stroking her disheveled hair.

The patient said one or two things to please her husband and then added:

"Nemesio, I hope you'll forgive me if I mention Olivia's problem again ... the poor thing's about to lose her home ... You must guarantee her a safe haven ... I think about her and her defenseless children ... Please, put my mind at ease."

Nemesio showed that he was moved, and answered politely:

"Don't worry about it, Beatriz. I've already sent a friend, an experienced builder, to the site ... Everything will be taken care of, without any problems. It's just a matter of time..."

"I'm afraid I might go at any time now..."

"Go where?"

Nemesio caressed her drawn, pale face, smiled with a touch of bitterness in his voice and added:

"All our trips have been put on hold while you're under treatment ... This isn't the time to think of São Lourenço[4]."

"My health resort will be of a different kind..."

"Now don't be so pessimistic ... Come now ... Where's the joy of our home? Have you forgotten that you taught us to do everything with joy? ... Don't be so gloomy ... I talked to

---

4   A town in the state of Minas Gerais, Brazil, known for its natural mineral water springs and spas. – Tr.

the doctor just yesterday. You'll soon be recovering in fine shape … Tomorrow I'll do what is necessary to fix up their shack … You'll be back on your feet in no time and we can have coffee at Olimpia's…"

Beatriz seemed encouraged by his thoughtfulness. She smiled broadly, reminding me of a flower of hope growing on a cactus of suffering.

Those lucid eyes dripped two tears of happiness, which Nemesio lovingly wiped away. Signs of hope and trust appeared on the woman's yellowish face.

Feeling mentally renewed, Beatriz believed in her physical recovery and longed to go on living for a long time in the cozy atmosphere of home. Showing how much better she was feeling, she asked Marina to bring her a glass of milk.

Her "care-taker" promptly did so, and as the patient sipped the liquid, I reflected on the kindness of that man who my companion had described in other colors.

Nemesio's thoughts had proven to be as pure as crystal so far. He held Beatriz in his mind, eyes, ears and heart. He was showing her the supportive understanding of a friend and the tenderness of a father.

Pedro looked at me and his eyes told me he was as astonished as I was by the unexpected scene.

A few minutes passed.

When Beatriz had handed back the empty glass, another picture unfolded in front of us.

Nemesio stood up, and behind the head of the bed, he reached out his rough masculine hand to Marina, standing on the opposite side, and grasped her white, delicate fingers.

He started whispering sweet things to his pleased wife while at the same time caressing Marina's soft fingers; the young girl relaxed bit by bit with a mocking smile on her face.

I looked at Nemesio in amazement. His thoughts were now of a different kind and were in complete contradiction with the impression of respectability he had inspired in us.

I instinctively looked at Pedro, and pointing at the two hands caressing each other, he exclaimed:

"That guy's a real enigma."

4

Back in the adjacent room, I tried to lift Pedro's spirits; he was positively downhearted.

He had obviously adopted an attitude of offended dignity, giving the impression that his incarnate family was still his possession. He condemned his son-in-law's behavior. He exalted his daughter's worthiness. He alluded to the past when he, himself, had overcome sentimental difficulties. Then, he apologized.

I listened to his outburst and realized how hard it is for all of us to rid ourselves of the illusion that we own other people. If it were not for the duty to respect his sentiments, I would certainly have outdone myself in delivering a long philosophical argument recommending detachment from such things; however, I only managed to comfort him:

"Don't worry about it, Pedro. I learned a long time ago that the doors of the earthly home are closed to discarnates when death closes their eyes."

I was unable to continue, however.

Nemesio and Marina left the room like two thrilled and happy children, obviously escaping from Beatriz's presence.

Their faces wore the expression of happy lovers when they exclaim the famous "Alone, at last!" and lock themselves in a room.

I instinctively got ready to leave, but Pedro stopped me. Looking half dazed, he insisted:

"Please, stay; stay! I do not praise indiscretion, but I have been at my daughter's side for several days now and I have to know what is going on so that I may be useful to her."

By now, Nemesio was rapturously holding Marina in his arms, as if he were back in high school. He was squeezing her small hands and stroking her silky hair, telling her about their future together. With the concern of an adolescent, he asked her not to be jealous; that they should be kind to Beatriz since she was at death's door; that they should be grateful to fate for having spared them the unpleasantness of a separation,[5] even if it were done on friendly terms ... He had talked to the doctor the day before and was told the patient would not live more than a few weeks ... And he smiled like a naughty boy, explaining that he didn't believe in life after death; but if he was wrong, he didn't want Beatriz to leave harboring any resentment against them. He was madly in love and wanted to be convinced that Marina felt the same way, so he looked into her enigmatic eyes, magnetized by intense attraction.

Marina returned his show of love. However, she displayed the odd phenomenon of her emotions being yoked to him but her mind to someone else, using every means possible to find in the latter the incentive she needed for that same emotion.

Nemesio voiced his own concerns.

---

5   Divorce was not legal in Brazil until 1977. – Tr.

He confessed his unexcelled devotion. He didn't want her to worry about a thing. He would sell his business and they would live happily in his bungalow in São Conrado, between the green of the sea and the green of the land. He would have the house remodeled and ready to welcome them when the time came. She needed to trust him. He was just waiting to become a widower to make her his wife forever...

All this was being said while accompanied by displays of love, in which sincerity prevailed on one side and cold calculation on the other.

I noticed something strange in all this.

They were communicating with each other using the tenderest expressions of reciprocal enchantment, but oddly enough, they seemed to automatically take on the feelings that we felt because we were watching their least gestures very closely, and prejudging their intentions based on the inferior experiences that we had overcome long ago.

Such thoughts, which we produced with complete impartiality, are worthy of note because, based on what I was finding in my studies, I must say that our wrongful expectations, combined with a spirit of criticism, established mental currents that stimulated the couple's mental anxiety, currents that flowed from us to them, increasing their sexual appetite.

Beatriz's husband was caught up in juvenile bliss. He whispered the desire with which he was awaiting her lasting affection in the refuge of the home.

However, the girl suddenly burst into tears.

Her lover kissed her face in an effort to soothe her convulsive tension.

For our part, however, we noticed that Marina's mind was set more and more on the young man occupying her imagination.

In light of the unmistakable sincerity of all the promises Nemesio was making to her, her mental conflict was obviously dreadful.

Having totally forgotten the vows he had made to his legal wife, who was now in need of all his faithfulness and tenderness, Nemesio had fallen head over heels for Marina. As for Marina, she was intelligent enough to understand how much his otherwise circumspect reasoning had been debilitated; thus she identified the perilous phase of the unfortunate estrangement that she had become part of, and felt bewildered amid the afflictions and remorse that were harpooning her heart.

Forced by the circumstances to grasp the problem, we examined the girl's mental screens, which flashed in her mind to reveal her story.

She had charmed Pedro's adult son-in-law, but did not really feel anything for him, except gratitude and admiration. However, now that events were impelling her soul towards deeper ties, she was frightened by the undue concessions she had made to him. Her spirit was disturbed by the recondite memories of her romance, reliving all the occurrences by which she had attracted the experienced protector to her subtle means of seduction, only to come to the amazing conclusion that she was desperately in love with that slender young man standing out in her thought through captivating appeals of her memory.

Inside her mind, she was waging a terrible battle of emotions and feelings.

Nemesio was trying to calm her down with phrases of fatherly solicitude. And in response to his repeated questions about the cause for all those tears, Marina began a lengthy process of complete deception, evoking problems at home to cover up the reality of the matter.

In an effort to avoid looking at herself, she told him all about her hassles at home. She emphasized the demands made by her mother; she spoke of financial problems; she alleged being terribly humiliated by her adoptive sister, and told him about her father's complete lack of understanding during constant quarrels...

Nemesio comforted her and told her not to worry about it. She would never be alone. He would share all her obstacles and difficulties, whatever they might be. She needed to be patient. Beatriz's death in a few days would be the landmark of their eternal bliss.

Nemesio spoke in a pleading tone of voice. And maybe perceiving that a mere show of words would not be enough to stop her sobbing, he took a checkbook out of his briefcase and placed a big check in her tear-moistened hand.

The girl seemed even more distraught, her face showing the apprehension of someone recriminating herself without any conscious justification, while Nemesio hugged her affectionately. In the silence of the room, I turned to Pedro but could not say a word.

Despite being discarnate, my friend now looked exactly like any ordinary incarnate who was outraged and furious. His furrowed brow changed his facial expression to indicate the vibrational imbalance that precedes serious fits of violence.

I was afraid this emotional calamity might materialize in an act of downright aggression. But something unpredicted happened.

Suddenly, a venerable spirit friend entered the room.

A rapturous expression of kindness marked his presence. A radiant halo encircled his head; however, it was not the soft light coming from this aura of wisdom that impressed me, but the invisible substance of love emanating from his sublime person.

I met his eyes with the feeling I was looking at a much loved friend whom my heart had been longing to see for a long time.

Calming fluids bathed me all over, as if I were receiving inexplicable radiations of pure bliss.

Where, on the pathways of destiny, had I first met that friend who had so suddenly impressed me with the sentiment of a brother from long ago? I scanned my memory during those unforgettable seconds, but to no avail.

In a heartbeat I was transported back to the pure sensations of my childhood. The messenger before us not only made me remember the feeling of being secure in my father's arms but also the love of my mother, whom I had never forgotten.

"O dear God! In what forge of life are these bonds of the soul born? In what shoots of joy and suffering, through countless incarnations of toil and hope, debt and repayment, is formed the divine sap of love that brings people together in a single vibration of mutual trust?

I looked again at the benefactor walking towards us and felt compelled to repress my delight so as not to overwhelm him.

We stood up immediately.

After greeting him, Pedro, somewhat composed, introduced me almost with a smile on his face.

"Andre, give brother Felix a hug…"

However, the newcomer anticipated him and came towards me with open arms, with the obvious purpose of stopping any words of praise before they came out of my mouth.

"So very happy to meet you," he said benevolently, "God bless you, my friend." I was dumbfounded. I could not make my lips utter the words I wanted to say to express my joy, so I just kissed his hand with the simplicity of a child, mentally begging him to accept the tears welling up in my soul as a sign of my silent gratitude.

Next, something equally unusual happened.

Nemesio and Marina were suddenly transported to another field of the spirit.

I could confirm my impression that our unhealthy curiosity and Pedro's rebelliousness had worked until then as stimuli for the animal magnetism enveloping the two lovers, both completely unaware that they were being examined in such detail, because all brother Felix had to do was look at them compassionately and they changed their attitudes immediately.

The sight of Beatriz ill cut across their mental field like a bolt of lightning. Their demonstrations of passion faded away. They looked like a pair of children, attracted to each other, whose thoughts changed suddenly in the maternal presence.

And that was not all. I could not read Pedro's innermost thoughts, but compassion suddenly flooded my soul.

If I were in Nemesio's shoes, would I have done any better? Such silent questions filled my conscience, forcing me to think at a higher level.

I looked at the troubled head of that family with different sentiments and saw him as a true brother who deserved my understanding and respect.

Despite regretting my inappropriate attitude of a few moments ago, I continued studying the spiritual transformation that was happening in front of us.

Marina started to show a positive reaction, as if she were being guided like a medium well prepared in advance. She recomposed herself from an emotional point of view and made it clear that she was not interested in any kind of physical contact at that moment. She politely said she needed to get back to caring for Beatriz. Nemesio, reflecting her inner change, did not make any objections and got comfortable in a nearby armchair while Marina quietly left the room.

I could see that Pedro was eager to talk, to get everything off his chest, but the benefactor that had conquered our hearts nodded towards Beatriz's husband and asked:

"My friends, our Nemesio is seriously ill without knowing it. Have you noticed his organic deficiency? ... Let's try to help him."

5

Having recovered somewhat from our astonishment at brother Felix's attitude, we began to work with him, applying magnetic passes to that friend who, unaware of our presence, remained lost in his own thoughts.

In response to Felix's hands as he expertly applied the magnetic energy, Nemesio exhibited deficiencies in his circulatory system.

His heart was considerably enlarged and displayed threatening problems with hardening of the arteries.

Nemesio looked well enough on the outside, but was seriously ill on the inside. However, the most pressing problem was the cerebral arteriosclerosis, the development of which we could clearly observe using tiny medical instruments.

Revealing his broad medical experience, brother Felix called our attention to a certain area of the body where the blood was not circulating properly, and stated:

"Our friend is in danger of suffering blood clots; moreover, a vessel could rupture due to high blood pressure.

As if he had perceived our activity and heard our conversation, Pedro's son-in-law, resting in the armchair, was instinctively answering the friendly interrogation to which we were submitting his memory, clarifying all our doubts by means of specific mental reactions. He thought he was just imagining things, unaware of what he was completely revealing to us, much like what happens during anamnesis, when doctors encourage patients to talk about their medical history. He remembered the slight dizziness that he had been experiencing of late. He rummaged through his memory to answer our questions. He recalled past events, concentrating on all the details. He tried to reconstruct, as much as possible, the period of discomfort he had experienced suddenly with his loss of consciousness in the office a few days ago. He had suddenly felt weak. Absent. His thoughts disappeared, as if they had been expelled by an internal hammer. A dreadful fainting spell that seemed to have lasted forever, when in fact it had lasted just a few seconds. He had come to, feeling confused and despondent. He had worried about it for several days.

In order to feel calmer, he had described the experience to an old friend two days ago, since he did not know how to unravel the phenomenon.

The screen produced by his imagination was so detailed that we could see Nemesio and the friend who was sharing his confidences as if they had been filmed.

Beatriz's husband unconsciously recalled precise information about the dizzy spell he had suffered, the consequent restlessness, the conversation he had had with a business colleague, and the friendly understanding they shared.

We also heard his friend's advice. He must not postpone doing something about it. He needed to see a doctor, explain what he had felt, and define the symptoms. He warned Nemesio several times. It was obvious that he was exhausted. He could recover in some health resort in Rio. A vacation wouldn't hurt. To his mind, any kind of dizziness was like the ringing of a bell at the door of the apartment of life. Something serious was knocking at the door.

Nemesio, still silent and unaware that he was communicating with us, mentally repeated his arguments... It was difficult to make an appointment with the doctor. He had too many responsibilities and time was short. He was accompanying his wife during her painful, final hours of existence, and could not spare the time to look after himself. He couldn't argue with the usefulness of the warning, but said that he would have to put the treatment off for the time being.

However, at the bottom of his thought, and by means of information secretly filed in the coffers his soul, he showed us other reasons which he had not had the courage to reveal.

Softened by the touch of the benefactor's love, Nemesio silently told us his most secret fears.

He was like a naughty boy who behaved willingly and obediently only when his parents were around.

He disclosed why he refused to discuss anything related to his health. He was afraid of finding out what kind of shape he really was in. He was in love again and felt like he was back in the springtime of his physical body. He felt spiritually young and happy. He said that Marina's love was like rediscovering the youthfulness he had left behind.

Recalling memories and thoughts, he showed us the course of events that had influenced his precarious notions about life, thus giving us the opportunity to understand his psychological reality.

His wife Beatriz, about to discarnate, was in his heart like a relic that would soon be reverently housed in the museum of his dearest memories. Imperturbably upright and simple, she had transformed his lust into admiration and his juvenile flame into the warmth of serene friendship. Ignoring the benefits of a constructive routine, he had replaced his deceased mother with his wife. Instinctively, he longed for her benevolent smile and the blessing of her approval. He wanted her around, like someone who had got used to an invaluable piece of furniture. He felt good when, arriving home sweaty and tired, he looked into her eyes.

Nevertheless, Nemesio, with his materialist upbringing and practical, though generous, personality, did not grasp the fact that noble souls find in matrimonial love the fruit of sublime joy, whose pulp is seasoned and made sweeter by time, eliminating all the temporary whims of the rind.

He insisted on hanging on to all the emotional impulses of bodily youthfulness. He kept himself up-to-date on the most recent theories about the libido.

From time to time he would travel to nearby cities for bohemian nights out, and upon returning, he would tell his friends that he had gone in order to keep his heart from rusting. After such escapades, he would return home and offer Beatriz expensive bouquets which she was thrilled to receive. Over the next few weeks he would appear to be more understanding and loving. However, going back to his routine, he was unable to dedicate himself to the mental constructions that only discipline favors and guarantees. So, like an animal breaking through a fence, he would once again cross the boundaries that moral commitments established.

Sometimes he would look at his unwaveringly selfless and faithful wife and ask his soul what would happen if she decided to adopt behavior similar to his. This really scared him.

"That'll never happen," he thought. If Beatriz showed interest in another man, even if superficially, he would kill her. He wouldn't hesitate.

In those moments, conflicting emotions agitated his limited mind. He did not have the least bit of interest in his wife, but he would not tolerate any competition for the possession of the woman on whom he had conferred his name.

He would become restless and imagine things, but then would compose himself, remembering the odd case of an old friend that had wasted his life as an alcoholic amid the wealthy inheritance from rich relatives, and who had always trampled his dreams as a young boy by saying, "Nemesio, a woman is like a slipper on a man's foot. When it wears out, you must get another."

It was no wonder that, watering the roots of his character with the dirty water of such a philosophy, Pedro's son-in-law had turned sixty with his sentiments completely wrong concerning the respect a man should have for himself.

For all these reasons, during these difficult and gloomy times, Nemesio had refocused his attention on his self-preservation.

He had recovered his taste for dressing with distinction, selecting outfits and tailors. He had refined his masculine sensibility and had become a regular listener of radio fitness programs, which, by the way, had helped him get rid of an oscillating obesity. He had started to go to parties in order to update his language and improve his posture.

He did not mind the few gray streaks in his thick hair. He began to use designer colognes and colorful ties, displaying elegance always in fashion.

He had hired skilled instructors to refashion his personality, and he did his best to be more attractive, reminding us of an old building being remodeled.

"Obviously" – he reasoned, apprehensive – "I'm not going to resign myself to any treatment unless it increases my ability to enjoy pleasure." He would peremptorily refuse any measure indicated to readjust his physical body, since he considered himself perfectly able to control his own feelings. Euphoria, the main thing; medical measures, only if they could lift his spirits and make him feel younger.

Brother Felix explained:

"Nemesio is completely spent due to his destructive habits. Emotional carelessness has thrown his nerves out of control and fake aphrodisiacs have drained all his strength without him being aware of it."

On hearing this, Beatriz's husband looked worried, indicating that he had mechanically absorbed the impact of the serious diagnosis.

"What if I get worse?" he asked himself.

Marina's image came to his mind.

Nemesio pondered it anxiously.

Yes, he would agree to work on his health, but not now … Only after he had brought the girl to live with him via the vows of marriage. Until he had her in his arms under the protection of a legal commitment, he wouldn't accept medical treatment. He had to stay fit and look young in her eyes. He wouldn't willingly heed any kind of discipline or advice that might get in the way of the long outings, trips, entertainment and drinking sprees that, as a man in love, he felt he owed her.

Brother Felix did not argue. Instead, he assisted him by applying magnetic resources over his entire cerebral region.

When this lengthy procedure was finished, a taciturn Pedro could not hide his consternation. Disapproval gushed from his mind, forming thoughts of criticism, which, although respectful, reached Felix and me as a deluge of negative vibrations.

Perhaps that was why Felix silently suggested to Nemesio that he leave the room, which Nemesio did immediately, feeling better after having received the support that the spiritual friend had offered him.

The three of us continued our conversation.

Felix smiled, patted my friend on the back and said:

"I understand how you feel, Pedro."

Encouraged by the kindness in the benefactor's voice, Nemesio's father-in-law burst out:

"I just don't get it! I just cannot go along with giving so much care to such a rascal. A man like him, who has betrayed my fatherly trust in him! Who can't see that he's a blatant polygamist? A shameless man of sixty who taints the presence of his dying wife! Ah, Beatriz, my poor Beatriz, why did you marry that brute?"

Pedro was completely beside himself. He had returned mentally to the narrow circle of the human family and wept helplessly, making it impossible for us to help him control his emotions.

"I'm really trying," he moaned, "but it's futile. What's the use of my efforts here if I hate him so much? Nemesio's a fake. I've studied the science of forgiving and serving. I've counseled others to serve and forgive, but now... Separated by a simple wall, I see suffering and vice under the same roof. On one side, my beloved daughter lying in a bed, resigned and waiting for death; on the other, my son-in-law and this woman who is an insult to my family. God in heaven! What else is in store for me? Have I been called to help a sick daughter or to practice tolerance? But how can anyone put up with a man like that?"

We urged him to settle down but it was useless.

"I used to believe," he stammered in despair, "that hell, after death, meant having to leap into a fiery prison, but now I can see that hell means having to return to the earth to be around the family members we left behind ... That's the real purgation of our sins!"

Felix held his hands kindly and advised him:

"Settle down, Pedro. For all of us, the day always comes when we must practice what we preach. Besides, Nemesio must be understood..."

"Understood?! Isn't it enough just to have to see him?"

And he added almost sarcastically:

"Do you know the name of that fellow that has been on that girl's mind?"

"Yes, I do," replied Felix kindly. "But let's start by accepting Nemesio as he is. How can we expect a child to be a grown-up, or someone who is insane to think rationally? We know that growing up physically does not necessarily mean growing up spiritually. Like us, Nemesio is a student in the school of life, but he doesn't have the benefit of the lesson we are learning. If we were in his shoes, what would become of us if we didn't know what we do know? We would probably wind up in much worse circumstances."

"So you mean that I should approve of what he is doing?"

"Nobody applauds infirmity or praises a lack of equilibrium; however, it would be low to withhold compassion and medicine from a sick person. We need to remember that Nemesio is not someone to be despised. He got tangled up in dangerous suggestions, but he did not abandon the wife who is receiving his assistance. He is being deceived by some very bad emotional excesses, which are sapping all his strength. Nevertheless, he didn't forget solidarity and gave free room and board to the woman who works for him for pay. He believes he still has all the strength of his youth, when in fact, his body has aged prematurely. He has passionately devoted himself to a young woman who doesn't love him in return, although she does respect him … Aren't these reasons enough for him to deserve our benevolence and care? Who is most capable of helping? The one who walks blindly or we who understand? I cannot praise his deplorable behavior in the realm of the sentiments; even so, I must confess that, although he belongs to the category of those who are illiterate about the truths of the soul, he has not yet failed completely."

In a significant tone of voice, the instructor emphasized:

"Pedro, Pedro! For each one of us, the progressive purification of sex involves a burning furnace of continual sacrifice. It is not for us to condemn anyone for wrongs into which we ourselves might fall, or into which we might have actually fallen in the past. Let us understand so that we may be understood."

Pedro did not say anything, obviously influenced by our venerable friend. And when I looked at him after a few moments of expectation, he was praying humbly.

6

Back in Beatriz's room, we made sure Nemesio and Marina had left. The maid was keeping an eye on the patient.

Pedro was disgruntled and refused to talk. He kept to himself, making it clear that he was trying to overcome unconstructive thoughts.

He had composed himself a few moments earlier and had asked brother Felix to forgive him for his fit of rage when he had poured out all his rebelliousness and despair.

It had been uncalled-for, he admitted humbly. He had been uncharitable and insensitive, and he was sorry. Brother Felix had enough authority, that if he had wanted to, he could have removed Pedro from the charitable endeavor he had requested in order to help his daughter. Pedro asked for his tolerance, however. He confessed with bitterness and disappointment that his fatherly heart had at that critical moment shown that it was not yet ready to ascend to the appropriate level of detachment.

Felix, however, embraced him kindly and told him with a smile that spiritual growth often entails sentimental outbursts, with thunderclaps of rebelliousness and showers of tears, the consequence of which is the unclogging of the pathways of the emotions.

He told Pedro to forget about it and start all over again. To do so, he could rely on time and the upcoming opportunities. And that was why Nemesio's father-in-law now stood before us, changed and helpful.

Following brother Felix's recommendation, Pedro said a prayer as Felix and I applied magnetic passes to Beatriz.

She was moaning and groaning; nonetheless, Felix was able to alleviate her pain and help her fall asleep. He also took measures so that she would not leave her physical body during the usual hypnosis of sleep because it was not advisable for her to be away from her exhausted physical vessel for the time being. Her organs were extremely weak and she would be very lucid, spiritually speaking, and it would not be wise to suddenly expose her to too many active impressions from the different plane to which she would be going in the near future. The best thing for her was a gradual change, with the light intensifying little by little.

We went out, leaving Pedro's daughter in nourishing, restorative sleep.

Felix's face reflected deep concern as we accompanied him to a spacious apartment in Flamengo[6], where we would meet Marina's relatives.

It was getting late.

We went down a narrow hallway to the living room, where we encountered two discarnates making jokes about the horrible topic of vampirism.

It is worth mentioning that, despite the fact that we could see their movements and hear their vulgar language, they had no

---

6   A district of Rio de Janeiro. – Tr.

idea that we were there. They threatened to cause trouble. They argued violently.

They were dangerous rascals, even though they were invisible to the incarnates living there, who had no idea they were under their evil influence.

Judging from such company, it was easy to imagine the dangers the occupants of that cement abode were exposed to without any means of spiritual defense.

We went on into the living room and found a man of fine features. He was engrossed in reading an evening paper, and from his relaxed posture one could guess that he was the head of the family.

The accoutrements, although modest, evidenced refined, feminine taste. The somewhat course lines of the old furniture seemed smoothed out by the light decorations.

Crystal vases containing bunches of red carnations harmonized with the red roses that were skillfully painted on two gold-framed canvases hanging on the walls. However, an offensive, out-of-place bottle of whisky sat on the beautiful tablecloth that completed the elegance of the table, releasing alcoholic fumes that matched the breath of the man sitting on the sofa.

Felix gazed at him with the expression of someone who was compassionately tormented at seeing him:

"That is brother Claudio Nogueira," he explained, "Marina's father and head of the family."

I looked him over. Our unwitting host gave me the impression of one of those middle-aged men who wanted to remain forty-five years old, thus bravely fighting the ravages of time. His face was expertly cared for, and its firm lines deterred the vague threat of wrinkles. His hair was combed with distinction; his nails were buffed and his loungewear was impeccable. His large brown eyes were glued to the newspaper as he tried to find a reason to produce an ironic smile on his thin lips. Between the fingers of the hand resting on the arm of the sofa was a lit cigarette, very near an end table, on which a full ashtray was a silent warning against the abuse of nicotine.

We were curiously examining the scene when something unexpected happened.

Right in front of us, the two unfortunate discarnates approached Claudio unceremoniously.

One of them put his hand on Claudio's shoulder and shouted insolently:

"Drink, my friend! I need a drink!"

His raspy voice may have hurt our sensitive ears, but Claudio could not hear a single sound. He went on reading, undisturbed. Nevertheless, even if his physical eardrums had not registered the order, his mental waveband was attuned to the intruder.

The inappropriate guest repeated the order several times like a hypnotist who wants an order obeyed.

The result was not long in coming. The man stopped reading the political editorial that had engrossed him so much. He could not explain his sudden lack of interest.

"Drink! Drink!"

Claudio finally accepted the suggestion, convinced that he felt like having a shot of whisky solely for himself.

His thoughts had suddenly changed, like a power plant whose current is switched in a different direction because it is needed elsewhere.

"Drink! Drink!" And the thirst for alcohol took complete control of his mind and took shape. The pituitary mucosa became excited, as if it were more strongly impregnated with the pungent smell floating in the air. The malicious spirit scratched

Claudio's throat lightly and he became restless. An indefinable dryness afflicted his larynx. He wanted to feel calmer.

The cunning, uninvited guest perceived that his victim had given in to the suggestion and latched on to him: a light touch at first; then an enveloping embrace, followed by a full embrace and reciprocal association.

Both of them were integrated with each other in a perfect, extraordinary example of fluidic grafting.

On several occasions, I had studied the passage of the disembodied spirit through dense matter. When I was readjusting to the environment of the spirit plane after my latest discarnation, I myself mechanically analyzed my impressions as I passed through earthly obstacles and barriers. I recalled that, in those exercises, I felt as though I were breaking through clouds of condensed gases.

This time, however, something like a complete splice was occurring.

Claudio-the-man was absorbing the discarnate like a shoe adjusting to the foot. They melded with each other as if they were going to inhabit one body: same height; same girth; synchronized movements; complete oneness.

They stood up at the same time and turned around in the small space, totally integrated into each other, and picked up the bottle.

I was not able to tell which one had taken the initiative, that is, if Claudio had come up with the idea, or if the obsessor had proposed it.

The first gulp rolled down the throat, which now exhibited a strange duality. Both simultaneously smacked their lips in pleasure.

Then, the pair split apart. Claudio was about to sit back down, when the second discarnate rushed at him and protested:

"Me too! I want a drink too!"

The fading suggestion in Claudio's mind was rekindled.

Completely passive in the face of this assault, Claudio mechanically reconstructed the feeling of unsatisfied thirst.

That was all it took for the other vampirizer to smile and possess Claudio, repeating the phenomenon of complete oneness.

Incarnate and discarnate were juxtaposed on each other: two conscious parts at one in an impeccable system of mutual compensation.

I approached Claudio in order to impartially investigate how extensively he was mentally enduring that process of fusion.

I could see right away that he remained free inwardly. He was not experiencing any kind of torment as he yielded. He merely hosted the discarnate and willingly accepted his guidance. There was no symbiosis in which he was the victim. There was only implicit association; a natural mixing.

The experience was based on percussion: appeal and response; all the strings absolutely in tune. The discarnate suggested; the incarnate agreed. The former requested; the latter conceded.

Allowing his senses to be ensnared, Claudio believed he had not drunk enough and took another swallow. The curious math did not escape me: two gulps for three entities.

When Claudio was released once more, he sat back down on the couch and continued reading the newspaper.

The discarnate friends went back out into the hallway, joking sarcastically. Pedro respectfully asked questions about responsibility.

How were we to view the problem? If we had just seen Claudio reduced to the role of a puppet, how were we to understand the issue of justice? What if instead of a case of drinking, we had witnessed a crime? If the bottle of whisky had instead been a gun used to kill someone, what then? Would Claudio be at fault for having yielded, or would the obsessor be to blame for having commanded him?

Brother Felix calmly explained:

"Now Pedro, you need to understand that we are dealing with individuals who are free enough to decide and lucid enough to reason. Whether in the physical body or acting outside of it, the spirit is master of its attributes. Responsibility is not a note with an expiration date. It is as valid on this plane as it is on others. In the scene we just observed, Claudio and his visitors were three consciences in the same arena of choice with its consequent manifestations. All of us are free to suggest or assimilate this or that. If you were urged to participate in a robbery, you would obviously refuse, but if in your right mind you did agree to do it, you would never forgive yourself."

Our mentor paused for a moment and then continued:

"Hypnosis is a complex topic that requires an examination and re-examination of all the moral ingredients connected with it. The alienation of the will has its limitations. There are all sorts of appeals everywhere. Experiences are lessons and we are all learners. Enjoying the company of a master or following a wrongdoer is our own decision, and we will reap the consequences either way."

Pedro realized that Felix was more interested in explaining things to us instead of sending the two obsessors away, so he wanted to press the matter, like a student who is eager to complete the lesson.

He remembered that, when we were at his, Pedro's, house, Felix had done his best to defend it against that sort of spirit. Amaro, the helpful caretaker, had been stationed beside Beatriz for the purpose of getting rid of meddlesome discarnates. Consequently, her room had become safe for her. Here, however…

So, he asked the reason for this difference.

Felix had the look of surprise of a teacher who does not expect such an intelligent question from his student. He explained that the other situation was different. Nemesio's wife was in the habit of praying; thus, she was immunized spiritually. She effortlessly repelled all disparaging thought-forms directed at her. Moreover, she was ill and about to discarnate. To leave her at the mercy of insane entities would be mean. Protecting her against them was only right.

"But…what about Claudio?" Pedro insisted. "Doesn't he deserve a fraternal show of charity so that he can be freed of such dreadful obsessors?"

Felix smiled good-heartedly and explained:

"*Dreadful obsessors* is how you see them." And he went on: "Claudio is in perfect health. His mind is clear and he can think straight. He is intelligent, mature and experienced. He has no physical handicaps that would require special attention. He knows what he wants. He has all the things he wants. He is living the kind of life he wants to live. It is only natural that he is now experiencing the influence of the kind of guests he deemed desirable. He has complete freedom and all the valuable resources of education and discernment to join the missionaries of the good who work among incarnates, thus guaranteeing spiritual growth and happiness for himself. If he chooses to house guests like the individuals we have just seen, that's his affair. While we ourselves were still incarnate, we would never think of throwing people out of somebody else's house just because we did not see eye to eye. Now, looking at the world and things of the world from a higher perspective, we know it would not be acceptable to change such behavior."

The topic developed and took on further aspects.

Feeling curious, I jumped in:

"But brother Felix, surely if Claudio were free of them, he would be more respectable."

"That's perfectly logical," he confirmed. "No one would argue with that."

"So, why not undo the bonds that keep him prisoner to those two scoundrels exploiting him?"

The clear reasoning of a high order spirit made itself present:

"Claudio obviously doesn't see them as scoundrels. He sees them as esteemed partners, as dear friends. On the other hand, we cannot be too opinionated, because we have not yet investigated the cause of the connection between them. Circumstances may be healthy or unhealthy, just like with people, and if we want to treat a patient correctly, we have to get to the root of the illness, confirm the symptoms, prescribe the medicine and test the results. On this side of life, we see a problem in the raw, so to speak. When did these three become attached to each other? In this life, or in a past one? Nothing would justify an act of force on our part in an effort to separate them with the purpose of being helpful. That would be the same as separating generous parents from their ungrateful children, or noble spouses from their less-evolved partners under the pretext of assuring cleanliness and goodness in the evolutionary process. Responsibility matches one's knowledge. We don't have the means to keep friends from falling heavily into debt and making appalling mistakes, although it is fair to help them as much as possible in order to make them see a danger in a timely way. Sometimes, the higher authorities in the spirit world take special measures that impose afflictions and suffering on certain persons in order to save them from falling into imminent moral disasters – if they deserve such exceptional help. On earth, exact justice restricts people only if they would compromise the equilibrium and safety of others in the area of responsibility that life has drawn for them, but it lets them act as they feel is best. So, should we adopt rules that are less worthy when compared to those that guarantee harmony amongst incarnates?"

When he had finished his remarkable explanation, brother Felix was surrounded by a shining aura.

Entranced, we had no words to express our wonder before such wisdom and simplicity.

The instructor looked at Claudio with kindness and started to give him a paternal embrace, but perhaps afraid of missing the opportunity, Pedro humbly and respectfully asked to be forgiven for insisting, but he still had one point he would like to have clarified.

He asked our patient mentor about those who promote wars. Felix had said that justice tacitly keeps people from doing things that may threaten social stability. So, how were we to explain the existence of leaders who could be considered veritable tormenters of entire nations?

Felix summed up what he had said by repeating some of the words he had already used:

"I said 'restricts' people in the sense of 'correcting' or 'restraining.' I also said that all individuals live in the area of responsibility that the law has delimited for them. We need to understand that, if people's responsibility depends on the amount of superior knowledge that they have acquired, it is easy to see that the commitments of their conscience take on the level of the authority that has been attributed to them. A person with a large amount of authority can lead entire societies to the peaks of progress and development, or drown them in stagnation and decadence, all to the exact size of his or her decisions for good or evil. Of course governors and administrators must at any time be ready to answer for what they have done. All must give an accounting of how they used the resources that were entrusted to them in the area of their influence, for they automatically begin to reap what they have sown, whether good or bad."

But we could see that Felix did not want to dwell any longer on philosophical matters.

The look on his face was the expression of someone who wanted us to wait until later to ask any more questions. He approached Claudio and enveloped in with the soft radiations of his kindly, searching look.

There was a light, gentle atmosphere of expectation.

The benefactor could not hide his emotions. Mentally, he seemed far away in time. Then, he stroked the head of the man with whom neither Pedro nor I had in fact considered worthy of it, like a charitable doctor encouraging a difficult patient.

Nevertheless, that emotional moment was very brief, because brother Felix returned to us mentally and said:

"Who knows whether or not Claudio will turn into a man renewed for the good, one capable of educating those two spirits? Why should we reject all three simply because they are ignorant and wretched? And which of us can be sure he will never need someone else's help? Manure may have a very unpleasant smell; even so, it fertilizes the soil, helping plants that, in turn, help us."

The benefactor kindly indicated that the conversation was over and that it was time to get back to the work at hand.

7

We went into the bedroom next door and found a frail young woman. She looked to be in a lot of pain as she sat on one of the beds in the charming, clean room, enveloped in torturous thoughts that revealed her secret drama.

Brother Felix introduced her.

Her name was Marita and she had been adopted by the owners of the house just after she was born twenty years ago.

One look into her eyes was enough for me to feel sorry for her. Although she exuded the fragrance of youthfulness, that human rose was almost child-like. She was brooding with her hands folded under her chin and she seemed to be carrying the exhausting burden of chronic, painful problems. Her wavy hair looked like a beautiful, velvety brown headdress. Her face was sculpted in lovely lines, her dark eyes contrasting with the white of her face, and her small hands and pink nails completed the pretty mannequin of flesh that housed a frightened, wounded child inside.

Sadness hidden by makeup. Affliction disguised as a flower.

Felix suggested that I approach her gently and mentally ask her to tell me something about herself.

Since our contact with Nemesio, our benefactor, probably without realizing it, had made me practice a new kind of anamnesis: how to consult spirit patients mentally with the tender understanding that a father owes his children in order to probe matters that might be useful in helping them.

Compelled to assist her by myself, I collected my emotions.

I recalled the paternal sentiments I had experienced while incarnate. I focused my gaze on that thoughtful creature and imagined her to be a daughter of my soul.

I silently asked her to trust us and unburden herself. She could tell us her remotest memories and unfold her past. She could recall everything she knew about herself without leaving anything out.

We meant to help her, but we could not act randomly. She would have to pull from the chamber of her memory scenes stored there since childhood and project them onto her mental screen so that we could analyze them impartially and do what we could to be of assistance.

Marita immediately registered my request. Although she did not understand why she instinctively felt constrained to remember the past, she focused her mental impulse on her earliest memories.

Scenes from her childhood began appearing on her aura like a movie.

We saw her as a little girl, faltering as she took her first steps.

And while we watched the parade of innocent scenes showing what had happened to her after her birth, she articulated answers to our requests.

No – she remembered, thinking she was addressing herself – she was not really the Nogueiras' daughter. Marcia, Claudio's wife, had adopted her. She had been born to a young suicide. Aracelia, the mother she had never known, had been hired as a maid by the couple that destiny had chosen to be the baby's parents. When Marita was old enough, her adoptive mother told her the brief story of the poor, simple woman who had brought her into the world. She had just arrived from "upstate" Rio de Janeiro and was looking for a modest job. She had been sent to the Nogueiras by one of her acquaintances. She was pretty, spontaneous and loved to party. After finishing her housekeeping duties, she would go out to have fun. She was extroverted and made a lot of friends, with whom she went out dancing. She was joyful and communicative, but also hardworking and reliable. Sometimes it was very late at night when she returned to the room the family had reserved for her; even so, she was always at work bright and early the next morning. She never complained. She was always helpful, from washing the clothes to cooking. Consequently, although her employers did not approve of the company she went out with, they did not feel entitled to reproach her.

Marcia was always straightforward in her references. She fondly remembered Aracelia. When Marcia gave birth to Marina, her only daughter, she and Aracelia became even closer friends. Aracelia outdid herself in her love and devotion to Marcia. However, right at the same time, a big change took place. The devoted maid got pregnant and began to experience a lot of physical pain. No matter how hard the Nogueiras tried to get her to tell them the name of the man responsible for her plight, she would only cry, nullifying any possibility of trying to arrange for a dignified marriage. They knew that going out partying so often had obviously held many hazards. The Nogueiras took pity on the young mother-to-be and gave her all the help she needed, including taking her to a good hospital so that the baby could be born under as much care as possible.

At this point in her bitter reminiscences, the girl stopped as if she were tired of thinking about the matter. So, that was how she, Marita, had been born.

Her eyes welled up with tears as she compared her mother's trials to her own. Nevertheless, in order not to be distracted from my examination, I asked her to please continue.

Marcia had told her – she went on – that upon returning home one day, she had found Aracelia extremely depressed. She cried all the time, and was irritable and depressed. Neither warnings nor medical care were of any use. On the night when she swallowed a large dose of poison, she had talked animatedly with Marcia, giving everyone the impression that she was recovering. However, the next morning she was found dead. One hand was grasping Marita's cradle, as if at the last minute she had decided she did not want to say goodbye, after all.

Extremely emotional, Marita tried in vain to tell us everything she knew about herself. She was sure of only one thing, and that was that she had awakened to life in Marcia's arms; that from the very beginning she had considered Marcia as her real mother; and that she was connected to Marina as if they were full-blooded sisters from infancy. They went to school together and they shared childhood together. They went on outings, attended parties, and enjoyed fun times and games together. They read the same books and dressed in the same colors.

I continued with my analysis, but perhaps because it was getting late, brother Felix said goodbye, explaining he had urgent matters to attend to. Work in the institution for which he was responsible did not allow him to stay longer.

He very kindly reaffirmed his trust in me. With the tact of a mentor who asks instead of demanding, he said that he was expecting a lot of attention on my part on behalf of that naïve girl for as long as our fraternal help was possible. When Felix made his request, I noticed his discomfort. I understood that he, a high order spirit, was there only because of his extreme generosity, like a wise, distinguished professor who comes down from his lectern to encourage his students still struggling with their ABCs.

He smiled in disappointment, perceiving the interpretation that had come to my mind, and he subtlety explained that he had several reasons to consecrate himself to the happiness of that home. The family stubbornly refused to engage in any religious or beneficent activity. No one was interested in cultivating the habit of praying or learning. Not one of the four family members had any interest in serving his or her neighbor. Consequently, despite his paternal love for Claudio, he did not feel authorized to place spirit workers under his guidance in the house, unless there were serious objectives on which to base his decision.

Since that was the case – it would only be satisfying a personal desire – he only felt compelled to visit that home from time to time, or to ask for the collaboration of itinerant friends.

Pedro and I were very sorry to see him go. We pointed out our deficiencies but promised to do our best, nonetheless. We would watch over the place and if something came up, we would appeal for his assistance.

Felix smiled and told us that Amaro, Beatriz's healthcare giver, and several coworkers were at work in the neighborhood. They were all dedicated friends who were ready to help, although they were under no obligation. Optimistic, he added that, in case we did need him, our concerned thoughts would work as an alarm signal.

So, we were alone with our work.

At the end of this short break, we continued the analysis. I noticed that Pedro was trying harder to be useful.

Marita had set her memories aside for a moment, but automatically returned to them, exposing on her mental screens what was accessible to her.

Immersed in her imagination, as if she were daydreaming, she found herself in her mother's lap or hanging on to her sister in the innocent security of someone who was fully adjusted to the family scene. She saw Claudio holding her in his arms like a tender rosebud, providing the tenderness of a real father.

Oh! The fleeting happiness of childhood! ... The sweet certainties of those early days! How she wished she could go back in time and sleep in simplicity!

Suddenly, her soul shivered, as if a merciless scalpel were slicing its nerves. Marita burst into an explosion of tears. Her mind was being colored by a party nine years ago, the one that celebrated her graduation from elementary school. She saw herself in the upscale school saying goodbye to her classmates, praising and thanking her teachers, and happily receiving kisses on her long, flowing hair. Afterwards ... at home, the strange look on Marcia's face, and in the bedroom, the locked door.

The conflict that would haunt her entire life had begun. The unexpected revelation had wounded Marita's spirit like a bruising stone. It only took a few seconds for her childhood joy to be shattered; she felt like an adult, all grown up and suffering in an instant. Come to find out, she was not the family's daughter, after all; she was an orphan, adopted by the dear hearts she loved so much, thinking she was really theirs. The revelation had broken her heart. For the first time, she had wept, afraid of sheltering herself in the maternal lap that had always welcomed her in difficult times. She felt bruised, alone. Marcia went on, kindly explaining and explaining. Until then, Marita had been a smiling, outgoing girl, but was now tormented as she listened and listened ... She wanted to ask why all this was happening to her, but her voice stuck in her throat. She had to accept the truth ... resign herself ... suffer. Her adoptive mother had tried hard to dilute the bitterness of the news by being particularly gentle, but had not forgotten to say in a grave tone of voice: "You need to grow up knowing the whole truth; better today than tomorrow; if they do not know the truth, adopted children usually cause big problems, especially if they learn the truth from other people." And before the silence of Marita, who was trying to hold back the tears, she added: "Now, don't cry; I'm just explaining things. You know we have raised you as our own daughter, but you had to know the whole story. We adopted you in consideration of Aracelia, so friendly, so kind."

This news was immediately complemented by Marcia showing her some photographs and mementos that her suicide mother had kept in a small wooden box.

Astonished, Marita nervously fondled the pictures and costume jewelry – possessions of a poor woman. It was moving to her to see the cheap necklaces and rings. That was all that was left of that mother she had never known. She looked at the face in those photos yellowed by time and felt a profound and irresistible attraction to those big, sad eyes, which seemed to transport her from that room to a completely different world.

However, her mind had not matured enough to grasp the anguish of that woman smitten by suffering. The image of her discarnate mother had lasted only a moment. She had been hurt too deeply to think about anything but her own pain. She had heard Marcia gather up those tender vestiges of the past and say goodbye, but had not paid much attention to her. Those words kept resounding in her head: "We adopted you in consideration of Aracelia, so friendly, so kind."

So, this was how they were sending her off to the station of orphanhood, her real destination? What about the kisses of the family to whom she had always thought she belonged? And what about all the pampering she thought she could share with Marina on equal terms?

She had gotten the impression that Marcia had decidedly undertaken to speak to her without the least manifestation of the effusive love that had always characterized her gestures. True, Marcia had been loving enough, but she rationed her caresses, as if she wanted to establish from that moment on a strict boundary between Marita and the rest of the family. That was why she felt robbed and hurt. She had simply been sheltered, tolerated, fooled. She was not a daughter; she was an orphan.

Her precocious intelligence grasped the whole situation, although, on that particular day, she was unable to be thankful for her parents' compassion, because she was feeling assailed by her childish pride.

Following a brief pause in those emotion-filled reminiscences, Marita showed us a heartwarming, unforgettable scene.

For my part, I had never registered such deep pain felt by a child.

Ah! She had never forgotten that event. After Claudio's wife had left her crying and disconsolate, she saw the skinny, nameless puppy that Marina had rescued from the street a few weeks earlier. The little thing had approached her and licked her hands, as if offering to share her bitterness. Marita, in turn, petted it as if she wanted to transfer to it the whole load of love that she used to believe Marcia had given to her. And weeping as she hugged the affectionate little dog, she exclaimed, "Ah, Jewel! You aren't the only one who was rejected! I was too!"

From that day on, her life had changed. She had completely lost her spontaneity.

From the day of the revelation that had never left her mind, she considered herself unworthy, deceived, dependent.

Such mental suffering, which she had incurred at eleven years of age, was mitigated only by the incessant dedication of her adoptive father, who devoted his love to her to the same degree that Marcia and Marina withheld theirs.

But as a female, she was alone.

Mother and daughter deliberately made it a point to abstain from any opinions whenever she asked them which outfit she should wear. She was left all to herself, without any assistance with regard to the care that a young girl owed herself, although Marcia did listen to her with maternal tenderness on occasion concerning the questions she had about her private life as a girl and woman.

Whenever there was an opportunity for a friendly chat, Marita could see that Claudio's wife did have an enormous storehouse of understanding and sympathy, but it lay hidden under the weight of conveniences and conventions, like a treasure buried deep in the roots of a stolid thorn bush.

Marita would take advantage of those moments of intimacy between them and would open up about all the doubts and perplexities that lay hidden in her imagination, just waiting for the right opening.

Marcia would seem to ignore the distance between them and would respond amid kisses in a lively demonstration that the heat of dedication and trust of before had not vanished from her heart. She would smile and be thrilled. Her maternal instinct would expand into wise and sweet comments. She would also try to help Marita deal with the first problems in the life of a young girl, giving Marita the impression that she had found once again the momma that she thought had been hers at the foot of the cradle, when those lovely, fine hands, now distant, stroked her hair.

However, such luminous moments never lasted long.

Marina would arrive home and the atmosphere would change immediately.

Marita was astonished to see the sudden difference. Marcia delighted in a show of dual personality.

The spiritual, loving, warm mother disappeared and the critical, impersonal Marcia appeared.

Marcia would suddenly come up with something for Marita to do in the adjacent room, something to keep her away. She would assume different airs. Or she would suddenly complain of some pain that she had not even noticed before.

Marita would watch this reversal of the picture in amazement.

Acting together, mother and daughter completed each other, doing little things to depress and humiliate her. A small spot on her clothes was a reason for sarcasm. A light organic indisposition provoked a complex string of jocular and indiscreet admonitions. She was occasionally invited to go shopping with them downtown, and if, by chance, the shops did not make deliveries, the pair did not hesitate to load Marita with a lot of shopping bags, thus making her embarrassment and subservience even worse by their use of derogatory and cruel jokes. Whenever Marcia and Marina were around Marita at the same time, it was an unparalleled trial that she was forced to bear in silence. On those occasions, Marita would feel her heart race uncomfortably, as if she were having to endure a test of tolerance and patience before examiners who would evaluate her reactions amid jest and cruelty.

She soon realized that her sister, an only child, would not share even the least bit of domestic pampering. She believed herself to be the only one entitled to it.

After Marina found out about her sister's origin, her behavior toward her changed completely. She found excuses to expose Marita's past in conversations with her friends. She wanted to make sure there could be no doubt that the two of them did not belong in the same social environment. Marina criticized Marita's tastes and attitudes. And Marcia made no secret about whose side she was on.

When Marina was not around, Marcia did not hesitate to show Marita the same love as she had shown in the past, maybe enriched with the pity that she, a poor girl, inspired in the present. But this only made Marcia's coldness toward her even worse. Marita longed to rest on a devotion she could count on. She felt the weight of loneliness, having no blood relatives to share the connections of friendship. Her letters to Aracelia's relatives never merited a response. Information from her mother's distant hometown said that the whole family had migrated to different parts of the country in search of a better life.

She was very self-critical and understood her situation only too well. She was alone.

Marita, believing she was deliberately revisiting memories of the past, felt she needed a break from her reflections, like someone carrying a heavy burden wanting to stop and put it down for a moment in order to appraise the obstacles on the road ahead.

I weakened my detailed observation of her wordless exposition.

She felt relieved and wondered if her isolation from her family might not have exaggerated too soon her need for new acquaintances outside the narrow circle of trials at home.

Locked in the thoughts that adorned her fantasies, and afraid of expressing them for fear of ridicule, she resorted to avoiding everybody.

Like a bird exhausted from trying to use its wings too soon, she wondered why she had been refused emotional nourishment in the nest where she had first stretched them.

But before she could get comfortable in some dark corner of her mind in order to wallow around in useless self-pity, we asked her to please return to the analysis we were conducting for the specific purpose of helping and protecting her.

She obediently returned to her elucidations and revealed her first days as a store clerk.

The memories streamed forth.

They showed us the busy shop where Claudio had gotten her a job as a clerk. It catered to the feminine world: costume jewelry, perfume, light fabrics, readymade clothes, etc.

The day after her adoptive father had brought her a cake decorated with seventeen tiny roses to celebrate her birthday, she started her new job.

At first, everything was uncertain and new.

She soon found herself embroiled in a battle of feelings. New acquaintances. Renewed ideas.

She formed comforting relationships, expanded her interests, shared confidences, won affections.

Her imagination ran wild, urging her to dress to the nines in order to make herself attractive to the hero that would surely come to rule over her emotional realm and offer her a home, a bit of paradise where she could soothe her heart, relieve her pain and find happiness.

A simple girl, all she knew about love was what she had read in romance novels, where nameless Cinderellas wound up dazzled in the arms of princes who rescued them from obscurity to offer them glory. She loved novels and films that ended with altruism being rewarded or with supreme human aspiration being appropriately crowned.

Fate, however, scorned her innocence.

She compared real daily life to an implacable pruning that cut all the flowers in the garden of her youthful dreams.

Disillusionment had first struck her spirit through a coworker who repeatedly gave her tickets to the movies. Marita knew his fiancée, a distinct young teacher who had become her friend.

What would be wrong with going to a good movie with him from time to time? That initiated moments of fraternal camaraderie. The closeness of propitious minutes. Copacabana, here and there. A cup of coffee in a cafe when the wind was cold. Ice-cream on the beach when it was too hot. Nothing more than friendship. Just a friend playing the role of the brother she never had.

But then, one night he showed up completely unsettled. He had not brought his fiancée, because she had gone to Petropolis. A natural event, albeit rare. There was nothing to suggest unpleasant consequences. No reason to be worried.

They chatted casually on the sands of Leme Beach. The full moon suggested calm, joyful thoughts as they enjoyed the fresh breeze from the sea.

Working in the shop had been a bath of copious sweat on a hot day.

They talked about the customers who were always in a rush, and they remembered the difficult ones. They laughed, feeling as carefree as college students enjoying a break from classes.

The young man, however, did something unexpected by talking about sizes. In his opinion, the measuring tape was not enough in certain cases. One had to use psychological means to reassure anxious customers when they were interested in buying only fragments of materials.

To illustrate, he asked her to give him her small hand so he could compare it with his. Marita offered him her right hand without even thinking about it.

But she became frightened when she felt his rough masculine hand gripping her fingers.

She tried to break free, but he made his unfortunate intentions very clear. He pulled her to him, stammering words of love.

With the vertigo of someone feeling the effects of a bolt of lightning out of the clear, blue sky, Marita wanted to scream for help, but the blood was boiling inside her head.

She was impetuously dominated by those lips that were glued to hers, and fainted for a few seconds.

The seductive breath of the first man to hold her in his arms was filled with the magnetism of a snake as it hypnotizes the trustful bird.

But she fainted for only an instant. Her profound, invincible female reaction, coupled with conscience, quickly surfaced. The notion of commitment flashed in her mind. That was all it took for the sex urge to be defeated and neutralized. She thought about his absent girlfriend and understood all the peril to which she had exposed herself.

Yes, she did aspire to be someone's wife, to be the companion of someone who was hers in turn. She humbly grasped her condition as a human being, a girl craving affection, anticipating the emotions of motherhood; but she would never agree to lower herself by being disloyal or promiscuous.

She summed up all the strength she could, and feeling a sudden surge of resistance, she pushed her trembling persecutor away.

Upon breaking free, she exploded into hot, pain-filled tears.

Questions from her sincere soul burst forth, frank and blunt.

What about his commitment? What would become of the honest girl that had surrendered her destiny to him? Was his heart that corrupt? Didn't he have a mother and sisters, for whom he demanded esteem and respect?

Pale and confused, her coworker said he was sorry and stated impudently that he had no idea she was so old-fashioned.

He had been engaged for months. Even so – he emphasized cynically – in his opinion, it was only natural that, while he and Marita were still young, they should enjoy themselves. He went on to say – according to his liberal philosophy – that, although they know the correct route, all sensible travelers are free to taste the fruit hanging from trees beside the road.

He mocked her tears and left, laughing loudly and sarcastically. He started hounding her at work.

And there were other problems and temptations.

The boss's nephew, a recently married, handsome lad, insinuated his intentions, beginning with a birthday present and ending by asking her to help him in his office, where he attempted unspeakable proposals. Marita had won a new enemy and suffered injustices.

Meanwhile, she noticed that Marina was going through significant changes. Favored by her devoted mother, she had earned a degree in accounting, which had definite advantages. And because she began making so much money, Marina spent money lavishly on designer clothes, extravagant hairdos, drinking sprees and trivialities.

At this point of Marita's mute confidences, the profile of a young man appeared clearly. Upon projecting his image on the landscape of her most recondite thoughts, the suffering girl was transfigured.

Her inner firmament became cloudless. Complaints were set aside; worries were forgotten.

Marita's aura became so bright when she recalled the young man that the phenomenon induced the most beautiful appreciations of poetic enthusiasm. She was a thinking vase that had the privilege of being shaped and molded at will to contain a favorite flower, a lake of consciousness that can suddenly hide all the detritus in its water and transform itself into a soft and crystalline mirror to reflect a star.

Marita loved her chosen one with the strength of the tree standing on its main root of support; with the selflessness of mothers, who would happily die in making the ultimate sacrifice if that was the price they had to pay for their children to go on living.

Enrapt with the mental frame, which was like a living altarpiece that inspired religious reverence, I asked myself where else I might have seen a similar picture: a young woman constructing that face in her mental field.

I searched my memory and found him. He was the young man whose face inhabited Marina's mind and controlled her heart in partnership with Nemesio.

Both girls were spiritually attached to him by identical ties. Their preferences crossed; they were partners in the same destiny.

I glanced at Pedro. He was observing me closely, doing a psychic analysis. His face was filled with bitterness.

He received my mental signal and whispered in my ear:

"We still don't know the whole story. Do you know who that is? My grandson, Gilberto, Beatriz's son."

I made a gesture, asking him to wait for an opportunity that might be appropriate for the conversation, and I prepared myself inwardly for the effects of the emotional impact. I, who had approached that tormented child, imagining myself in the position of a father helping his daughter, could barely keep from gasping in amazement and falling into the inappropriateness of destructive compassion.

I did not know which caused me more pain: the thought of Marina, divided between father and son, or this sad girl, so deeply wounded emotionally.

I stifled my personal feelings and proceeded with the analysis at hand.

The girl's silent confession continued with lively, clear reminiscences.

She had met Gilberto exactly six months ago in her boss's office. She was providing some information related to work, and Gilberto was representing the interests of his father regarding the real estate business.

How dazzled she had been when she received his first affectionate, inquisitive look! From then on, links of intense affinity began to yoke them to each other, without her being able to explain her ever increasing thirst for his company.

On their first outing – which had preceded a string of further, happy ones – they were delighted to discover that Marina had recently been hired as an accountant at the firm where Gilberto's father was the most important person.

They laughed at this coincidence with the innocence of two children.

Marita had entrusted herself to him completely. She loved him and felt loved in return.

From the moment he had supported her on his arm, ready to embrace and protect her, vaster horizons opened up to her soul. She put up with the daily pinpricks, transforming them into notes of forgiveness and happiness. Nature showed her new wonders. She felt like a different light had shone in her eyes, enabling her to discover the beauty of the sea. She couldn't explain the music in her content and enrapt ears, the music of the harangues of children, and the songs of birds. She cut ties with her domestic Calvary. Time flew sweetly by in her heart.

Loving and being loved anaesthetized her sensibilities: no weight to bear; no notion of suffering.

She had given herself to Gilberto, copying the passivity of the plant that surrenders to the gardener, or the spring that offers itself to the thirsty.

Nemesio Torres' son had promised to marry her. He talked about their wonderful future; he stimulated her dreams of motherhood and happiness. He was just waiting for an upcoming raise to make her completely happy.

In spite of all this, her heart was now broken, smitten. She was convinced that Gilberto had left her, that both of them had been too eager to satisfy their hunger for pleasure, and had plucked the flower of happiness too soon.

Marina had come into the picture. Always Marina...

The day before, Marita had overheard Gilberto and her sister in a conversation that left nothing to imagination. Without their knowing she was there, she had heard their voices full of ardent tenderness.

At this point in those bitter memories, like a bird suddenly wounded, she lay on the bed and wept convulsively.

8

I had finished making notes for my analysis, when I noticed that the patient was weeping in prostration. Since it was impossible for me to continue my examination, Pedro asked if he could have a word with me.

"Of course," I said.

"Andre!" he exclaimed, not trying to hide his perplexity, "What does this mean, my friend? Did you see that? My grandson; that young man is my grandson! ... How can that be? Four people entangled so! ... A woman caught between father and son, a young man between two sisters! I had no idea! For days now, I've tried to help my poor Beatriz; that's all. I had no idea about the troubles surrounding her. Ah, my friend! As a father, I would feel better if she were suffering in a madhouse."

And nodding toward Marita:

"Was she revealing the whole truth?"

"Pedro," I answered, "you know that every family group can be seen as a kind of machine made of different parts, although they interact with each other according to their function. Each member of the group is part of the realities that mesh with the whole. Marita was being truthful. She showed us what she knows. She is a part of the truth we are looking for. If we want to discover what you call 'the whole truth,' we will have to consult the persons that make up her inner world."

My friend smiled like someone who has brought understanding and conformity together.

However, yielding to the discomfort with which he imagined he was reverencing justice, Pedro complained angrily:

"Can you believe it!? Gilberto! Just a boy ... If only his father could help! ... But Nemesio's a basket case. There's no way ..."

He looked compassionately at the tearful girl and added:

"Look at the poor thing. Good character ... Faithful ... She yielded herself trustfully. Why blame the porcelain vase if it has been violently broken by an animal? And this animal is a boy I love so dearly! ... She could have been the ideal wife he idealizes, the worthy mother, a homemaker for an honest man ... But there goes Gilberto, lured away by a worthless thing. Marina and Marita ... It's hard to believe they were brought up under the same roof. They're adoptive sisters, like what happens to a snake and a dove!"

During a brief pause, it did not take me long to figure out what to do.

I unduly played fortuitous counselor and asked him to calm down.

We were there to correct, to watch-over, to do our best ... Certainly, the good that could be planted in that family would rebound in help for Beatriz. We should think of her first. His anger would only undermine her spirit, and he, Pedro, embittered, would project onto his daughter negative fluidic elements that would sap her strength.

Patience and fraternal activity would serve as our support.

Besides, we could not tell when Beatriz's physical suffering would come to an end. It was all right to predict, to calculate ... But higher authorities might order a lengthier stay in the flesh. She might have to continue attached to a relatively better physical body for months – years perhaps – although every prognosis indicated discarnation before long. But what if the opposite were the case? Exasperation or discouragement on our part would mean the end of our power to be helpful. It would not be hard for our supervisors, despite being helpful and compassionate, to remove us from Beatriz's bedside. They had the means to reassign us easier, smoother, more comforting tasks elsewhere. They would do so on behalf of the patient to keep her from the harm we could cause her with our load of disconcerting vibrations.

Pedro patiently tolerated my advice.

He asked for understanding. He had left the family a long time ago – he justified himself – in order to focus on wisdom and detachment. But now, upon returning, he was being forced, at every moment, to confront inwardly the man he used to be. He was self-seeking, overly attached to his blood kin, absorbed in the well-being of those he considered the flowers of his heart. He knew he was going through a difficult trial. He knew he was being analyzed, observed and evaluated concerning his assimilation of the principles of charity and indulgence he had begun to administer under the influence of wise, kindly mentors that had opened to him the doors of the schools of spiritual growth in the higher realms.

Like any human being possessed of assets and liabilities, he said he was willing to control himself, and reminding me of some of my young, former colleagues who felt confident yet hesitant at the same time regarding problems of self-control, he asked for my help so that he could remain as calm as possible in the presence of his instructors.

My friend's submissiveness impressed me.

He believed he was temporarily disturbed – he said humbly. He shared his daughter's hardships. He had returned instinctively to the aggressiveness and extroversion that marked his temperament in the past; however, he promised he would change his attitude. Nevertheless, he asked me to overlook any inappropriate comment when he was with me. There was always a moment when, despite working hard on his inner development, he felt that long-accumulated excitations weighed on his spirit like a cloud of burning fumes. Then he would either express them or go crazy, as if he were carrying exploding bombs in his chest.

I told him to compose himself. There was no need to feel so ashamed. I understood everything completely. For my part, I was not one bit better than he was. I, too, was a discarnate individual, and I knew only too well the difficulties of the inner struggle, in which we are always our own enemies in the arena of the inferior qualities that we must sublimate.

It was unwise to continue our conversation while we were trying to work.

The frail girl was unburdening herself in tears. Weeping out loud, although discreetly. Sobbing.

I was about to intervene when something unexpected happened.

Claudio knocked lightly on the door, obviously disturbed by the moaning that Marita tried in vain to control.

I breathed a sigh of relief.

Undoubtedly, the troubled paternal soul had come to the unfortunate girl, anxious to restore her energies, and using magnetic stimuli, I urged her to open the door.

The girl used her will and strength to control her weeping, answered my appeal and staggered to unlock the door.

Claudio entered, but he was not alone. One of the two discarnate spirits who had modified his personality – the first one that had induced Claudio to drink the whisky – was actually entwined around his body.

The word "entwined" in human language seems to be the one that best describes the example of shared possession we were studying, although it does not explain very accurately the entire process of fluidic envelopment. And we use the term "shared possession" because, actually, one individual has exactly the same burning, dishonest objectives as the other, thus euphorically completing one another, dividing responsibility into equal shares.

As was the case when they had drunk together, they gave the impression of being two beings in the same body.

At certain moments, the obsessor would move away from his companion, but only a few inches; nonetheless, he continued to enlace him, copying the movements of a cat so as not to lose contact with his prey. Thus, the two of them were unrestrictedly attached to each other.

This made Claudio look different. The hypnotizer, whose spirit sight could not detect us, controlled Claudio's sentiments and ideas, while Claudio gladly let himself be controlled. His obedient eyes had that crazed look that is characteristic of someone who is insane. Claudio's face had become transfigured. His was wearing a weird smile. To Marita's limited perception, he was just an ordinary man; nevertheless, to us he was two male personalities in just one representation. Two spirits externalizing debased impulses and sharing identical passions in the same tonic of total affinity.

Pedro looked at me in astonishment. But although he was less-experienced, he was not the only one who felt amazed, shocked. I, myself, in the spirit world, had grown used to disturbances of the sentiments; but now I was terribly concerned.

That room, previously filled with the painful memories of a child, had been transformed into a cage, where Claudio and the vampirizer, strangely animalized by their unhappy desires, were like a cunning beast, calculating the easiest way to catch its prey.

If an incarnate clairvoyant were to see Claudio at that moment, he or she would see him wearing a different physiognomic mask.

A spontaneous, conscious example of mediumistic incorporation[7] could be observed in all its savage plenitude. The phenomenon of the communion between two intelligences – one incarnate, the other discarnate – was right there in front of us; as such, it manifested itself as violently as a hurricane or the sea, which are channels of expression for the still-uncontrolled forces of terrestrial nature, although, in this instance, from the human perspective, everything had happened in the apparent silence of the mental plane.

To us, however, it was not only their thought-forms, with their structures, colors, sounds and corresponding movements, that warned us about the libertine intentions of the animalized pair; it was also frightening to hear their voices, in a dialogue clearly audible to us.

The seemingly silent words left Claudio's head and went to his adopted daughter, as if his skull had become a sound box containing radiophonic equipment.

---

7   This is a mind-to-mind process as the spirit cannot expel the incarnate spirit from its body to make it its own. See *The Mediums' Book*, Ch. XXIII, by Allan Kardec (International Spiritist Council), and *Missionaries of the Light*, chapter 16 'Incorporation,' by the spirit Andre Luiz, psychographed by Francisco Candido Xavier (International Spiritist Council). – Tr.

Magnetizer and magnetizee revealed the same level of sensuality.

We recalled the race to the bottle a few moments ago and could see the obvious peril the defenseless girl was in. The only difference this time was that Claudio still had enough energy left to argue, even under hypnosis – a hypnosis that he was enjoying, by the way.

The obsessor was urging Claudio to cast aside his remaining scruples:

"Now, yes, now! ... This is what love is, Claudio ... Waiting, sometimes for years and years, in order to win happiness for just one minute. There are millions of women in the world, but this is the only one that can actually slake our thirst. Rest stops are everywhere along the way, but the migrating bird flies for miles and miles, longing to rest in the down of its own nest ... To satisfy physical hunger, any old food will do, but love ... In love, happiness is like a circlet, of which the man has half and the woman has the other half. In order for euphoria to vibrate perfectly, the two halves have to be of the same substance. No one can fuse a piece of gold to a piece of wood. Paganini may have played the violin using just one string, but that string was in harmony with him. He would never have been recognized as the genius he was if he had only had a violin with strings made of hemp even if they could make sounds. Each man, Claudio, if he wants to be accomplished in the realms of vitality and happiness, must find the woman who is magnetically in tune with him, the partner who is in complete affinity, capable of offering him the inner plenitude that transcends conventions and forms.[8]

---

8 We understand the negative character of this discarnate spirit's language as he is in a deplorable state of ignorance, but we feel it is our duty to reproduce it here – even though it has been diluted – as a warning to sensitive, loving individuals, who, sometimes, ignore their own reasoning and wind up falling into awful mental suffering for the sake of their heart. (Note by the Spirit Author)

He paused a few seconds before continuing, pleadingly, proclaiming cunning sophisms:

"Get on with it! Marita is ours, ours! ... We are thirsty men, suffering men ... we feel compassion for the forsaken sick and give them the medicine they need; we are sure support for beggars who wander around aimlessly. So, do we deserve any less sympathy? Are those who have gone insane, craving love, worse than the wretches who collapse in the streets for lack of bread? You, Claudio, have been suffering from a dreadful want of love. A beggar in the square does not have the slightest notion of your afflictions. What good are big salaries and experiences in brothels, when true love is crying out, unsatisfied, in the flesh? You live at home like a dog in the gutter: beaten, wounded ... Marita is your compensation. Isn't the grower entitled to the ripe fruit? You have sheltered this girl in your arms; you have held her to your heart; you have watched her grow up, like someone that has watched the growth of a flower now in bloom, and you have wound up discovering that she is just your type. Aren't you tired of seeing her and desiring her ardently every day, resigning yourself to the torture of distance while living so close to her?"

"But I brought her up as my own daughter," Claudio sighed, thinking he was talking to himself.

"Daughter?" insisted the seducer. "A mere social artifice. Just a woman ... And who says she's not longing for your kiss as well, with the thirst of a doe tied to a tree beside the spring? You're no neophyte; you know that all women love to surrender after playing hard-to-get."

Claudio felt like he was mentally divided into two distinct personalities: father and would-be lover. He felt conflicted and became discouraged.

He knew the girl had already promised herself. She had chosen Gilberto, the young man whom she frequently went out with. So, it was impossible that she loved him, Claudio, in secret. He had no doubt about that. Feeling jealous, he had secretly followed the couple on their Sunday outings, without them ever knowing he was there. He had never heard what they said; nevertheless, he had seen their gestures. He believed he had been right to ask that imbicile to commit himself. He had calculated, calculated. However, when he was about to ask the police authorities for their advice, he had been shocked by the unexpected. Claudio was a man with a very busy night life and he had begun to run into his daughter in places of pleasure, not only in the company of Nemesio Torres, the gentleman who employed her, but also with Gilberto, his son, in a compromising attitude. For some time now, he had considered Marina's irresponsible behavior as an inevitable calamity. At first, he felt tormented: a father troubled by the licentiousness going on in his family. However, Marcia, his wife, dictated the rules. During the first years of their marriage, a wall of discord had been erected, discord that emanated from within their souls in awful waves of instinctive aversion, the existence of which they had not suspected in the least before the wedding.

At first, quarrels and arguments. After that, indifference; complete weariness of each other. Unilateral affairs. Each of them living their own life.

Marina, obviously, had followed in her mother's steps. She too had disconnected from him. In his opinion as a man, she was a free woman, tolerated at home, provided she kept the job that enabled her to support her fantasies. At home, they usually gathered around the table like three intelligent animals, disguising their reciprocal spite through convention or witticisms.

In his mind, however, Marita was something apart: a flower on the thorny branch of those punishing antagonisms.

He had deliberately encouraged her to stay later at her job. He had invented ways to force her to have lunch in Copacabana so that the bickering at home in Flamengo would not torture her spirit.

He kept a constant eye on her, and listened to what her bosses had to say about her.

Once she was settled into her new condition, he himself, whenever possible, would ensure her independence.

Since he loved her with affection mixed together with tyrannical selfishness, he was deeply hurt by the humiliations frequently inflicted on her by his wife and Marina.

He wanted Marita for himself, with the tenderness of a dove and the brutality of a wolf. He did not go along with the pair's insults and sarcasm towards her. Such attitudes led him to give Marita more freedom, which she used for spending more time with Gilberto, since, by nature, she stayed away from parties. Marcia and Marina were always more interested in extravagances, which they indulged in like two carefree sisters, and did not even notice this fact. Marita's absence was more of a relief than a worry. Feeling sure that they could never warp her character, they were happy at not having to put up with her physical presence.

Deeply engulfed by the rationalizations resulting from this brief self-examination under the control of the vampirizer, Claudio remembered that several days earlier he had come to the conclusion that Gilberto was cheating on both women, but after thinking it over for a long time, he had decided to keep quiet.

Wouldn't it be best to weigh the advantages? To accuse Marita of being reviled would result in losing her trust. To tell her about Marina would insult her and afflict her with awful wounds of a moral order. Shrewdly, he let time pass because in his opinion it was best to let Marita be bruised by the circumstances.

Then, when she turned to him, weary and disappointed, he could perhaps easily transform her into the lover he wanted so much.

Goaded on by his invisible guest, Claudio mentally listed the hurried thoughts that came to mind. Thus urged by the former, the latter let himself be deluded by imaginary expectations, which led to another set of issues. Totally enveloped by the obsessor's subtleties, he examined himself and tried to figure out if he was thinking rightly at the moment. Might he be mistaken? Could Marita be giving herself to Gilberto while thinking of him, Claudio, whom she was avoiding due to the scruples of conscience? For weeks now, the girl had seemed more distant. He had found that to be odd. Might she be telepathically picking up on his apprehensions, or was she deliberately avoiding him in order to hide the love that was possibly driving her heart to desire him?

He, himself, was offering his obsessor the arguments that were undermining his resistance.

Until now, for good or ill, he had managed to hide from the girl the sentiments that were overflowing his soul. But hadn't he finally reached the limits of the puzzle? Was he supposed to suffer until he went crazy?

The hypnotizer's face displayed the immeasurable thirst of gross sensuality. He smiled gleefully and whispered mentally, winning complete control:

"Claudio, you need to understand that in matters of love the woman never makes the first move. Remember the old saying: 'Oranges growing along the side of the road are free.' And a philosopher once said: 'Pleasure that has not been fought for is like beef without salt.' Get on with it! Let's go!"

Analyzing Claudio on the inside, hunting for means with which Claudio himself could reinforce the magnetic possession, the obsessor looked hard at him for a few seconds. And obviously exhuming Claudio's disrespectable illusions regarding love, illusions he had held since childhood, he began to hammer away:

"Cigarette! Remember the cigarette and the mouth! Marita is a woman like any other ... Cigarette, cigarette in the window ... Cigarettes, cigarette cases, cigarette holders and cigars do not choose their buyers ... Flesh is a flower that has bloomed in the soil of the spirit, that's all. The gardener does not have to know the essential formation of the flowerbed, nor does he know what exists at the roots of the plant. Solomon used to say, 'Everything is vanity'; we would add, 'Everything is ignorance.' However, on the surface of situations and things, one can see clearly. A flower that nobody picks is fragrance that is lost. Time not spent on love is like a petal in the manure; a withered rose, an ornament for the ground; rotting flesh, fertilizer for the weeds. Now's your chance – take it!"

We could see that the discarnate spirit was not just an alcoholic. Alcohol was merely an escape valve, since the words he chose to exert his influence and the cunning way he was sensitizing his partner before taking his mind over, suggested techniques used by consummate exploiters of human passions.

This persecutor was no petty tramp.

The extreme eagerness with which he was driving Claudio to the girl, along with the passionate way he was gazing at her, seemed to come from far away. But the occasion did not lend itself to any investigations going back in time. The situation demanded immediate attention. It was necessary to surmount obstacles and come up with measures to protect the poor, defenseless girl.

The strange duet continued between the two friends, who understood each other without using their mouths.

The magnetizer pressed; the magnetizee resisted.

Finally, Claudio took two steps forward to the edge of defeat.

Ideas, contradictions, stimuli and rapture clashed violently with each other in the narrow confines of his skull. The terrible internal battle of a few seconds ago was losing strength. The animal nature had expanded its domain. The discarnate seducer was finishing up his work.

No more the crying out of the spirit. No more the clash of silent random thoughts.

Yes – he deduced, deliriously – he was a man, a man ... Marita, uncontestably younger, was but a woman. So, he did not have to belittle himself. She was weeping, but he could comfort her and warm up her heart.

Mad with lasciviousness, he enveloped her in a long gaze and concluded that if it were not for fear of seeing her run away for good and finding himself disgraced, he would embrace her in his arms like a fearless lad seeking to swallow her tenderness.

Meanwhile, the final arguments were losing their force. Within him, the last barrier that had been restraining his impulses came crashing down. He submitted himself completely to the vampirizer's commands. They merged into one.

Marita looked up at him with pleading eyes, imitating a hunted bird that has no alternative but to hope for the hunter's mercy.

Yoked to his unfortunate companion, Claudio sat down beside her and assumed the airs of a protector who had decided to surpass the limits of pure and simple affection.

"From what I can see, that rascal Gilberto has been using you," he whispered in a sweet voice.

Then, he took her little right hand in his shaking ones, barely able to disguise the double lustfulness possessing him.

Marita felt the impact of the degraded energies that were requesting her compliance and tried not to show her repulsion. She had heard her father's remark in a mixture of surprise and revolt, but she controlled herself and began to respond, trying hard not to blame the young man and attributing to herself her emotional instability. However, to the degree that her adoptive father increased the liberty of his attitudes, Marita lost her will to talk and stayed silent, as if her interest in the problem had disappeared all of a sudden. And in split second, she listed in her mind the bitter impressions of the past few months ... She had noticed the reserved change in the way Claudio treated her. She felt very uneasy at the way he was staring at her. She was scared. Even so, she reprimanded herself. She had devoted to him the respectful love of a true daughter and it was unthinkable for her to defile the immaculate sentiments he had held for her since infancy. She fought against her suspicions, not wanting to believe she was being looked at by him with any sort of indecent purposes in mind.

Even so, no matter what arguments she wielded against herself, an unexplainable sensation was warning her spirit, exhorting her to police the ways with which Claudio was now surrounding her. For the most inane reasons, he was exaggerating his care for her with sentences that had double meanings.

Tortured by doubt, she affirmed her distrust and disavowed herself inwardly.

At that moment, however, her defensive instincts urged prudence; they warned her to be careful, be on her guard. Her spirit had sensed the presence of the "other," so without wanting to, she gathered all her strength and adopted a posture of flight.

She felt unsafe in Claudio's presence.

Her heart was pounding irregularly as she felt he was pondering ways to embrace her, avid for affection.

"Don't try to deny it, dear," stammered Claudio, a bit shaky. "I don't want to upset you, but I've been thinking ... You weren't made for that thoughtless boy. I know you ... I'm not just your father by heart; I'm your friend, as well ... That guy..."

Marita gathered her courage, and anticipating his hesitant allusions, she naively explained that she loved Gilberto, that she trusted him, that he, Claudio, didn't have to worry, and added, almost smiling, that her tears at the moment had nothing to do with any disappointment, but were due to some unknown physical problem. She had suddenly decided that it might be best to reveal her soul a bit more, thereby nipping any possible misunderstandings in the bud. She continued her confidences and told him honestly about her hopes of receiving an engagement ring. She was determined to measure Claudio's reactions, in order to steer, uncompromisingly, her own behavior.

But she got confused when she saw the indignation painted on his face. In the dim light of the room, she could see his face contorted in the grimaces of rage.

She understood that the storm in that willful spirit was about to snap; however, she continued presenting reasons in order to see how he would react.

The explosion was not long in coming.

Claudio clenched his fists, interrupted her and exclaimed angrily:

"I know, I know; you don't have to bore me ... however, I want you to more fully grasp my devotion to you."

Drawing even closer to her, as if he wanted to enwrap her in his very breath, he continued – acting for himself and for the "other" – with his intricately carved complaint:

"My child, you need to hear me out and get what I'm saying."

And assaulting her emotions in order to undermine her resistance:

"You can't imagine what I've been going through. Imagine the tragedy of a man who dies, little by little, unhappy, alone ... a man who gives everything, but receives nothing in return ... You grew up witnessing this ... unhappiness, loneliness. You surely feel sorry for me. This house is my desert. I come home every evening, dead tired, and not one friendly soul is here to greet me. Marcia may be in her forties but she lives for gambling and parties ... You are young, inexperienced, but you must realize this. Forgive my outburst, but my own friends feel sorry for me for having to live such a life ... Can't you see the conflicts of a poor devil, chained to a dishonest wife? But that's not what hurts. At first, the wound bleeds but the calloused heart doesn't feel it. I got used to detesting her ... I give her the money she demands so that she'll hurry up and leave, and that is what consoles me nowadays ... Moreover, Marina, whose affection could give me some comfort, makes a point of humiliating me with her licentiousness! I'm a failure. There are days when I think I'm the saddest clown in the world..."

Under the obsessor's control, Claudio's voice stuck in his throat.

His appearance had changed completely.

As a result, Marita yielded, genuinely sympathetic, and concluding he had accomplished his purpose, Claudio added dramatically:

"You, only you, have kept me bound to this unhappy home. Just the other day, the bank offered me an excellent salary in Mato Grosso, but I thought of you and turned it down ... For you, my daughter, I put up with Marcia's insults, Marina's

ingratitude, my problems at work, and the worries of every day
... Do you know what I mean?"

The girl sighed, trying hard to expel the sensual vibrations
with which the "pair" had enveloped her head, and said calmly:

"Yes, Daddy, I do understand we have our problems ..."

"Our problems!" he repeated, acquiring new strength
to help him reach his objective. "Yes, my child, they are our
problems, but you have to remember that we should also have
our hopes and joys. I long for the time when you see me as
something more than just a father."

He fixed his gaze on the poor girl, who could not hide her
immense surprise, and in a supreme effort to reveal himself, he
emphasized:

"Marita, I may seem like an old man, but you make me
feel young again ... My heart is yours, yours..."

The obsessor, with grimaces of lust, could foresee the
final blow.

But Marita perceived the unmistakable intentions of that
passion-struck man as he held his aged and well-cared-for face
over hers, and tried to pull back.

"No; no!" she cried pleadingly when she felt his breath.

However, Claudio's strength had doubled due to the
power of the "other," and he held her tightly in his arms like a
misbehaving boy.

As if we had rehearsed her defense beforehand, both Pedro
and I leapt towards her, offering her our hands so that she could
escape. The victim thought she was using only her own resources
and managed to stand up in a marvel of lightness. She stood and
faced Claudio, who looked at her with the wary expression of an
animal that has just been wounded.

"Please, Daddy! Don't make my life even more miserable
than it already is ... Spare me the humiliation!"

Under the impact of this unforeseen rejection, the head of the family seemed to disconnect himself from his discarnate friend, reminding us of a beast that had somehow managed to escape from the spell of the tamer. Even so, Claudio's partner carried a load of passion that made it too hard to give up so easily. He recovered his domination so quickly that he imposed his own physiognomic mask on Claudio's face. He clenched his fists and emitted lethal vibrations of rage. A dreadful conflict ensued in both men's minds: in one of them, disappointment and despair; in the other, malice and aggression.

The adoptive father bore a strange burden of anguish mixed with rebelliousness. He was incapable of understanding the contradictory sentiments that were almost driving him insane, and began to clamor inconsiderately:

"This is an outburst of a whole lot of accumulated suffering. I've done all I could to forget but I have failed ... What am I do to with this urge? I'm a leaf blowing in the wind, my daughter! Ever since I first saw you as a little girl, I have had to bear this obsession ... If I were a religious man, I would say I have a demon living inside me, a demon that is constantly pushing me towards you. Whenever I'm around you, I just want to think of you as being the daughter who grew up in my arms, but I can't ... I've read a lot of books on science to try to understand what is happening, but the mystery continues. I thought about going to see a doctor, but I was too ashamed of myself! ... I see only you in everything! I hate Marcia; I despise Marina ... I've prayed for widowhood so that I could offer myself to you without conditions, but it does not come ... I'm jealous with a jealousy that consumes my soul in flames ... I hate that inconsiderate, irresponsible Gilberto."

Claudio's voice had become softer, taking on a woeful tone. It betrayed his emotional upheaval. The persecutor scornfully duplicated everything that Claudio said with emotion, which caused an unexpected about-face. The caring father gave way to the violent would-be lover. Tenderness turned sour, like curdled milk. Showing himself to be totally out of control, he sneered at Marita, traumatizing her with horror, and chided, crazed:

"No, No! I will not let myself be humiliated like this. You know I'm no fool! Two weeks ago, I followed the two of you to Paqueta Island without your knowing it ... I followed your carefree, happy outing, as if I were a dog beaten by fate ... When night came, I saw you embracing, exchanging promises and saying silly things to each other in Ribeira ... I hid in the bushes and saw everything ... ever since, I've been going crazy ... From what I saw, you must have been doing such things for a long time ... You! You, whom I imagined to be untouchable, giving yourself to a numbskull! Foolish girl! You think I don't have good reason to throw you out? You think I don't have the guts to face that rich daddy's boy?"

Changing his fatherly approach, Claudio roared like an animal:

"Marita, you had better remember that you're not a kid anymore! You're just a woman, nothing but a woman, a woman."

The girl sobbed desperately. Realizing that her careless behavior was no longer a secret, she did not dare raise her eyes.

Pedro, still astonished, turned to me and asked:

"See that? Is this man crazy or just shameless?"

I feared his impulsiveness and made him remember brother Felix's sensible, Christian attitude. I discreetly told him that I was praying, begging for help from the higher realms, because at that moment, we did not have the resources to prevent a passionate attack of dolorous consequences.

"Praying?" Pedro asked in disbelief, completely disillusioned. "I don't think angels care about cases like this.

Here, my friend, and in other places where I have seen many old beasts dressed up like ordinary people, only the police…"

Of course, angels did not come in person in answer to the silent prayers I had been uttering since the disagreeable scene first began; nevertheless, help did come.

We heard the sound of the front door being unlocked. Someone entered the house, making a lot of noise.

The shock was providential.

Claudio became frightened and detached himself from the hypnotizer, who stood beside him extremely disappointed.

Marita recouped her strength and lay back on the bed, while Claudio quickly composed himself.

In awe, we witnessed Claudio's amazing ability to pretend like nothing was happening. Without the obsessor's interference, he started to think up excuses to justify himself.

Acting almost mechanically, he cunningly unlocked the bedroom door and opened a nearby window seconds before a slender woman entered the room asking apprehensively:

"Everything all right in here?"

Marcia, his wife, had come home unexpectedly.

She said she was concerned because she had heard a loud voice as she was opening the door. But donning the mask of convention, Claudio spilled the story he had made up a few minutes ago.

He looked meaningfully at Marita and set Marcia's mind at ease by telling her unceremoniously that he had come home just a while ago and had smelled gas. The maid had left the gas on so he had shut it off. He suggested to Marcia that she tell her to be more careful the next time. Justa, the maid, should check all the appliances thoroughly before leaving. He said that he was still concerned so he had opened the windows to air out the place. As he was putting his pajamas on – he continued with a very serious face – he had heard agonized moaning. He ran to the girls' bedroom and found Marita crying but unconscious. She was talking in her sleep, as she often did. He had woke her up in alarm, but alleged that everything was now in order.

The girl, immersed in the dim light, covered her face with a handkerchief to hide her tears and pretended to be asleep, as if she were going from one dream to the next.

Marcia chuckled, completely unaware of the volcano she was facing, and Claudio, as if wanting to make up for her indifference, went back to the living room and made a gesture inviting Marcia to join him.

9

As they sat in the living room, the couple looked at each other awkwardly. Two sworn enemies enjoying a friendly truce.

Marcia presented a very clear picture. She was the usual example of women who fight valiantly against the onslaught of time. No one would ever attribute forty well-lived years to her. Her abundant hair, which medicinal liquids kept perfectly dark and shiny, was arranged in an attractive hairdo that garnished her face, like women who use makeup for artful effects, and who never let themselves be seen unless their pores have been restored to the caress of nature. Slender, with the characteristic look of those who constantly use appetite suppressants to maintain their ideal weight, she came across as a real fashion figure. Her dress was made of white linen lightly imprinted with tiny pink flowers, giving it a certain diaphanousness that accentuated her almost autumnal beauty.

This was the same person we had seen on Marina's mental screens, but now she was exhibited differently, like a kind of book – clearly identifiable but exposed in a livelier, richer binding.

Due to genetics and co-existence, she had obviously influenced her only daughter's traits, because as she sat there she reminded us of Marina in every detail, although she was much more at ease and mature. Rather than displaying their true condition as mother and daughter, the pair could easily be mistaken as two sisters, although Marcia seemed to be kindlier due to the studied gentleness of her manners.

Although her smile was spontaneous, it had the artificial ruse of those who deliberately avoid other people's problems so as not to be held back. Sweetness crafted with polite selfishness; always ready to smile; never ready to be bothered.

Even so, her eyes – ah! Her eyes betrayed her sibylline soul. Gazing at her husband, she seemed interested in capturing his smallest reactions in order to use them to her own advantage.

She was not trying to detect any vestige of his behavior; she wanted to remain emotionally hidden. Calm and poised as she flirted with her husband, she was like a deft traveler who was bent on cheating the customs officers so as to be able to continue her trip without getting caught with smuggled goods. On the other hand, the husband looked like one of those customs officers, experienced with being bribed, more interested in profiting from the situation than in reporting travelers who were as clever as he, himself. Suddenly, at a time in which he had almost been caught red-handed, Claudio outdid himself in being nice. He was ready to listen to Marcia with the apathy of an astute dog that had stopped walking to pay attention to the guiles of a cat.

To Claudio, the circumstances made it worth it to study everything, to listen to everything. After all, what had happened had been inevitable. Marcia had come into Marita's bedroom at a psychological moment. It was crucial for him to appease any misgivings she might have, at the cost of a tolerance that he had not had for a long time. Consequently, he was sprawled out on the sofa, calm and obliging.

Still, we could sense mutual mistrust in both of them. Two mouths that understood each other; two heads that did not see eye to eye. Each sentence came out, pre-fabricated in the throat, disguising the thought.

In a sweet voice, Marcia commented on the problems with the buffet for the charity dance she had helped with. Too many people. Some kids had gotten drunk and had caused trouble. They had stolen some things! So, she was exhausted.

She suspected that in spite of his almost affectionate mood her husband was not interested in a long conversation, so she wanted to make that rare moment last a bit longer; as a result, she made her voice even sweeter.

Affable, she offered him a silver cigarette case.

Claudio refused politely. He did not want to smoke. Marcia tapped the tip of a cigarette several times on the small metallic case, flicked a tiny lighter, and after enveloping herself in a cloud of smoke, she relaxed in the armchair, indicating that she wanted to feel more comfortable.

"Can you imagine?" she said carefully, "I left long before the soiree was ready to end. I was waiting for the auction of the donated gifts, when I got a strange feeling. I felt afraid. I asked Margarida to take over and I left. I was worried because I felt as if there was something wrong at home, perhaps something to do with the electricity, or maybe a thief ... But now I see that you may have had the same hunch. You got here before I did and fixed the oven ... Fortunately, everything turned out OK. Even so, I can see that my return was providential because for many days I've been hoping for a few minutes when you would be calm and in a good mood – like now – so that we could discuss a serious matter ... Something that affects us directly and which I cannot decide without you."

Pedro and I immediately noticed the regimen of attack and counterattack in which those two enemy souls lived, socially enchained to each other due to the demands of their trial. Deducing that his wife was about to take advantage of his temporary benevolence to remind him of his responsibilities, Claudio took off the friendly mask he had worn to start with and adopted a defensive posture. His smile turned into a frown. One could notice a touch of sarcasm on his face. He took the initiative to speak, trying in vain to disguise his bitterness. He was too tired. He alleged exhaustion from working extra hours and asked Marcia to be as brief as possible. He wanted to read, to think, to recoup his strength.

Marcia pretended not to see his ironic look and commented on her own exhaustion.

Perhaps he did not know it, but she had submitted herself to several exams ordered by her gynecologist. She had not slept at all for several nights; she had been suffering from arrhythmia, shortness of breath, a strange feeling of heaviness and hot flashes … Her doctor thought she might be experiencing the early stages of menopause and had prescribed the tests. She had continued feeling weak and moody. Problems around the house were wearing her out. One of the maids had quit, and since then she had had to do the ironing, wax the floor, and to a certain extent, help with the cooking so that Justa would not feel overwhelmed. The refrigerator had broken down and had cost a lot of money to fix. The bills at the end of the month had gone up. Marina had contributed two bonuses from having done an extraordinary job, but it had not been enough. She needed fifteen thousand cruzeiros[9].

At this point, Claudio looked at her sarcastically and asked:

9   Brazilian currency at the time – Tr,

"That's it?"

That question, loaded with scorn, hovered in the air like a lash from a whip.

Marcia could not respond, under the impact of this unexpected thoughtlessness.

Her husband had not shown the least bit of concern about her physical problems. He was deliberately ignoring them. While she was describing them, she had been unnerved by the hard expression in his cold eyes. She recognized that icy attitude of profound disdain. As she was complaining, she got the feeling that Claudio was asking her mentally, "Oh, why don't you just die?" On other occasions, he had asked the same question but with clearly spoken, repeated words. Why did he hate her so much? – she asked herself. She did not expect any tenderness from him since the constant friction between them had incinerated it; however, she thought she still deserved a little of his attention. After all, whenever he himself felt a bit under the weather, she would stay at his bedside even though she did not love him. She would call the family doctor. She would immediately do everything he prescribed. Even so, when she had told him about the tests, which were important for avoiding a compromising surgery, she received two dry monosyllables, which her husband had thrown in her face like two jabs.

Silence hung in the air until Claudio said he needed to go. But Marcia stopped him, exclaiming angrily:

"No, don't! I need you here. This isn't just my home. Can't you see? Marina and Marita ... We raised our kids with love and care ... While they were still very young they were angels; now that they've grown up, they're a nightmare. I've suffered in silence, but now ... this can't go on without your getting involved. Between one and the other, you cannot be indifferent. I welcomed Marita into my arms as if she were my own daughter.

I have put up with insults and have neglected my health, my time ... I haven't held back; I've done all I could ... She has never lacked anything, but now..."

"What about now?" asked Claudio, surprised.

"Can't you see the humiliation Marina is constantly exposed to?" replied Marcia in sudden tears, as if she could cry at will. "Can't you see the problems our daughter's going through?"

Claudio laughed sarcastically.

"Oh, come on, Marcia; enough dramatics! You talk about Marina as if the scatterbrain had been condemned to hang. I don't get it. She looks as happy and misguided as ever. If I have to get involved in any of her problems, it will be to warn and stop her. If it weren't for you giving her everything she wants, along with your bad examples, I would correct her, even if I had to put her in a reformatory."

"My God! I don't believe this!" Marcia exclaimed.

She stopped crying, alarmed at the conversation having taken this unpredicted turn. "It's the truth," Claudio continued mercilessly. "Just yesterday, because of my job I had to go to a cocktail party put on by one of my bosses in a nightclub. But I had to fake a headache and leave. Do you know why? Because our daughter, whom you believe to be a saint, was there, in the arms of a rich old man. And he wasn't kissing her like a father. I was so embarrassed that I asked a colleague to apologize for me. I rushed out before Marina could see me.

"Oh, the poor thing!" Marcia objected, cheeks afire, utterly shocked.

Both of them were automatically taking off their masks. They were two spirits facing each other with undisguised loathing; two sworn enemies, aversion against aversion.

The bitter dialogue continued:

"Poor thing? Why?"

Marcia looked him up and down with an expression of sarcasm and began accusing him:

"I refuse to discuss your presence as a mature, married man in such a place, because I don't believe your story about having to ingratiate yourself to your bosses so late at night. You've always been immoral, undignified, and a liar, but because I love my family, I'm willing to forget all that so you can grasp the full situation."

Trying to come up with the right way to sensitize him to the outcome she had in mind, Marcia calculatedly lowered the harshness of her voice and softened it in order to seem less aggressive.

"Claudio, please listen to what I'm saying," she continued almost mellifluously, "Marina has never hid the truth from me. Don't be malicious. Ever since Nemesio's wife began to worsen, Marina has been caringly dividing her time between her obligations at work and her boss's home, where the poor woman is dying little by little … You have to admire her selflessness, because she wouldn't have to be interested in the Torres family to the point of staying up at night with them so many times simply out of a spirit of sacrifice … I don't know if you have ever seen her when she comes home in the morning with bags under her eyes and sunken cheeks."

A complex reaction was taking place in Claudio's inventive mind, however. As he listened to Marcia's offensive words, he felt like hitting her. He blushed with indignation, but controlled himself, not because he was giving up his scornful attitude, but because he was sure Marita was eavesdropping. He longed to win her at any price. Especially now that he had already declared his love, he had no intention of backing off. He would continue his pursuit.

Marcia, deceived, had accepted the nightmare story and believed Marita was sleeping, since she had accepted his presence in Marita's bedroom without saying a word.

Claudio, on the other hand, knew Marita was listening. He would not do or say anything that was incompatible with the gallantry that he had started to develop. If he were to yell at Marcia, it would only push Marita away. Therefore, he decided to put up with Marcia's mockeries and insults, whatever they might be, while studying the best way to manipulate the conversation to his best advantage.

Moreover, the discarnate friend beside him was reinforcing the hardness of his soul and influencing his thoughts. The lies of one complemented those of the other. Together, they agreed that it would be best for them to examine all the details and speak with intention. They would manipulate Marcia in order to get to Marita. Marcia would be their tool. They would use her as a trampoline to reach their goal.

All these considerations flashed in Claudio's mind while Marcia tried hard to defend her daughter. Dominated by new thoughts, he did not smile but softened his facial expression, like someone who had resigned himself to the dictates of patience.

Marcia was somewhat disarmed by Claudio's impassivity, which she interpreted as benevolence. She continued:

"It just so happens that Mr. Torres is completely lost in the face of a tragedy that his fortune cannot relieve. Gobs of money, yet a broken heart; business thriving, yet death knocking at the door. Marina felt sorry for him. She devoted herself to the sick woman so much that she ended up discovering that man's suffering. He knows he's about to become a widower … That's why she has been trying to cheer him up as best she can."

"But why like that?! Drowning themselves in alcohol and nighttime pleasures like two ill-behaved children?! They weren't exactly praying for Beatriz's health."

"Don't be sarcastic. If you were in the same situation, you wouldn't seek consolation in tears; you would look for something to get your mind off your problems. I don't see anything wrong with Mr. Torres escaping to a happier environment at such times in order to recover a bit, and I don't see anything wrong with him treating Marina like his own daughter and the spoiled doll she has always been. Everything has been up front and transparent. Beatriz and Nemesio only had a son; they never enjoyed the love of a daughter or adopted a girl like we did. Since I'm her mother, Marina tells me everything. You know she's very sensitive and caring. She feels sorry for her boss and tries to make him feel better."

"Make him feel better?" Claudio teased, mocking once more.

"Sarcasm won't do us any good," said Marcia, feigning disappointment. "Marina has been acting properly, so much so, that our conversation should clarify a very serious matter."

She changed her tone of voice to be more persuasive, sweeter, and went on:

"You know that a few months ago Marita fell in love with Gilberto, the Torres' son ... Watching the two of them always together, I really believed the young man felt the same way about her."

Mixing discretion with malice, Marcia began to tell Claudio about the tête-a-têtes, the outings, the phone calls, the notes ... She told him she had been very anxious a few days ago when she had caught them off by themselves on a Sunday trip to the Tijuca Forest. She had been upset at finding them completely alone, under the trees... As a woman and mother, she was worried about her adopted daughter.

At this point, Claudio had fire in his eyes and his heart was pounding as he grasped what she was hinting at.

So Marcia knew about it, too. Claudio was not fooled by her distrustful tone of voice when confiding in him. Obviously, she knew some details that she would prefer to keep hidden. It was not only Paqueta, then ...Tijuca Forest had also been the stage for the meetings and kisses that Claudio detested. He would never have expected such news under his own roof. He had no idea Marcia knew so much about what he thought only he, himself, knew ... At that moment, he completely forgot the little girl that had grown up in his arms, and he disregarded his condition as a father called to defend her name. Instead, goaded by jealousy, the wounded animal erupted, the wild man who usually lay dormant in politeness.

Rubbing his fingers against the palm of his hands in a personal gesture that always meant displeasure, he stood up, took a few steps around the room and exclaimed:

"Ingratitude!"

Marcia watched the scene with the glee of someone who has accomplished her ends, because from the very beginning of the conversation, she had aimed to create a climate that was favorable for her real daughter to the detriment of the other. She believed that with such a reproach, her husband had summed up in just one word his obvious disgust for the girl she wanted out of the way. She did not realize that the reality of the matter was that Claudio's indignation was rooted in the bitterness of a rejected lover; consequently, she wore a smile of triumph.

However, we were able to analyze Claudio's mental screens and see how much he suffered from Marita's rejection. Mentally, he saw himself facing Gilberto, sizing up his strength. Ah! If only he could get his hands on him at that moment! He would pour out the entire weight of his rage on that young man and break every bone in his body...

"I'm touched by your reaction against Marita!"

Registering Marcia's reticent remark, Claudio realized the inadvisable role he was beginning to play. He had almost given himself away completely. He had gone beyond the limits of circumspection for his own sake, and made an effort to compose himself. He realized that Marcia approved of his repulsion, seeing him only as a father wounded by the circumstances. He let her get comfortable with that interpretation as he mentally fenced himself in on the defensive. He repressed the despair that possessed him and sat down again to relax his tense nerves. He erased every trace of outward agitation and appeared suddenly calm.

Marcia, whose intent was to accumulate advantages for her daughter, had no idea she was being deluded in this game, in which husband and wife were two cunning partners making calculated blows against each other. Assuming she was in complete control of the situation, she said calmly:

"I find your respectable attitude as a father encouraging and pleasing. Thank God, I can now see you as the head of our home and family."

Claudio listened, attentive.

"I think you should know," she continued, "that Gilberto actually wants nothing to do with Marita; she's just infatuated with him. The boy's actually in love with Marina, and everything points to an advantageous marriage, one we cannot afford to lose. "

Claudio skillfully deduced that the chance for him to take revenge was now. Pretending not to know the web of sentiments involving the two girls, he commented on the new aspects of the problem in a loud voice in order to be clearly heard by Marita, whom he knew was eavesdropping in the adjacent room. After emphasizing the excellence of his adoptive daughter's character, highlighting the love and tenderness he would always offer her, he stated jocularly:

"Ah! That rat! ... So, this farce of hanging around with Marita is nothing but pandering and trickery ... That rascal's playing games. It's lovers' billiards – hitting one ball in order to hit another."

He listed some poor girls whose trust had been betrayed, and explained that Marita was susceptible to a psychosis of serious consequences. If Gilberto wanted to marry Marina, he should make it very clear. He, Claudio, would not be against it, but he demanded transparency.

Marcia suddenly felt flattered because he seemed very open to the idea, so she gave more details about Marina's confidences to her.

The young man had confessed. He admired not only Marina's personal charms but also her fine upbringing. At first, they had only greeted one another from time to time. However, he had needed someone to help him translate some French texts. Marina had displayed her competence. The work she did was so good that it had received the praise of the Embassy. Ever since that enterprise, they had worked almost as one. Marina had told her that the ever-solicitous Nemesio, himself, had already begun to call her his daughter-in-law.

Claudio deliberately interrupted her from time to time:

"Marcia, I don't hear so well; please, speak up a bit."

Marcia raised her voice and said that, despite Beatriz's health, the couple was, at the moment, translating some beautiful English poems, writing sentimental notes in the margins that expressed their mutual love, composing a beautiful album whose reading had brought forth tears of emotion from Marcia. The love between the two was as clear as water. It was necessary to help their daughter materialize all her hopes. She affirmed that she felt relieved to have realized in time that Gilberto's upbringing did not suffer the deficiencies of Marita, for whom he would not be a happy partner. She was absolutely convinced that it was Claudio's and her responsibility to guide the situation. She added that the help that Marina devoted to Beatriz had tightened the bonds between the two young people, and believing that Claudio was angry, anticipating probable problems for their adoptive child, she finished by saying wittily that Marita would turn out all right. Young women's inclinations were their own problems.

Claudio did not believe a word of it. As a father, he was disappointed in his daughter. Her nighttime visits to bohemian hangouts, her embarrassing treatment of her boss, left him no doubts. On the contrary, Marcia's enthusiastic news about Marina woke him up to more aggressive realities. It meant that Marina did not have any scruples between the older man and the younger one. Otherwise, as husband, he could not let himself be deceived. He saw his wife as a woman who had not been faithful to her commitments at home, a woman that he, himself, had created with his examples of uncontrolled emotions. He had nothing to complain about. Living amid an unworthy social circle, Marcia had turned into a cunning and cruel individual. She had learned to put on a front in order to win. Of course, she had not told him everything she knew. She was probably as informed as he was about all of Marina's excuses regarding Mr. Torres. She was capable of covering up all inappropriateness, perhaps encouraging irresponsibility if there was profit in it for her. However, this was the right moment to gain Marita's trust, and for that reason he softened his hardened spirit, stifled his rebelliousness and went along with the farce, feigning trust in the girl they both loved as a daughter. He would try to distract her, to renew her, and working with Marcia, he would try to get Marita included on a sightseeing trip to Buenos Aires. He had been invited along by friends from the bank. Marita would forget; she would forget.

The conversation continued, but work called us back to Marita's bedroom, where the girl's suffering was exploding silently in vibrations of intense pain.

10

Marita was stretched out on her bed, weeping inconsolably.

The revelations she had heard in that dialog in the next room turned her heart over like pincers of fire. She felt abandoned; she wanted to die.

So – she thought to herself – all of Gilberto's devotion was superficial! He had appropriated her soul and had thrilled her sentiments, only to leave her without commiseration.

In fact, she remembered that a few weeks earlier he had asked her if she knew any other languages. Somewhat vexed, she had told him she had barely finished elementary school.[10] The young man then took a poem by Shelley from his pocket. He read it in English and then translated it into beautiful verse. Then, he suggested she attend night school. He would help her because he was acquainted with some distinguished teachers. She had laughed and said she wanted a home – the school of a home with him. It was only now, in her heartbreak, that she finally realized the extent of his disappointment when he left her.

---

10 In Brazil, until 1970, elementary school was obligatory and lasted only four years. Later on, with the enactment of the new Law of Directives and Bases of National Education no. 5.692/71, mandatory schooling was extended to eight years, with the merging of both Elementary School and Lower High School. – Tr.

Ah, yes! He wanted to marry an educated girl. You fool! – she said to herself – You're nothing but an ignorant fool! Marina was different: she did speak other languages.

Everything was already planned, decided.

That was why Marina had been avoiding her the last few days. The more she had tried to please her sister, the more standoffish she was.

Now, she could also understand why Gilberto had seemed bored and irritable. However – she asked herself sadly – if he despised her so much, why had he abused her trust? Why the rapture with which he had enchained her soul to the unforgettable feelings of a girl that had suddenly become a woman? Hadn't he sealed a marriage pact with her? Hadn't he shown extreme tenderness on their Sunday outings, when they enjoyed a more intimate togetherness?

Incapable of doubting the authenticity of the love she had received, Marita turned mentally to the sister that was robbing her of the little bit of joy in her life. This new misfortune – she conjectured – was Marina's fault. She was absolutely certain that Marina had seduced Gilberto and had caught him in a web of craftiness like no one else could. Gilberto had taken the bait. A bird in the snare. Now that she grasped the entire plot, she felt irremediably hurt. She was overwhelmed with tears, under the weight of family considerations. It was vital that she remember that she was an orphan and an uneducated girl. Nothing would be left to her; all to Marina. Marina deserved everything; herself, nothing.

Marcia's little speech a few moments ago was like the torture of a defendant who has just heard an unappealable sentence. Marita wept, unwilling to accept her situation. The possibility of losing Gilberto made her think about either murdering Marina or "disappearing." She remembered the tragedies published in the press, but fratricide was repulsive to her heart. On the other hand, the idea of suicide, like a seed buried in the depths of her being and summoned forth by the faint outline of her soul, had suddenly begun to germinate. She toyed with the idea and the unfortunate suggestion took on a body. Negative thoughts began to assail her. To surrender Gilberto and forget all her plans hurt much more than dying – she thought, disconsolate. But would such cowardice be justified? So, she rejected the summons, and in tears she promised herself that she would be brave. She would struggle to be happy. She would talk to Gilberto and together the two of them would banish the pending threat. Still, if Gilberto refused her arguments, what would become of her life, if, in addition to the blow she had just received, she still had to deal with the ghost of her adoptive father's weird urges afterwards?

Why was life being so cruel? Should she forget about the young man she loved in a natural consecration and accept the passion of the older man, whom she had learned to respect as a father, and who was beckoning her to a kind of relationship that was totally unacceptable to her? She had been terrified as she listened to him a few moments ago. She had heard a touch of triumphant glee in his voice on account of the happiness with which he would get Gilberto out of the way on the field where he promised to seize her for himself.

Claudio seemed to be addressing her from the next room, although he was speaking to his wife. All those flattering references with which he was praising her in front of Marcia confirmed his decision to make her yield, to divert her from Gilberto. Between disgust and pity, she remembered his caresses, which only that very evening she had managed to understand.

How could she get away from him?

Like a flower yielding to the gale of trial, she kept asking herself: Why? Why?

Weighing the latest events, for the first time she felt afraid of that family nest to which she felt bound through the bonds of the heart.

Suddenly, she remembered her mother ... Ah! She had never imagined that a woman's heart could meet with dilemmas as afflictive as those she must have had to deal with from one moment to the next! How her mother must have suffered at leaving her at the dawn of life? Marita had never really known the circumstances surrounding her birth. But she now concluded that perhaps her mother had also drunk from the same bitter chalice from which she was drinking right now! How many nights of mental agony she must have spent alone, caressing her in her womb! What insults had she suffered? What privations had she endured? She, who knew nothing at all about her father, reflected on the suffering of her mother, young and abandoned, as she waited in vain for her father's love and protection night after night. When Marcia had told her about Aracelia, she had described her as a "frolicsome girl." Could that be true? Maybe she had laughed in order not to weep, using the noise of parties to hide the cries of her soul ... Who knows? Maybe she had devoted herself to some forbidden young man, who had been stolen from her love as a young woman.

With tears streaming down her face, she wished she could be a child again ... Why hadn't her mother lived so that they could struggle together? They could have dedicated themselves to each other. They could have shared in each other's suffering...

In the shop where she worked, she had often heard people talking about communications with the dead and experiments having to do with the continuation of life in the Beyond ... Could it be true? – she asked herself. If Aracelia, now free, was alive somewhere, it was obvious that she would be following her daughter's Calvary and sharing in her unhappiness.

Mechanically, she begged her mother's spirit to bless, strengthen and protect her ... In spite of not having any defined religious beliefs, she said a silent prayer, one that was worthy of being called a profound invocation.

We were trying to console her and ease her mind when two discarnate women entered the room unexpectedly.

They greeted us affectionately and said they were familiar spirits connected to that domestic refuge.

Of the two, the one that seemed the lesser experienced approached the girl as she prayed. She was having a hard time controlling herself. She trembled, trying to wipe her silent tears. The spirit leaned over the bed like any unfortunate and afflicted mother would do when afraid of waking a loved one.

Although we had not been advised ahead of time, there could be no doubt. This was the girl in the picture Marita kept as an image on her mental screen. Aracelia, supported by the sweet affection of her venerable friend, was right there in front of us! A loving mother, she had perhaps come from far away to mitigate her daughter's anguish ... We were truly moved as the poor mother knelt down to kiss Marita's hair ... Oh! The mysterious secrets of Divine Providence ... Who can explain in human words the essence of the love that God has placed in the maternal heart?! ... The woman gently leaned down and embraced Marita lovingly, like a plant enfolding the only flower that had been born from it.

The suffering girl suddenly calmed down. Divining the visit she had longed for, she released her tension, mentally sensing the presence of her mother, whose face she was lovingly attempting to recall and reconstruct.

At the same time, another moving scene was superposed on the first.

As Aracelia prayed and wept in profound silence, she searched mentally for another woman, whose memory renewed her energies.

The discarnate mother saw herself as a little girl alongside the simple laundry woman who, in her last incarnation, had brought her onto the stage of human life. She was grasping the hem of the skirt of that sickly young woman, whose legs were immersed in the river, washing clothes to make a living ... The sounds coming from the memory were so acute that she could hear the sound made by her mother's hands as she scrubbed the soapy clothes ... She recalled the gentle look in her mother's eyes asking her to be patient ... She saw herself sitting quietly on the sand, waiting, waiting, after her mother had put her fragile body there, a short distance away, in order to do her work ... She also remembered how happy and joyous she felt when her mother put her to bed to the sounds of the old lullaby in her hollow brick house. Gazing as if she were searching the infinite reaches of space for those warm arms that time had taken away, Aracelia situated herself in such a way that Marita's head was in her lap. Emotional to the point of tears, and as if her own lips were the lips of her humble and sickly mother, whom she would never forget, Aracelia, in tears of resignation, sang softly:

Beautiful angel of my life,
Rest, my sweet darling.
Sleep, sleep in my arms,
While the night has not yet come.
Sleep, my dear child;
Weep not, my charm;
Sleep, sleep, my life,
O treasure whom God has given me...

As if she had been suddenly magnetized, Marita fell into a deep sleep.

That done, the other woman, who was watching over Aracelia, drew her gently to her, and with the clear intention of consoling her, she held her while addressing us sadly:

"Brothers, our Aracelia is not yet in any shape to help her daughter."

And she added amid kindness and disappointment:

"Please, forgive our interference. In certain times of difficulty, we mothers have nothing to give our children except an old lullaby!"

Then, she left, supporting Aracelia, who had collapsed in her arms, sobbing...

We had not yet recovered emotionally, when we saw Marita's spirit leave her physical body, displaying the anxiety of a child looking for the warmth of her mother's arms in vain ... But, as happens to most spirits while incarnate on the physical plane, she looked insecure and mentally hesitant ... She staggered around in the room, and when I realized that Pedro was about to support her, I restrained him and reminded him that our direct intervention might hinder Marita's desires. In order to be of more effective help, we should leave her alone, under our discreet watch so as to identify her innermost needs.

Suddenly, something unexpected happened.

Marita's raptures went up in smoke and her child-like mood vanished. Aracelia's daughter disappeared and her feminine personality appeared, strong and clear.

Marita could not see us. Her mind was fuzzy, something characteristic of very young persons who are still incapable of detailed impressions when they are taken to an unfamiliar place; however, as is also the case with them when they have their mind set on something, be it a toy or a piece of candy, Marita concentrated all her thoughts on one, sole point: Gilberto.

She wanted to see Gilberto, to hear Gilberto.

Such impulses, emitted repeatedly, galvanized her will, lending her thoughts a bit of clarity, although they were only directed at her womanly longings. This partial concentration gave her an inner support point and, seemingly in control of herself, albeit completely bound to her ardent desire, she left the room and went down the long flight of stairs that bordered the elevator, exiting the large building like a sleepwalker magnetized by her own thoughts.

We followed her closely but entrusted her to her own discretion.

Our job was to study her extroverted impulses and to consult her intentions. But we had no doubt about where she was headed.

In a short time, Claudio's adopted daughter arrived at Nemesio's place, with which we had already become familiar.

Instinctively certain about whom she was seeking and disregarding any conventions of shape or number, she went inside with Gilberto's image in her mind.

Driven by the indefinable perceptions of the soul, she headed for a large, back bedroom, and although we could not tell right away if we had been right in leaving her alone so that we could observe her reactions, she was hit by a terrible shock.

We, ourselves, were astonished, but we could only help her afterwards.

Upon entering the room, Marita found Gilberto in Marina's arms, and screamed, appalled:

"You bastard! Bastard!"

However, her strong language had no effect at all on the young couple. They were completely absorbed in their exchange of affective gratifications.

Pedro and I did not say a word. We automatically rushed over to the smitten girl and tried to control her convulsive rage.

A few minutes later she woke up in her physical body, reminding us of a small, wounded wild animal back in its cage. She slowly opened her eyes and had the look of an insane person whose muscles have relaxed after a dangerous fit of rage. She felt her sweat-drenched forehead. She turned on the light, eager for physical reality. She looked around at the walls and confirmed the fact that she was in bed in her own home

Little by little, she calmed down and regained her strength; however, what she felt was a kind of tense, bitter tranquility.

Was that a nightmare? – she asked herself, terrified, or, who knows, maybe a fit of madness?

Her head ached and she felt ill, feverish.

Marita had returned to her physical body too quickly for us to anesthetize her memory.

Her mind retained the details of what she had seen and heard, and imprisoned again between the superficial impressions of the bodily senses and the notion of the deep truth, which she could not understand, she began to weep in agony and could only get back to sleep with relative calm when daylight broke.

11

We continued working together to assist Beatriz, who was growing weaker and weaker by the day. We also checked in on Marita at the end of our day's work.

November had arrived with torrential rains.

One particular day, after a few hours of intense heat, enormous clouds hid the hilltops, shortening the sunset with water and fog. The wet streets of Copacabana were at the peak of rush hour and were even noisier than usual. Everybody on the sidewalks seemed to be competing in a race – an improvised marathon. Busses, coming from the north part of the city and from downtown, unloaded long lines of people, obviously anxious for the tranquility of home. Cars, reflected in the mirror of the wet asphalt, honked their horns impatiently trying to get the traffic to move. Commuters covering their heads, jostling each other as they waited for busses and taxis.

Claudio's adopted daughter arrived at the tall building, struggling against torrents of water.

The bus ride from Copacabana to Flamengo had not taken long, and the distance from the bus stop to the apartment was just a matter of steps; even so, she took off her raincoat before entering the elevator as if she had just gotten out of the swimming pool.

Everything was cold and dark around her; however, with eyes heavy from fatigue and sleeplessness, Marita's tormented soul was even gloomier than the rainy evening. On the way up, a neighbor had called her attention to some ornaments she was carrying in a basket. The girl glanced down at the colored paper that was going to be used for a birthday party in one of the other apartments and automatically made a brief compliment before silently focusing on her own thoughts. She felt relieved in having arrived home.

Nobody was waiting for her.

Alone, she stretched out on her bed and tried to review the events of the day before, but her stomach was demanding food. She remembered she had not eaten a thing all day. She got up and searched the kitchen, but did not find anything appealing. In spite of her lowered body temperature, reflected in her cold hands, she felt excited, hot. She was tired of thinking; her nerves were a wreck. Iced tea sounded good. She opened the refrigerator again, found some and filled a glass. Her blinking eyes stopped on the telephone a few steps away. She could not help herself. She dialed. From the Torres' residence an imprecise voice told her that Gilberto had gone out. She felt even worse...

She dragged herself back to her bedroom and opened the window. She wanted to find some relief in the fresh air.

She bent over the windowsill and contemplated the city below. Under the rain, the cars looked like animals on the run.

The girl thought and thought ... As she pondered the illuminated windows outside, she deduced that thousands of people lived there, perhaps enduring problems like hers or even worse. She asked herself in vain why she felt so strangely attached to Gilberto, when hundreds of young men lived nearby with excellent qualities to interest her heart.

She felt discouraged, dissatisfied. She longed to forget, to escape from herself.

She thought about putting on a jacket and going back down to the street for some distraction, despite the bad weather, but decided against it, not only because of the downpour but because of her body, which did not want to move even if her spirit did. Exacerbation and exhaustion. She tried to get comfortable on the bed and engulf herself in a novel she had started, but then she remembered Claudio. Her adoptive father was rarely late, and since last night, she could not think of him without being afraid. She got up and got ready for bed. Cautiously, she turned off all the lights. When he arrived, he would surely think she was out.

Shut off in the darkness, she threw herself on the bed with the abandonment of someone who has thrown off an inconvenient burden, and started to ponder ... She realigned in her memory all the hopes and dreams, trials and frustrations of her short existence, letting her tears dampen the pillowcase.

A few minutes later, she heard Claudio moving from one room to another. Due to the subtlety of his footsteps, she could tell when he approached her door to peek into her room. He tried the knob but did not insist. She and Marina had the habit of locking their rooms whenever they left at night. She heard the unmistakable noise of a bottle being opened, and then a bit later she could tell that he had gone back out onto the street. She could also tell how upset he had been by the way he slammed the door as he went out.

She felt relieved and less disturbed.

Marita really was alone because even the two obsessors had left with their companion.

The hours dragged by, slow, difficult…

It was 11:00 p.m. sharp when Pedro and I began the magnetic treatment. We prayed, asking for Christ's blessing and brother Felix's help with the exhausted girl.

We mobilized all the meager resources available to us.

At first, she reacted negatively and struggled to stay awake, but she finally gave in and fell asleep.

We worked cautiously, reducing her ability to move, in order to keep her from going to Gilberto, as had happened the night before.

In fact, disengaged from her physical body, she expressed complete alienation and did not show the least bit of interest in her surroundings.

Totally absorbed in the passion that consumed all her energies, she asked repeatedly:

"Gilberto! Where's Gilberto?"

She tried to regain her balance; however, she teetered unsteadily.

"Somebody help me!" she begged desperately. "I have to meet him, meet him…"

We rushed to her assistance.

We were about to leave when a kindly discarnate woman greeted us, saying she had come on behalf of brother Felix. He was waiting for us at an assistance outpost.

Helpful, she embraced the patient maternally and we set out.

The newcomer, who introduced herself as sister Percilia, said that our destination was a nearby neighborhood, where a respectable Spiritist-Christian institution would offer us shelter.

I noticed that she and Pedro exchanged warm greetings, revealing that they had already met. However, Percilia did not dwell on personal matters. More focused on her job than herself, she talked to the fragile girl and encouraged her. She made an effort to decentralize her attention by pointing out scenes and events on the way, but to no avail. The girl expressed no other thoughts, words and objectives, except those that related to Gilberto. It was pure fascination, influencing all her reflexes. Every time Percilia pointed something out, she responded by asking where and when she would at last be taken to Gilberto. Percilia would reply, showing admirable maternal sense without any impatience or boredom, as if she were talking to a sick daughter, trying to readjust her by means of loving solicitude, a behavior that Pedro and I were compelled to imitate. So, neither Pedro nor I felt inclined to regard negatively any of the girl's naïve remarks that indicated clean and innocent sexual impulses, rendering her, at that moment, an extroverted child.

When we arrived at the place where the spirit-related activities would take place, we were greeted by Felix in person, accompanied by two friends.

The instructor told us he had received our request, emphasizing, modestly, that since he had some spare time, he had decided to come and see what was happening.

Marita looked at him absent-mindedly, indifferently, completely incapable of grasping the importance of the wise man who was covering her with fatherly kindness.

Mentally pinned to her memories of the young Torres, the questions she asked would have really offended us, had we not been aware of her predicament.

Supported by Felix, who was leading us with enormous tolerance, she entered the building asking if we had finally arrived at the club where she usually met Gilberto. When taken to a spacious room, where she would receive the magnetic help she needed, she wanted to know why the dance room had changed so much. Noticing a small team of discarnate spirits, who were involved in a task of assistance in the opposite corner, she commented that the band should keep playing, and hearing the cars honking out on the street, she tried to find out if Gilberto had come to dance with her.

With her reasoning obliterated as it was, she projected the mental creations she fabricated in her mind, without the slightest notion of outer reality.

Felix listened to all her juvenile talk with the tenderness of a father – serious but not stern, understanding but without a sentimental attitude, which could compromise his authority as a true educator. He answered all her questions with all the kindness and circumspection owed to someone who is ill, making sure not to hurt her feelings or encourage her illusions.

He had her sit in a big armchair and put her to sleep under light hypnosis.

Marita stopped talking, lost in pleasant memories, while the instructor gave her soothing passes.

The magnetic treatment was long and detailed.

Next, Felix asked her what she wanted most from us; Marita, stammered shyly, asking for Gilberto. She said she was not sure if this place was actually the same club where they usually met … She asked for help, protection … With the impulse of a child eager for its mother's lap, she turned to Percilia and wept quietly, as if begging us not to stop her.

Without the patient's grasping the depth of what he was saying, the compassionate brother Felix told us that, unfortunately, the treatment he had given her was only superficial and would only help her sleep physically; that her juvenile passion had developed into a serious psychosis; that the poor girl had surrendered to emotional insanity to the point of falling into the worst kind of possession, the kind in which the victim happily accepts the imbalance in which he or she is consumed.

He emphasized the fact that he had examined Marita's body with the intention of interrupting her mental alienation just as it was beginning, perhaps with the help of some serious illness that would force her to stay in bed and also modify her mind, predisposing her to a different attitude. However, the girl's body was not capable of receiving such providential help. Marita was extremely disoriented and weak, and would discarnate if he tried. There was no choice but to wait for her own mental resistance.

Felix asked us to escort her back home, and Pedro, Percilia and I set out.

Marita did not seem to be any better as far as her mental state was concerned, but the magnetic help did have an immediate, healthy effect, because readjusted to her physical body, she began to rest peacefully. When we left, she was fast asleep.

We said goodbye to Percilia under a starry sky. Pedro and I were alone again. Maybe because he sensed my unspoken question, Pedro asked:

"Andre, do you know who that woman was?"

I shook my head and he said:

"She's the same woman I saw in the night club the day I attacked my son-in-law in a thoughtless gesture. She's the stranger who helped me back to Beatriz's room; the only difference is that today she wasn't wearing the luminous badge ... But I'm positive. She was the same person..."

12

Pedro and I were still speculating about Percilia, when somebody greeted us affectionately.

It was brother Felix. He had come to say goodbye.

Although a spirit admired for his selflessness and knowledge, and revered by all the sowers of the Good, when he referred to the protagonists in the family drama we were involved in, his eyes would well up with tears.

His face revealed not only fraternal sympathy, but immense love for those four souls brought together again in that pleasant corner of Rio.

We stood motionless, breathing the soft breezes that gently rippled the waters of Guanabara Bay as the dawn sky enhanced the twinkling stars. We were endeared by his paternal kindness, as if he were an ordinary man taking a break with us on the seashore.

The devotion he displayed as he revealed the treasures of his heart through words was so pure and so great, that as the often-restless Pedro listened to his comments, he willingly did what he had promised: not one impulsive comment; not one thoughtless interjection.

The instructor's attitude as he discussed the struggles of the physical plane enlightened and captivated us. Grandeur in every sentence; the light of sentiment in each idea.

Without even asking, he had won our willingness to lend our assistance to Claudio's household, the stability of which was in danger, according to Felix himself.

He felt sorry for those four creatures – he explained kindly – thrown into the ocean of the earthly experience without the compass of faith. At first, he tried hard to open a spiritual path for them, but had failed. They were too deeply immersed in the mists of illusion, hypnotized by the temporary pleasures of the carnal senses, like birds trying to eat the rotten peel of a fruit instead of tasting the rich flavor of the pulp inside.

Revealing a little more of his inner self, Felix told us he had been present when Claudio was reborn; that he had accompanied Marcia from birth; and that he had closely followed Marina and Marita's reincarnations, enabling us to imagine, without boasting of any virtue or superiority, all the tears that overcoming such obstacles must have cost him.

He had pledged his devotion, friendship, trust and time in order to involve them is some sort of charitable endeavor to cultivate their latent spirituality, but Claudio and Marcia, once again on the physical stage under the inevitable and providential forgetfulness of the past, were recapitulating certain unfortunate experiences.

In the spirit world, before they had begun their earthly task again, they had analyzed the needs and regrets that were afflicting their consciences and had promised to use the reward of a new internment in the physical vehicle to work on their inner sublimation and correct the excesses of former times by means of sweat in serving others. However, when they had not yet fully reached the prime of their corporeal energies, they had embraced passions that were frustrating all potential for liberation any time soon. He, Felix, and other friends had tried hard to help them, but all attempts had been fruitless. The four spirits resisted every kind of reparative suggestion and immediately rejected any new constructive project.

Kind friends from other times tried to offer them their invaluable help, but ended up being disappointed, leaving the four to their own fate.

Claudio and Marcia, especially, decided money and uncontrolled sex were the most important things in their lives, and they were doing nothing but upsetting the tranquility at home. Consequently, Marina and Marita did not have any foundations for true happiness. Still very young, the two got involved in perils and temptations, from which they could not disentangle themselves without dolorous scars on their souls.

Claudio's rebelliousness had been so strong that, at that critical and threatening time in his life, he did not have anyone he could count on beyond Divine Providence, except for a few friends. Even so, these friends – he added modestly, obviously pondering his own difficulties – were not close enough for him to ask for special help. They had countless responsibilities of their own and could only offer him sporadic and uncertain support.

We understood what our humble benefactor was driving at and we promised our full commitment to the assistance plan he would outline.

We embraced the opportunity; fulfilling it would not be difficult for us.

Besides the time my superiors had granted to me to work with Pedro, I also had permission from the appropriate authorities to pursue a two-year training period in any one of Nosso Lar's organizations that was involved in sexual psychology work for educational purposes. I knew that brother Felix was the director of one of the best institutes of that kind, so I asked him to endorse my request.

I would be happy to have the chance to study and work, profiting from his experience and receiving his sponsorship.

The instructor reaffirmed his humility, saying that the endeavor for which he was responsible might not meet our expectations, but he felt obligated to support our studies.

Pedro noticed my enthusiasm and did not hesitate to share it.

He would make the same request.

Our friend was truly moved and said that such decision would be a great comfort to him because, responding to the dictates of kindness and gratitude, he had been given permission to welcome Beatriz in his own home as soon as she left the physical sphere after discarnating.

Having Pedro – the father she had never forgotten – and her together would bring him great happiness.

Both of them would enjoy the blessing of each other's company and would rejoice remembering the past and making new plans for work and happiness.

As Pedro was expressing his gratefulness, Felix lovingly said goodbye and left.

Pedro and I outlined plans and discussed means to carry them out.

Pedro demonstrated new energy and hope. Yes, he would wait for his daughter, trusting in the future. He wanted to completely recoup his spiritual balance and was anxious to reeducate himself in order to be more useful to her. He would use every means possible to support and strengthen her.

We were both euphoric and decided that very dawn to concentrate all our efforts on Beatriz, who was about to leave her sickly cells behind. Realizing that the Nogueira family needed our constant attention, we thought it would be best to take turns.

My friend, however, was right in arguing that his daughter was on the edge of the final transition and that he was afraid he did not have the serenity needed if he had to face any possible constraining obstacles by himself. After all, he was only human and he loved that suffering daughter. He wanted to embrace, to encourage her, although he did not consider himself worthy of giving her support and consolation.

Wouldn't it be better if he stayed at the Torres residence while I helped to bring peace to the Nogueiras?

This arrangement would last for only a few days while Beatriz's liberation was still pending.

On the other hand, if possible, I would return to Nemesio's home to share Beatriz's last moments with him. There we could attend to the imperatives of our moral edification by studying and serving to make good use of the time.

I thought that was a sensible idea.

So, late that morning, I was back at Claudio's apartment for the purpose of investigating the scene in order to decide on the proper course of action. It was my task to determine the most important details from one moment to the next; to discern points for support; and if possible, to listen to the two discarnate brothers, who were playing such a lamentable role in the drama.

I went in. Marcia was conversing happily with the woman in charge of the heaviest domestic chores about a charming program on their newly installed TV.

Everything was calm; the vampirizers were out. All was cleanliness and order.

At one point, the figure of Marita came to mind. I had become quite fond of the poor girl. She was like a spiritual daughter who deserved all my care and attention.

I anxiously hurried out onto the street and I soon saw her in the charming, colorful shop smiling at the well-dressed customers.

I embraced her paternally, silently wishing her peace and optimism. She answered instinctively with vague feelings of balance and hope.

I could tell she had gotten much better.

The magnetic treatment had worked very well. Marita did not know why, but she felt serene, stronger. She was rested and felt renewed. She had rediscovered the joy of working and was talking light-heartedly while pointing out differently patterned cotton fabrics.

My presence caused her to reflect. Although she was engaged in conversation with friendly customers, she had begun to think, to think...

After a few minutes, her memories urged her to pick up the phone and call Marcia to ask her if she was planning on coming to Copacabana that afternoon. Marcia said she was, so Marita asked her to meet her at 4:00 p.m., if possible. They could have a snack together; she had something to tell her.

I felt it would not be fair to bother her at work, where she had to divide her attention among discontinuous thoughts, so I decided to wait for a more appropriate chance to see if there were any problems for which I might be of assistance.

At 4:00 I pondered the seriousness of my task as I accompanied mother and daughter to a small, ice-cream shop.

In an atmosphere of secrecy, Marita began to unburden herself hesitantly. She spoke discreetly and humbly.

She asked Marcia to forgive her for troubling her just then, but she couldn't help it. She knew how much this was going to hurt and she would do anything to avoid it, but she would regret it if she did not say what she had to say. She had hesitated for a long time before deciding to reveal her secret, but since she was her daughter, she felt she should confide in her.

And with the naiveté of an inexperienced girl, she described Claudio's confession in all its details. She had felt appalled and had suffered beyond description. It had never even occurred to her that something like that would ever happen. If she had other relatives, she would not hesitate to move in with them in order to avoid a scandal. However, she was alone and dependent. The only family she had was the Nogueiras, whose name she had proudly borne since childhood. She was disoriented, frightened. She was asking for advice.

Marcia smiled as she listened. She did not interrupt once as she ate her ice-cream with delight.

Such passivity cooled Marita's attitude and she began to reduce the confidences and allegations she had meant to share. And with unspeakable surprise, not only to Marita, who was anxiously waiting for her to say something, but to myself as well, because I did not expect Claudio's cunning expedient of defending himself beforehand, Marcia's serene face expressed complete disbelief. She informed Marita that just yesterday Claudio had invited her for a private conversation about some things that he was feeling uneasy about. That night, he told her that he hadn't had the courage to mention the matter that troubled him, because he had thought it best to reflect on the troublesome incident before rushing to any conclusions. Nevertheless, after giving it some serious thought, he had decided that Marita needed psychiatric treatment.

Marcia adopted a tone of voice mixed with anxiety and warning and continued...

Claudio had told her that he had been greatly relieved when she came into the bedroom the night before because just a few minutes earlier, as he had awakened Marita, who was sleepwalking, she assailed him with kisses and inappropriate words. This explained the voices that Marcia had heard and which had concerned her so much. He added that he had given it a lot of thought and had come to the conclusion that Marita was mentally imbalanced. He had asked Marcia to help him find a psychiatrist to deal with the problem. He would finance the treatment. In fact, he was so worried that he would do even more ... He would arrange for her to take a trip to Argentina to restore her obviously altered energies.

To my utter astonishment, Mrs. Nogueira adopted the posture of a counselor.

She advised Marita to try to forget about the incident. She explained that she had not come here to discuss it, but in light of her allegations, she felt she had no other option but to open her heart to her. As a wife and mother, she would strive to keep the peace. She did not believe in taking sides. Yes, Claudio was indebted to her as an ungrateful husband, no denying it. But when it came to his daughters, he had always behaved as a model father. It was unfair to accuse him of any wrongdoing. The whole thing was just a product of Marita's imbalanced imagination. It was just a phase in the life of a love-struck girl.

And the verbal hammer turned to the refrains of the past: Aracelia's parties, Aracelia's friends, Aracelia's disappointments...

Seeing in the girl's eyes the painful impressions caused by those memories, Marcia mercilessly changed tactics and began telling Marita some stories she had heard about sleepwalkers doing incredible things.

She argued that she and Claudio had analyzed the incident with the love of true parents and with no spirit of criticism whatsoever. They remembered that when Marita was a child, she had woken up many times in the middle of the night, screaming, throwing a fit and complaining of inexplicable terrors. They had taken her to the doctor, who had prescribed tranquilizers. She also recalled, good-naturedly, the opinion of an old family friend that had told her and Claudio that Marita suffered from *nyctophobia,* and that only afterward they had looked the word up in the dictionary and had learned that it meant "fear of the dark."

Marcia laughed about those amusing recollections, completely unaware of how serious the problem was. She touched Marita's shoulder and advised her to be reasonable.

The girl, as bewildered as I was, did not have the courage to argue with her mother. She had no idea how to unravel the tangled mess her seducer had woven. She adopted the stance of a child, seeming to agree in silence.

Nevertheless, she felt repulsed inwardly.

Claudio had set the trap and her adoptive mother had fallen into it.

Marita had no way to prove her allegations. She could do nothing but endure her predicament and wait.

Marcia, with the clear intention of avoiding the matter, and furthermore, of displaying sincere compassion for the supposedly mentally ill girl, invited Marita to join her to check out the lovely articles in a nearby boutique.

Marita acquiesced, and the failed understanding ended; but for me it meant a serious warning. I realized I would have to double my efforts of watching over her.

Five days passed without any incidents worthy of mention. I had completed exactly one week of contact with my new friends, when, upon sharing my concerns with Pedro, I received a visit from a kind friend whom I had asked for help. He informed me that a certain woman had gone to the bank, looking for Claudio in order to talk about the matter with which we were involved at the moment.

The sun was high in the morning sky when I left for the bank. I found the woman sitting in a small waiting room next to the large office, where a team of employees was busy doing the bank's accounting.

The woman was waiting for Claudio, who was out at the time.

The newcomer was well-dressed, but she exhibited the air of women, who, after having lost their illusions, end up by selling pleasures that they can no longer enjoy.

I was unpretentiously studying that person who had appeared in our story, when Claudio arrived, pleasant and cheerful as usual. He was accompanied by one of the discarnates, as if the vampirizer were his shadow. I was no longer surprised at seeing them in such close association, thinking and talking in complete symbiosis.

Claudio and the woman knew each other, because Claudio immediately addressed her by her name – Crescina – and he bent his head in a way to make whispered conversation, which suggested the two were used to the secrets that were transmitted from lips to ears.

"Anything new?" he asked, rubbing his hand together and exhibiting a mischievous smile in anticipation of new pleasures.

The visitor, however, was slightly embarrassed about the purpose of her visit.

She had been visited by Marita a few hours ago, and, truthfully, it had been impossible to deny the girl the favor that she had tearfully begged of her.

She informed Claudio that at 8:00 the next night the girl wanted to meet Gilberto, a young man who often visited her business. Consequently, she had chosen a room in the back – number 4 – because it was cozier and more discreet. The poor thing – she said sympathetically – had made her request in complete confidentiality. She seemed very nervous, even desperate, so it was impossible to say no. She, herself, was a woman with two daughters. She had agreed.

But that was not all. Marita had paid her generously to deliver a note to the Torres' son.

And in front of the stunned eyes of Claudio, who, due to the vampirizer's eagerness, was becoming more and more curious, Crescina took from her purse a small piece of paper, on which the girl had written a note imploring Gilberto to meet her at 8:00 p.m. that night at the indicated place. She did not want to bother him. She was merely asking him to be there and was waiting for an answer.

Claudio read and re-read it amid jealousy and indignation. Yes – he thought to himself – this was a pure insult. Gilberto had that much control over Marita! The room in the back – number 4! He knew that room. What an odd coincidence! It was the same room that he sometimes chose when he went to Crescina's happy place of "rendezvous" for entertainment and rest ... Without even realizing it, Marita had the same tastes! ... Spite was crushing his soul as the "other" remained attached to him with a cunning expression on his face.

The patron of nighttime rendezvous interrupted a lengthy pause and repeated the fact that it was not fair to deny Marita the favor. However, she added slyly, Claudio was a client, so she had decided to advise him of the matter, not only as a show of loyalty to her customers but also as a way to avoid any trouble that might bring the police, who had never interfered in her business.

Thus she had come and wanted to know what she should do.

Claudio swallowed his anger; I could see he was thinking hard, trying to come up with a way to handle the situation.

Although Claudio was completely unaware of the fact that he was used to absorbing the suggestions of an outside intelligence, he was eagerly seeking its stimuli, believing himself to be knocking at the door of his own imagination.

Obsessor and obsessed began exchanging impressions brain to brain. A few moments of silent, mechanical adjustment, which an ordinary observer would regard as an extremely quick confabulation, and the two souls came to an implicit agreement.

I arrived at that conclusion based on the fact that they both suddenly calmed down. I did not feel capable of verifying their plans and intentions, because I had to divide my attention between them and the woman, whose information I could not afford to miss.

Claudio mouthed a yellow-toothed smile and thanked Crescina for being so helpful. He then began to tell her the fantastical story he had just invented. He told his surprised friend that Marita really would become engaged to the young man in perhaps just a few days, and that although he considered the requested rendezvous as pure foolishness by two young people, he asked Crescina to go ahead and deliver the note to confirm the meeting.

Obviously, he added, feigning good humor, the kids might have had a lover's spat and wanted to make up. No, he was not going to cause them any trouble. He would rather talk to his daughter about it the next day.

Still — he continued after a short conference with his invisible friend — he would be happy to pay her for a small favor, since as an interested father, he wanted the rendezvous between the "almost engaged" couple to materialize. He asked her to deliver the note only after 2:00 that afternoon, when Gilberto was sure to be at the office.

Crescina promised to do as he wished, collected the generous tip, and promising that she would call Marita after delivering the note, they shook hands with a smile and she left.

Alone again, Claudio, always influenced by the obsessor, did not waste any time.

He went to the phone but then hesitated for a moment. He realized that this was the first time he would be talking to the man he despised.

His hesitation did not last long, however.

He resolutely dialed Gilberto's number.

When Gilberto answered the phone, Claudio arranged a meeting, using a courteous tone of voice. If possible, he would like to meet with him in order to ask him for a favor that would be of mutual interest to both of them; but his discretion was necessary. They should meet immediately.

Gilberto stammered on the other end of the line, denoting strong emotion, and acquiesced without having said much.

Both looked at their watches. It was 11:00 a.m. sharp.

He, Claudio, would take a taxi to meet Gilberto in Lido before going on to Flamengo for lunch. The young man had nothing to worry about. They knew a lot about each other, even though they had never met in person. Furthermore, he would easily recognize Gilberto by his car.

In fact, a few minutes later the four of us – Claudio, Gilberto, Claudio's spirit obsessor and I – all met at the appointed spot.

The young man was very pale and looked like a guilty student before his teacher, but the broad, artificial smile with which he was greeted put him at ease sooner than he expected.

They walked side by side, exchanging banalities about the weather, until they sat down in the corner of a bar to a glass of soft drink, which they barely touched.

Claudio tapped the tip of his cigarette every now and then to knock off the ashes, trying hard to seem natural.

Invariably linked to the vampirizer, he began by telling Nemesio's son that he understood the situation very well; that he knew to a certain extent that the young man was attracted to Marina, his actual daughter, and that although as her father he felt he had the duty to safeguard her happiness, he also understood he should not interfere in their private affairs; however – he added dramatically – he had raised Marita as his daughter too; he loved her dearly and wanted her to be as happy as the other.

The inexperienced Gilberto listened, both dumbfounded and moved.

The bank clerk condescendingly told him that, actually, only destiny could explain such a coincidence since he was sure that both girls wanted Gilberto equally.

I was astonished by the mask of paternal love that Claudio had put on.

On the inside, he felt strongly repulsed, but he skillfully repressed his impulse to smack Beatriz's son, who, now happy and at ease, was soaking up Claudio's every word.

Cunningly controlling himself, Claudio continued.

He emphasized that, of course, the foolish girl had misinterpreted Gilberto's displays of friendship and had fallen in love with him, and this passion had brought psychosis and illness upon her. He was troubled, worried. He would find resources to solve the problem, but to do so, he needed Gilberto's cooperation so that Marita would not suffer as much.

Claudio said he was counting on his help, and as soon as Gilberto spoke his first words of agreement, he lowered his voice and in a tone of confidentiality, told him that Marita had written him a note. He, Claudio, knew about it. Continuing his studied act of fatherly concern, he asked Gilberto if he had received it yet. When Gilberto said he hadn't, Claudio explained that the girl had written the note, asking him to meet her that night. Without Marita suspecting it, he had read the note and could repeat it word for word. He recited it by heart, giving Gilberto the impression that he was doing so in order to more surely express his paternal care.

After completing his role-playing, he asked the young man for a couple of favors: first, that he answer the note in writing, saying that he would meet Marita, and second, that he fail to show.

Claudio made up the story that the girl was misguided, sick. He was afraid a crisis was in the making. He had no other recourse, except to ask Gilberto for his cooperation because that very day he was procuring the necessary documents to send her and Marcia to Argentina for rest and relaxation. It would not be wise to give her a negative answer at that moment. Of course, Gilberto was free to decide for himself. He should do what he thought was best. However, as a father, he was worried about the consequences. Doing what he was requesting was not asking too much. If Gilberto went along with idea, Claudio himself would meet Marita at the arranged time, not only with great news about the trip – which was bound to please her – but with Gilberto's own excuse for his absence. It was understandable that, with the loving authority of a father and friend, he was responsible for the young man's excuses and would be very tactful.

As a final matter, he wanted Gilberto to tell him what to use as an excuse: business, work, problems at home, or an unexpected trip.

The Torres' son listened to everything, highly impressed.

The proposal seemed to him to be based on sound commonsense. Apart from that, he could now breathe freely and happily. He had found a person who would help him, step by step, to free himself from a commitment that was weighing too heavily on his conscience.

By now, Gilberto was feeling completely uninhibited. He had lost the last traces of the suspicion that he had brought with him to the conversation. Consequently, he put on a mask that he deemed appropriate for his own ends and stated that he had always seen his friendship with Marita as nothing more than a brother-sister arrangement. He stressed that he had in fact noticed some changes in her that bothered him, and since he was definitely attracted to Marina, he had cautiously kept a distance, expecting it and time to do their work.

Claudio listened, flabbergasted, admiring the coolness with which he justified himself and wondering which of the two of them was better in the art of pretending.

Gilberto was genuinely encouraged and said he understood Claudio's concerns and that he accepted his advice and suggestions. He would write the note and promise to show up, but he would not set foot out of the house, the more so because Marina had left for Teresopolis[11] that morning on company business and would probably not be back until the next day. Mr. Nogueira – as Gilberto addressed him – had his permission to meet the girl at 8:00 p.m. and tell her he could not meet her because of his mother's worsening condition. He would not be telling a lie – he said – since Beatriz was, in fact, dying little by little.

After getting what he wanted, Claudio's face reflected a happiness, which, combined with the great pleasure of his obsessor, appeared to be genuine concern – devotion, even. To end the conversation, he told Gilberto that he already knew about Marina's business trip, and he asked kindly about Beatriz's

---

11 A small city in the sierras a couple of hours from Rio – Tr.

condition, promising that he and Marcia would pay her a visit. He also talked about the domestic problems caused by lengthy diseases. He urged Gilberto to be optimistic, and even though he was a confessed atheist, he praised the faith one ought to have in God under such circumstances.

With the pact settled, they said goodbye with a warm embrace, while I myself left Lido for Flamengo, dreadfully worried and wondering about what was to come.

13

I was very apprehensive as I went back to Flamengo.

I had failed to grasp the details of the dark plan taking shape. Claudio's thoughts were entwined with those of the vampirizer in strange, vague purposes.

I immediately sent an urgent message to brother Felix asking him to meet with me, but his answer was not very encouraging.[12] He would come, but only that evening because of unavoidable obligations.

It would not be advisable to ask Pedro to come because he, too, was very busy, and maybe that was for the better, since there was a maze of moral problems, and any anger on Pedro's part could hinder our objectives and activities. Moreover, any other friends who might otherwise be able to help were completely unfamiliar with the case.

It was necessary for me to work on my own.

This was no time for useless worries. I had to make do with the resources at hand.

---

12 In light of the small devices on the physical plane used for sending and receiving long-distance messages, it is unnecessary to comment on the ease of interchange on the spirit plane. – Spirit Auth.

In order to intervene and not hesitate, I decided it would be wise to listen to Claudio's discarnate friend, whom I did not know anything about at all. At first, there had been two vampirizers; however, only one of them was constantly with Claudio: the one whose cunning intelligence had grabbed my attention.

Would it not be right to study him and try to find out what was bothering him?

I remembered previous experiences, when I had modified my outward form by means of powerful mental effort in order to become visible to other discarnates.

I wanted to make myself visible to this enigmatic friend, who obviously lived with the Nogueiras.

I could transform myself by making my body denser, like someone changing clothes.

I found a quiet spot on the beach and prayed for strength.

I concentrated hard, building each particular aspect of my outward form, making my features denser and changing the tone of my usual appearance.

It took me nearly an entire hour of difficult preparation until I felt I was ready to undertake the desired conversation.

I could not waste even one minute.

I went up to Claudio's apartment and knocked ceremoniously.

Everything happened as planned, because Claudio's constant companion came to the door.

He looked at me suspiciously from head to toe in an effort to discover my intentions.

I tried to be inconspicuous and made my speech as ordinary as possible.

This approach was indispensable for getting the information I needed from him. With that in mind, I feigned a complete lack of interest with regard to the people who lived there and made the obsessor the central focus of my attention.

I explained that I was looking for a friend, and asked about the other fellow I had seen there a few days ago, when they were walking down the hallway. I had been unable to stop at the time, because I had other business to attend to. However, I was pretty sure that he was the fellow I was looking for.

Speaking to him in a tone of natural acquiescence and fraternity was the simplest way I could think of to gain some of his trust and attention.

He seemed sympathetic and treated me with the condescending benevolence of a nobleman who indulges in giving a bit of consideration to a beggar.

Of a big, robust constitution, he touched my shoulder with his right hand, in a gesture of someone who is politely trying to get rid of a nuisance, and started searching for details. He studied me, scrutinized me as he asked questions.

When I told him of the exact moment I had seen them together, and based on the details I had given him, he said that the person I was looking for was an old friend, who came there on occasion to relax with a couple of drinks. Unfortunately, he was not in at the moment. As far as he knew, he was enjoying himself at a home in Braz de Pina[13], and he gave me the address.

I said I was disappointed. I asked him his name and thanked him for his kindness, saying I would come back some other time. I said I would appreciate it if he would tell me his name in case I had to ask strangers about him when I came back.

He did not hesitate, and answered politely.

His name was Ricardo Moreira, but I could simply ask for Moreira. He was well respected, had several relations, and had a number of friends in the building. If I happened to see him

---

13 A district in the Northern part of Rio de Janeiro. – Tr.

again with the colleague I was looking for, I just had to remind him of who I was.

Till now, everything was fine. However, it was essential for me to examine his innermost reactions. It was essential that I find out more about him, that I sound him out.

I told him I was exhausted, discouraged. If he was the butler there, I asked if he might be so kind as to let me come in for a few minutes to compose myself. I would really appreciate it. Just a few minutes. I was in need of a human, friendly environment.

The atmosphere changed completely.

I totally lost the ground I had gained.

Moreira gave me a dreadful look that pierced me like a vibrational dagger. He became sarcastic and shouted that the house had a master; that, regarding any "huskless"[14] ones living there, he was the boss; that if I wanted to come inside, I would have to get passed him; that there was a big sidewalk I could sleep on outside. He then concluded aggressively:

"What are you up to, anyway? Get lost! I don't like your looks! Scram!"

I had no choice but to hurry back down the stairs because he threatened me with clenched fists.

I went back to the welcoming seashore and started to pray.

I returned to my usual appearance and went back up.

Inside, Justa was serving Claudio and Marcia their lunch.

Moreira, who was now unable to see me, was sitting in the same chair as Claudio in such a way that he was obviously eating right along with Claudio by means of one of the various processes entailing fluidic osmosis.

The conversation between the couple was banal, but when I probed Claudio's mind, I realized that the theme of

---

14 A pejorative term used on the lower planes to designate discarnate spirits. – Spirit Auth.

the day was actively circulating in the mental system that he shared with his obsessor. I noticed their anxiety as they waited for news that could facilitate the unconfessable plan they were beginning to formulate.

Now, at the table, the duo exteriorized their dark intentions in thought-forms revealing two very sick minds. Everything was becoming clear, suddenly. They hatched their plan in silence. They would approach Marita like two hunters stocking a hare. They relished the attack; their thoughts revealed wanton maneuvers. They planned to catch Marita at Crescina's place, as if they were picking fruit from a tree.

Perplexed, I grasped the entire plot.

Pretending he did not know about his daughter's trip, Claudio asked his wife about Marina, but actually, he wanted news about Marita.

Marcia immediately took the bait. She told him that he had perhaps forgotten that Marina had told them yesterday that she would be traveling to Teresopolis on business for the real estate firm. Her boss couldn't make the trip and had asked her to represent him regarding a few important business deals. Of course, she would be back tomorrow. As for Marita, she had phoned home from Copacabana a couple of hours ago, asking them not to expect her for dinner. She might have to work overtime in her shop's accounting department.

Her husband cleared his throat, changed the subject, commented briefly on some political news, and the meal ended without further ado.

With the purpose of working effectively for everyone's good, I headed for Crescina's place and had no difficulty finding room number 4. It was an isolated room for couples, completely separate from the rest of the building.

Considering its large size, the place seemed to be very quiet. However, due to the noisy conversations of the unfortunate, quarreling, idle discarnates, it was easy to imagine how noisy the nights were.

After watching the comings and goings to size up the situation, I saw the owner of the place pick up the phone. I approached. Crescina was calling the Torres' office, asking to talk to Gilberto. When he picked up, she arranged to meet him in thirty minutes, at 2:00 p.m. sharp.

Everything was going as planned and on schedule.

When she returned home, Crescina phoned the shop and told Marita that Gilberto had answered the note. Everything was OK. She read the note, in which he assured her he would be there at eight. She should wait for him, trust him.

The poor girl was ecstatic, whereas the pain of my worries only increased.

I had to decide on a way to protect her: maybe contact an incarnate friend who was connected to the group. I had to block the consummation of the plan, or at least create a situation where help would arrive seemingly by chance; however ... I wandered from the place of "rendezvous" to the office, from the office to the shop, from the shop to the bank, and from the bank to the apartment in Flamengo, all to no avail ... No one extending spiritual antennae, capable of helping me; no one praying; no one concerned about the matter ... Everywhere, thoughts saturated with sex and money portraying scenes of pleasure and profits to the exclusion of everything else. I even approached one of Marita's supervisors and, by projecting her image on his mental screen, tried to instill in him the idea of making the girl work until late. But he thought he was thinking for himself and distorted the matter to involve salary problems. He began concentrating on economic advantages, ran numbers in his mind, filled it with paragraphs regarding labor laws, and summarily rejected my supposed influence, telling himself: "That girl already makes enough; I won't give her one cent more." There was nothing I could do but to stay at Crescina's place and remain on guard.

All my attempts had been useless.

Claudio arrived at 7:30 sharp, dressed up and wearing a small toupee that made him look a bit younger.

He cautiously inspected the place from a short distance. He and the other. Moreira was no less interested than Claudio.

I followed them.

Claudio went in search of a telephone and found one in a nearby coffee shop. He dialed, calling Fafa, the business's doorman, whom I had met during my investigations earlier in the day. When Fafa picked up, Claudio asked him to come and meet him in secret. It was a "business matter." Fafa would not be sorry. They both laughed on the line.

The doorman, a good-hearted, older man, whom the alcohol was beginning to excite in those early hours of the night, responded right away. Polite and knowing, although he wore a kindly smile that could have been for good or for bad, he inclined his ear towards Claudio's mouth in order to hear better. Claudio whispered solemnly that he was in urgent need of Fafa's help. He needed to find out about the young couple that was going to be in 4. The girl was his daughter. He wouldn't make a sound and he didn't mean to cause trouble, but he had to find out. No complications. He had to know who the seducer was in order to discreetly solve a family problem. He was asking for Fafa's cooperation because the doorman was a nice person. He had to have his help.

Fafa said that he understood and that the girl had already checked in. She had come alone and had gone in through the partially closed door. She was sitting on the bed browsing some magazines. And, in answer to Claudio's questions, he confirmed that it was her all right because he had seen her talking to Crescina earlier that day. Yes, he remembered her name; it was Marita, yes.

Claudio became even more secretive and asked Fafa to cause a blackout by unscrewing a fuse in the fuse box. The "repair" should require fifteen minutes of darkness. That would be time enough for him to find out what he needed, and neither Crescina nor the guests would know he was there. He would be hiding in the dark, behind the lamp post, and could easily identify the young man.

In spite of the old man being half drunk, he wore a sly expression on his face and said that that might pose a serious problem. He was ready to please Claudio, but secretly. He did not want to get involved with the cops.

Claudio slipped him two five-hundred cruzeiro[15] bills, and Fafa, now less nervous, asked what time it was right now. Claudio answered that they had only ten minutes, since he would require the lights out at 8:00 sharp.

The two of them went in different directions, and while I was lost in painful conjectures, a reinvigorating surprise visited my spirit. I had only walked a few steps along the street, when I was pleasantly greeted by brother Felix, who gave me an embrace.

I felt an enormous relief. Filling him in on all my concerns took only a few seconds.

The instructor found out all he needed to know.

Without delay, we headed for Crescina's place. The lights went out as we crossed the door and went in. I got the feeling that power outages were quite common because the darkness caused no alarm at all. A number of candles were being lit here and there.

---

15 Brazilian currency at the time. – Tr.

We went straight to the isolated room.

Claudio had stopped at the door, entwined with the obsessor. Both juxtaposed on each other. Both of the same sentiments and purposes. Both thrilled, their hearts pounding, foretasting their quarry, for whom there was no escape. As I watched the scene from a short distance, I saw both Claudio and Moreira stop short under the aura of Felix's balsamic energies; nevertheless, they were completely unaware of the marvelous phenomenon.

As I pondered the disturbing yet tender scene, I imagined myself to be looking at two wolves in human form, to whom a merciful messenger from Heaven was trying to deliver the word and inspiration of Jesus Christ.

Claudio and Moreira were interlaced in a mental swamp of lust so powerful that, in that volcano of sexual appetites, it would be almost impossible to find the smallest opening through which one could try to inject the smallest lofty idea.

A powerful fragrance of carnations invaded my olfactory system. Where had I smelled that same fragrance that same day? I was surprised to remember that it was the essence Gilberto was wearing when he met with Claudio in Lido. I looked closer and realized that Claudio had even gone to the extreme of wearing clothes similar to Gilberto's, including a tie of the same size and knot. No detail had been forgotten.

Before Felix and I could devise a way to detain the pair, they entered the room.

We, who could see in the dark, watched the poor girl stand up whispering words of ecstatic passion and intense longing, eagerly opening her arms without the least bit of caution … She believed her lover had come … It was him; there was nothing to fear … At that exact moment, in all her intentions and in all her nerves, there was just one thought, one purpose: to surrender herself…

Claudio and the other kept absolutely quiet, trembling with emotion.

There was nothing we could do.

Claudio, acting for himself and the other, pulled her to his chest and kissed her passionately.

The defenseless child, hypnotized by her own reflexes, surrendered, defeated... Brother Felix, driven by sentiments I could not evaluate, left the room. I followed.

Reaching the steps leading down from the door, the disheartened instructor stopped and gazed up at the sky ... As for me, I was feeling so troubled that I could not articulate a prayer. I could do nothing but respectfully keep silent before that tormented paternal heart, which had come down from the higher spheres only to suffer cruelly in silent prayer awash in a torrent of tears!...

Brothers and sisters, even if we cannot yet live holy lives due to the inferior instincts that torture our souls, still animalized due to the awful burden of a guilt-ridden past, minimize your moral failures as much as possible! If not for your own sake, do so for the deceased who love you from a more beautiful life! ... Discipline yourselves out of respect for them, invisible guardians who hold out their arms to you! ... Fathers and mothers, husbands and wives, children and siblings, friends and companions, whom you suppose are lost forever, but who very often follow you closely, adding to your happiness or sharing in your pain! ... When you are about to fall into the abysses of moral delinquency, think of them! They will help you benevolently and point out the pathway on the night of temptation like stars scattering the darkness! ... You, who know how to venerate mothers and selfless educators still alive in the material world, have compassion on the deceased, transformed into loving Cyrenians who share our crosses of well-deserved trials in silent suffering, when, many times, we are not worthy to kiss their feet!

Weeping bitterly before Felix, my poor, imperfect soul resorted to the Gospel and I found comfort upon remembering that Jesus, the Divine Master, had also been the sensitive, loving friend who wept before the dead Lazarus!

After nearly twenty minutes of expectation, the lights came on again and we heard a terrible scream, full of astonishment and horror!

Marita jumped out of the window as fast as a wounded deer and fled, disheveled…

But before we could make any gesture to help, someone rushed up to the door and knocked furiously. That someone was Marcia…

Claudio, assisted by his discarnate friend, composed himself. He looked at his wife, smiled ironically and exclaimed sarcastically:

"Oh, this is just what we needed! … You're here, too?"…

Marcia, who enjoyed playing poker with some friends not far from Crescina's place on occasion, maintained friendly relations with her and had been informed by her that Claudio had shown up and had perhaps gotten into a scuffle with the young couple.

The doorman had been afraid there might be problems, so he decided to tell his employer everything he knew. Crescina, in turn, believing that Marita and Gilberto were together, had immediately asked Marcia to come in order to avoid any possible disasters.

When the concerned Mrs. Claudio arrived, she had seen her daughter bolt through the window, and noticing her husband's embarrassment, she immediately understood everything that had happened…

"You bastard!" she shouted, outraged. "I refused to believe that poor girl! I could have prevented all this!

Marcia's voice took on a dolorous inflection:

"What were you thinking? I have every one of Aracelia's papers; all of her notes … She never had any other man but you! … You never knew about her last letter, in which she handed her daughter over to me, saying that she would rather die so that I could be happy! … The memory of that poor, loyal girl is the only good thing I still have in my heart … You destroyed the rest … Ah! Claudio, Claudio! How could we have fallen so low?! You're completely insane! You abused your own daughter!"

As if he had been hit by lightning, Claudio reeled and tried to support himself against the door. Marcia burst into tears. As for us, we had to leave.

14

Felix and I rushed to catch up with Marita.

The girl was hurrying along, confused and in a state of shock.

She had run almost all the way from Lapa[16], where Crescina's place was located, to Cinelandia[17].

She felt as if she had been hit by all the winds of adversity and had been blown from the earth. Betrayed in her innermost sentiments as a woman, the insult she had experienced transcended all her notions of suffering. She would have been grateful to the man she had known as her father even if he had used a dagger or poison on her, but she did not have the strength to forgive him for this offense. Repulsion shook her arms and legs. She was trembling, desperate. There was but one thing growing in her mind: suicide. She wanted to throw herself under a passing car. To die … to disappear – she thought in tears. Even so, she had to go on living a bit longer. There was still one enigma left: Gilberto. Why hadn't he come? Why had he let himself be replaced so cruelly? What kind of scheme could they have contrived? She had read Gilberto's reply; she recognized his

---

16 A middle-class downtown district, filled with intense night life. – Tr.
17 In downtown Rio. – Tr.

handwriting. He had written, saying he would come ... Why had he changed his mind? How could Claudio have found out about the meeting? Through Crescina?

Such unanswered questions shook her all over. She was out of her mind. She gnashed her teeth, wanting to scream.

Death; death! – she exclaimed mentally, pursing her lips which were opening without a sound.

But wait; she should confront Gilberto – suggested the last vestiges of her dismantled dream. Yes – she agreed in the whirlwind of incoherent thoughts – it was necessary to hear what Gilberto had to say ... even if it was just once. She had to know the truth, to die knowing the truth...

Who knows? Maybe he could hold out a thread of light to her that would rescue her from the darkness ... If he were to say: "Live; live for me," she would forget the insult of that night and go on living ... If not, everything would end...

Walking hurriedly now and ignoring the breeze that caressed her hair, she mentally rejected all our attempts at tenderness and consolation.

She refused to accept any idea that was not in tune with her feelings of repulsion.

If Gilberto had participated in the trap they had set to catch her, everything would obviously be over – all she had left was final contempt.

She reached Largo do Passeio[18] and stopped for a moment ... She looked forlornly at the trees she had always loved so much ... Their branches swaying in the wind seemed to be waving goodbye to her ... Marita sobbed in fear but kept walking... She got caught up in a laughing crowd coming out of the movie theater, and as she watched couples on dates sharing popcorn, she remembered Gilberto and the happy girl she used to be ...

---

18 In Lapa. – Tr.

however, she kept going, ignoring the pushing and shoving. When she got to Marechal Floriano Square, she sat down and racked her tormented brain...

She felt completely alone and forsaken. Pressing her head between her hands, she wanted ideas, any idea that might offer her a way out of that bitter hell of anguish.

Brother Felix embraced her and whispered thoughts of patience and good sense, but in vain; he suggested kindness and forgiveness, but it was futile. That young heart, although truly kind, was now like a transparent lake that a hidden volcano on the bottom had unexpectedly begun to rile. All of its edges opened like a fire hydrant through which waves of thought poured forth. No part of it was open to receptivity; not one point marked by balance and silence.

Finally, an idea came to her tumultuous mind, bringing her a thread of hope: A phone call! She could phone the Torreses. Of course, Gilberto would be at his sick mother's bedside. And Marina had left on business that morning: one more reason why Gilberto would be with Beatriz. Still – she reasoned – he would probably lie to her. Uncontrolled suspicion stung her heart like a thorn. But she saw no other answer. Talk to him! Hear what he had to say! She longed for the truth; she had to know; to know!

Incoherent ideas clashed inside her disturbed head ... No, she would not return to her home in Flamengo ... If she had to choose between going back to the Nogueiras and dying, she would rather die...

She pondered the circumstances; she analyzed herself; she thought and thought...

All of a sudden she had a strange idea. She would disguise herself and pretend. She would lie in order to find out the truth.

Yes, she would join the game using the last trick up her sleeve.

Marita had come to the conclusion that she and her sister had similar voices and mannerisms, due to their closeness from living under the same roof. She would phone Gilberto and pretend to be Marina. She would imitate her sister's voice as much as possible and would repeat words commonly used at home. She would pretend she had come back from Teresopolis earlier than expected. Gilberto would openly confess how he really felt about her.

The suffering child checked her watch. It was 8:50 p.m.

She wanted a familiar environment for the phone call. She remembered Cora. Cora was one of the Copacabana shop's customers, who had become a close friend. Marita would often go to her apartment when she had to make an important phone call. She got up, somewhat encouraged, and thought of catching a bus. But then she realized she had left her purse in the room when she had escaped through the window. She did not have any money but did not let that dissuade her. She hailed the first taxi that came along and asked the driver if she could pay when she got there. She was alone and had lost track of the time. The driver noticed her despair and embarrassment. He felt sorry for her. He said that he usually refused to accept passengers who begged a ride because they usually meant trouble; however, he would make an exception in her case.

We were all on our way to Copacabana.

When we arrived, Marita got out and asked the taxi driver to go with her up to her friend's apartment. She was welcomed warmly, as expected. Very embarrassed, she told Cora she was in trouble and needed to borrow some money. She would pay her back tomorrow. The spontaneous and kindly Cora did not hesitate. She opened a small drawer and said with a smile: "You only need four hundred cruzeiros?" Her husband was out. Marita gratefully said that that was plenty. She paid the driver and told

Cora she had worked late and then had gone to Leblon to visit a friend who was sick. Only now could she catch a bus home. But first she needed to make a phone call to a very close friend. Cora told her to go ahead and said she was going to make some fresh coffee. Marita could talk freely without being interrupted. Her two little girls had already gone to bed. Her husband had stood in for a colleague at work, and would not be back for a while yet. Cora went to the kitchen, leaving Marita to herself.

And there, in front of us, without the slightest awareness of the presence of our sympathetic hearts, Marita called Gilberto, controlling her emotions and imitating Marina's cheerful voice.

We listened to their youthful dialogue, which, sentence by sentence would remain engraved in our memory.

"Is this the Torres residence?"

"Yes."

"Who's speaking, please? Gilberto?"

"Yes, yes."

"Oh! Darling, don't you recognize me?"

"No. Who's this?"

"It's me! ... Marina! I just got back..."

"Ah! Ah! Marina...What a nice surprise! What's keeping you? Come on over ... we're all at home, waiting ... Why'd you call?"

"I just wanted to make sure you're OK. Did you have a good day?"

"I've missed you so much!"

"I really missed you too!"

"Then come on over..."

"And your mom? Is she better?"

"A little bit."

"Listen..."

"Just hang up and get over here!"

"Just a sec... Listen. I stopped in Flamengo to talk to my mom about some things ... I met a couple of friends in Teresopolis and they put some thoughts in my head. I'm upset ... jealous..."

"Why? What's the matter?"

"Marita..."

"Oh, her? I'm not a bit interested in Marita!"

"But I heard..."

"Heard what?"

"That you two were engaged. I knew you were together, but not like that!"

"Nonsense."

"They seemed to know so much that I thought it had to be true."

"A waste of time. They're out of their minds, OK?"

"I saw Dad a while ago..."

At that point, her voice faltered. She had heard enough to realize she was scorned, defeated. Even so, she had to find out how Gilberto had sunk so low. But at the same time, she was afraid she would reveal herself. She had to be very careful in analyzing the insult of which she had been the victim. The pause, however, was brief. Gilberto, on the other end, started to explain:

"So..."

"Tell me what happened."

"Well, by now you must've heard what happened. The old man came to see me ... He called and we got together and discussed everything."

"You mean that Marita..."

"Would you believe she wrote me a note asking me to meet her? The old man found out and asked me to tell her I would meet with her but that I shouldn't actually go. Get it?"

"So what did you do, after all?"

"I wrote her a note saying that I would be there, but arranged with the old man that he would go instead. It was his idea. You know I had to go along with it … It was the first time…"

"I'm confused! … I don't get it…"

"He asked me to agree to write the note because he didn't want Marita to be shocked. He said she had been depressed lately and said he would meet her, give her some fatherly advice and cheer her up with some good news: a trip to Argentina…"

"What?!"

"Argentina … A trip to Argentina."

He laughed and then said sarcastically:

"To put her in a nut house. Some sanatorium or asylum. It's the nut house for Marita, and the farther away, the better! Argentina for one and Petropolis for two."

Marita nearly collapsed.

She bent over and could barely hang onto the phone because of the sobs erupting within her.

We could hear Gilberto's voice shouting from where we were:

"Marina! Marina! What's the matter?…Tell me!"

Soaked in tears, Marita hung up the phone with the sadness of someone that was closing the door to her heart forever.

The girl spent a few minutes composing herself to look as normal as possible before returning to the living room.

Embarrassed, she mentioned the money she had borrowed. She asked Cora to forgive her for having bothered her and added that if she couldn't come back the next day in person, she would ask Nellie, whom Cora also knew, to pay her if she, Marita, didn't make it in to work.

Cora smiled cordially. Marita didn't have to worry about it.

Cora offered Marita the coffee, which she accepted, still feeling embarrassed. They chatted for a few minutes, when Cora noticed she looked faint, pale, and had tears in her eyes. Marita explained, trying to smile, that it was nothing. She claimed she had a cold and that was why her eyes were watering. She asked Cora if she thought Mr. Salomao might still be at the pharmacy since it was after ten. She wanted to ask him about some cold medicine. Her head hurt and her lungs were congested.

Her kindly host asked Marita to wait a second and ran to the phone. She came back right away, saying that the pharmacist would be waiting. But he was closing up, so she'd better hurry.

Marita thanked Cora and said goodbye. We followed.

Mr. Salomao was a calm, complacent old man, in whose eyes one could see the kindness of those who are willing servants of humankind in their respective fields. He welcomed her warmly.

Hiding her real intentions, Marita told him about the cold. She felt achy, dizzy. The pharmacist was old-fashioned and was used to playing the role of a doctor to his friends in cases that were not too complicated. He asked Marita to stick out her tongue. He examined it with the skill acquired over many years. He did not find anything wrong. He took her temperature. No fever.

He smiled paternally and advised her to go home and rest. She shouldn't be putting in so many hours at work – he said good-heartedly – and added that she could always buy medicine, but not her health. He prescribed aspirin for the headache, along with rest.

Marita bought the medicine and made a gesture suggesting she was leaving, but then turned around as if she had just remembered something.

"Mr. Salomao," she said with decided curiosity in her voice, "I'm not sure, but do you remember Joia, my old dog, the one that your grandkids sometimes played with on the beach?"

"Of course, I do. That intelligent animal playing hide-and-seek! My grandkids still get down on their hands and knees to imitate the way she used to walk!

"Yeah," Marita said sadly. "I'm afraid our little Joia doesn't have much time left."

"Oh, what's the matter?"

"The vet explained what was wrong with her, but I don't remember the name of the disease. But it's incurable. She whines all the time in torment."

She added that the animal had become a nuisance in the apartment building. The super had complained several times and so had the neighbors. Her parents were waiting for the vet to get back from Sao Paulo to euthanize the dog; however, they had told her and her sister they could use any medication that might give Joia the final rest. Joia was in bad shape, worn out. Marita said she was terribly sorry to lose the dog because she had been her companion in Flamengo ever since she quit school. Even so, she had to face the facts and spare the dog any further suffering. Mightn't he have some pills that would do the trick? She had heard about some sleeping pills, which, if given in too high a dose could cause painless death. However, she couldn't remember what they were called.

Mr. Salomao confirmed what she had said. Yes, maybe he did have some on hand and agreed that if the vet had condemned the dog, it was best not to save her.

Convinced by Marita's story, Salomao began searching his shelves...

Felix and I approached him mentally.

The paternal benefactor begged him to analyze the situation. He should take a good look at that young woman, so tired, alone, and far from home when it was already past ten. Disheveled hair, sunken eyes, no purse or coat. He, Salomao, was also a sensitive father and grandfather. He suggested that he refrain from giving her instructions about poisons; that he should be careful; that he should give her a mild sedative, making her think she was taking home the lethal poison instead. He should lie out of compassion, not ask questions and postpone any conversation for later.

That man had obviously been through enough harsh experiences to be sufficiently sensitive to register our appeals, because he immediately felt compassion for the girl. He discreetly observed her through the door, which had been left ajar. He was astonished at what he saw when she thought no one was looking.

Marita looked like a statue in a wax museum: wrinkled, lifeless. Only her eyes, although motionless, were active due to the flood of tears.

"Oh, my God!" he thought, filled with pity. "This isn't a cold. This is mental suffering; terrible suffering!"

Salomao stopped looking for the sleeping pills, picked up a few mild sedatives and went back out to Marita. Disguising his concern, he gave her the pills and told her:

"Here you go. Considering what you said about the state your dog is in, one of these should be enough."

"It's that strong?" she asked, trying to control her nerves.

"This stuff is very dangerous and is rarely used."

Pretending to believe her story in order to gain her trust, the paternal pharmacist told her that he could only sell it to her if she had a prescription. It was a big responsibility.

But she insisted. The pharmacist had nothing to worry about. The vet would write out the prescription later. She asked if she could buy ten of the pills. Better safe than sorry. She couldn't handle the moaning and whimpering at the foot of her bed anymore.

Salomao thought it over … He went back to the shelves and chose ten mild tranquilizers. If the girl did take all of them, they would help her by enabling her to fall asleep.

Marita thanked him and left.

Salomao recommended that she rest and take care of herself.

We followed her closely.

Slowly, she walked two blocks to Atlantica Avenue[19] and went into a bar.

She asked for a glass of water in a plastic cup. Careful not to spill it, she left, crossed the avenue, jumped down from the boardwalk onto the sandy beach and found a spot that seemed darker than the rest…

She wanted to die near the ocean, that serene, good ocean that had never rejected her – she thought in tears … She wanted to "leave" while contemplating that ocean that always kissed her without malice …

Just before what she thought would be her final act, she remembered the mother she had never known and imagined herself to be even more unfortunate than she. Although abandoned by the man she had given herself to, Aracelia had at least had a roof over her head at the time of her big goodbye. But not she. She had been mistreated, humiliated, despised. She would have to leave this world bearing a borrowed name, which she now loathed … She considered herself the scum of the earth, and believed everybody would be much better off without her. She recalled the joyful mornings on the beach, when she had so often felt the warmth of the sun and had breathed the fresh air coming from the sea. She imagined seeing the Sunday

---

19 An avenue that runs parallel to the beach – Tr.

crowd frolicking in the foam. She even imagined the noise of the children playing soccer or paddle ball ... No, she did not have a home to die in, but she did have the warm, friendly beach that always welcomed thousands of strangers, without ever having asked them any nosy questions, embracing everyone as true brothers and sisters.

She felt sorry for herself and cried for a long time, while Felix and I waited for her to fall asleep in order to prepare ourselves to face further problems.

Marita put the ten pills in her mouth and washed them down with the water in the plastic cup. Then, she sat down with her back against the stone drop-off from the boardwalk, as if she were meditating ... Her eyes were filled with what she thought were her final tears; she let the breeze caress her hair.

A gentle torpor anaesthetized her.

We checked the time. It was five minutes to 1:00 a.m.

Felix prayed for a few minutes.

I did not immediately understand whether it was because it was their duty as spirit caretakers, or whether it was because of Felix's prayer, but two discarnate patrolmen from our plane appeared and offered to help. Felix gratefully accepted, and as they kept watch, he and I began the operation of restoring the girl. We took measures to keep her from leaving her out-of-control body, applying comforting passes on all her force centers, providing various stimuli to parts of her brain and dilating her blood vessels. Detailed, lengthy measures: magnetic acupuncture from the spirit plane, something at which Felix demonstrated noteworthy mastery.

Almost four hours passed, at the end of which Marita slept peacefully.

Encouraged, I could see the hope shining in Felix's eyes ... Just then, however, a brutish street-sweeper left the asphalt and came in our direction to water down the sand. When he saw the sleeping girl, his curiosity was piqued. Measures by the two spirit watchmen were useless. The relatively young street-sweeper walked up to Marita and shook her, shouting: "Hey, wake up, tramp! "Wake up!"

I was completely heartbroken, not only for that mistreated child but also for the enormous pain expressed on Felix's face. I could see that he would have given anything to be able to materialize his hands and prevent that assault.

"Wake up, tramp! Wake up!"

He slapped her face, whose tears the wind had mercifully dried.

Frustrated, we watched as she opened her eyes, bewildered.

What kind of beast was this, who, seeing her tremble, began fondling her lewdly?

With her head spinning, she asked herself if she had died and was now in hell looking at a demon…

She tried to scream, but her throat was constricted.

Even so, she managed to stand up in a panic and climb back onto the boardwalk. A dew-drenched bench invited her to sit down but she was not calm enough to heed our suggestion. She stepped out into the street instead, indifferent to the traffic … She continued to stagger around, half awake.

Cars and motorcycles raced by. Pedestrians were heading to work for the day or were coming home from the night shift. City employees were picking up the trash.

The city was getting ready for a new day.

We followed the poor girl, our minds filled with dark foreboding.

Felix was like a venerable educator who had suddenly lowered himself to roaming the streets with the aim of saving a dear child. Between sympathy and respect, I felt pity as I watched the great instructor who had humbled himself and suffered because he wanted to help...

When a half-drunk group of young men on the next corner saw Marita staggering around, they burst out laughing and yelled: "Look who's had a few too many!" Drivers shouted insults at her, and without one human arm to hold her up, she was hit by a speeding car and knocked a good distance, like a piece of meat violently hitting the ground.

The car sped off; pedestrians gathered around.

Young girls returning home after a happy night out screamed in alarm. One of them burst into hysterics and had to be led away. Traffic came to a standstill and witnesses tried to determine who was responsible. People got out of their cars and gathered around the inert girl.

Her body had flown through the air and her head had hit the pavement. Her body had rolled a short distance before stopping facedown.

I was appalled. I did not have enough experience to deal with emergencies like this where quick measures were required. Nevertheless, amid the clamoring for the police to help, brother Felix sat down on the asphalt. Applying vigorous magnetic stimuli to the girl's head, he gave her enough strength to mechanically turn over onto her back so that she could breathe more easily. Some of the spectators saw this as impending death.

Marita lay motionless.

I had the distinct impression that the base of her skull was fractured, but this was not the time to ask questions. The emotional weight was too heavy for me to consider the technical aspects of the injury.

Brother Felix, like any profoundly human and suffering father, situated himself in such a way that Marita's head was in his lap. Then, holding his hands over her blood-filled nostrils, he looked up at heaven and prayed aloud:

"God of infinite Love, do not let your child be expelled from the human abode like this without preparation! ... Give us, O Father, the blessing of suffering, which grants us time to reflect! O God of Love! Just a few more days for her in this broken body! A few hours, at least!"

The instructor finished, smitten with anguish like any human being.

He motioned me over and asked me to go to the apartment in Flamengo to see what kind of help I might reasonably obtain. He told me to ask either Claudio or Marcia for support and compassion. He, Felix, would inspire someone to phone for help. Between him and me, the Nogueiras would be informed about the accident and mentally induced to pity ... He would stay there, keeping watch and doing everything he could to keep Marita from discarnating too soon ... We would join up when I got back from Flamengo.

Upon witnessing such a display of humble selflessness, I hurried off, not only to do what I had been told but also to unburden my soul. Sometimes we need the consolation of tears when no one is watching ... So much effort from that sublime benefactor to save a girl enduring such harsh trials! ... So much sacrifice from a mentor whose greatness had been shaped in the higher realms in order to offer his arms! However, to my mind, defeat seemed inevitable.

Before leaving Atlantica Avenue and heading for Tunel Novo[20], I heard several voices exclaiming: "She's dead! ... She's dead!" Unable to control my tears, I went back to see the effect of this news on Felix's face, and concluded to myself: it's useless,

---

20 Literally, New Tunnel, which connects the districts of Botafogo and Copacabana in Rio de Janeiro. – Tr.

useless! … But a strong feeling of hope bathed my soul! … It felt like imponderable streams of energy were pouring down from the clear, starry sky upon that little corner of Copacabana, caressed by the nearby ocean, as if asking us, in the whispering language of the waves, to trust in God…

No! … The battle was not yet over!

We had with us the nourishment of love and the light of prayer! … All was not lost…

The benefactor, holding that unconscious child in his fatherly arms, raised his eyes to the firmament and, immersed in deep silence, seemed to be talking to the Infinite.

END OF PART ONE

Part Two

(Medium: Francisco Candido Xavier)

1

It was almost 5:00 a.m. when we arrived at the Nogueira apartment.

The place was quiet. Mute, silent furnishings.

Marcia, however, was restless under the light quilt, still worn out from having tossed and turned for most of a troubled night. In the dim light of the bedroom, she rested an elbow on the pillow and her head on her hand, her mind far away. Her eyes were red and swollen from weeping. Her adopted daughter had not come home. She was anxiously waiting for the new day … She would phone the Torreses to see if Marina had returned. If necessary, she would call Teresopolis. She wanted to talk to someone in order to unburden herself. She was afraid; her heart was filled with foreboding.

I talked to her mentally in search of news about Claudio.

I perceived her unspoken answer. Believing she was recalling the events of that night, she remembered Claudio having come home a few hours ago, completely drunk. He had tried to lean against the walls for support, but had stumbled over the furniture. Marcia had inferred that he had tried to drown his remorse in several shots of whisky. She had heard him vomiting. She had listened to his insults outside the door but had kept it locked as a precaution. A binge followed by a hangover capping a criminal adventure … She did not want a scene.

Suddenly, she broke her line of thought. She rejected my influence convinced she had reached the breaking point ... She was finished with Claudio. Her bitterness had become pure disgust. She wanted a new start, a legal separation. She wanted out…

I left her engulfed in her negative thoughts and went to the room in the back. I found Claudio stretched out on the single bed, fully clothed – he had not even taken off his jacket. He was lying on his side, with drool coming from one corner of his mouth. He was snoring peacefully, and with him was the vampirizer, relaxed under the effects of the alcohol. Both were unconscious.

I was absorbed in my examination, when the phone rang.

Of course, brother Felix had found the means to open some door to me so that I could act favorably on their behalf. It was absolutely essential that I deal with the problem and provide the watch-care for which I was responsible.

I went back to the living room.

Marcia, wearing a babydoll, answered the phone with a bad feeling about what she was about to hear.

An ordinary male voice came through the handset.

"Am I speaking to Mr. Claudio Nogueira?"

"This is his residence."

"Is he in, please?"

Marcia immediately realized it would be impossible to communicate with Claudio at that moment, and said firmly:

"No, he's not."

"I need to speak with him or his wife."

Marcia had a lot of experience with phone pranks and was well-versed in social conveniences; thus, she supposed the call was related to some new nonsense Claudio was involved in, and asked cautiously:

"Who is this?"

"Zeca, the trash collector. I'm in Copacabana and I need to tell him there's been a bad accident…"

"What kind of accident?"

"Are you his wife?"

"No, but I work here. I'm the maid."

Marcia was afraid of getting involved in something complicated and decided it might be best to remain anonymous; consequently, before the caller could answer, she added:

"They're both out, but I can give them a message."

"Well," stammered the informer, "the problem involves Marita, the sales girl from the shop."

"Why? What's the matter with her? …Tell me.! …What's happened to her?"

Marcia was pierced through with anguish, while I concluded that Felix had somehow managed to get the support of a helpful street cleaner to tell them the news, thus preparing the soil that I had to plant with the seeds of compassion.

"Please, tell your bosses she got hit by a car."

"Where? How? When?"

"Well, I didn't see how it happened, but I'm positive it was her."

"Just now?"

"About half an hour ago. Nearby, on Atlantica Avenue…"

"Is she still there?"

"No, the ambulance took her to the hospital."

"Are you sure it was her?"

"I'm positive ... She didn't have her purse on her and nobody recognized her ... But I know Marita very well because she has been a friend of my wife's ever since she got here. My wife works in the same building ... Poor Marita ... Such a nice girl! She was the one who got a place for my two daughters at the school!"

"But listen," Marcia interrupted, terribly shocked. "How is she?"

"They say she didn't make it..."

Although hardened against emotions, Claudio's wife hung up the phone and went back to the bedroom, pale as death.

She threw herself on the bed, pressed her hands against her head, and thought she would go crazy.

"Dead! Marita dead!" she exclaimed to herself, grief-stricken.

She recalled the insult the poor girl had suffered that dreadful night, which the new morning had caused to vanish, as if it were expelling a nightmare, and her mind wandered ... Aracelia: servant and friend ... Twenty years ago ... Her suicide! ... And now her daughter, experiencing the same tragedy with the same man ... Obviously, Marita, in her shame, had sought death herself. Inexperienced, she had given up. Marcia was trying to arrange her arguments by deduction. Crescina had told her about the rendezvous with Gilberto; however, she had caught Claudio red-handed instead ... All the evidence implied that Claudio had tampered with the young couple's arrangements in order to afflict the girl with an unforgivable insult ... There could be no doubt that the poor girl had preferred death.

Meanwhile, I intervened, forcing myself to incline her to compassion. I assimilated her thoughts of sympathy and reminded her to think of Marita's troubles that night ... She should stop being so passive ... She should rouse Claudio, call to him, plead with him ... If her husband was in no shape to grasp what she was saying, she herself would have to go out on the street ... look for the girl ... call the police and think about her as if she were her own daughter ... She should rush to the Copacabana emergency room, talk to the doctors and nurses, go to the morgue ... Somebody would help her find the creature Divine Providence had placed in her hands ... Who knows? Maybe she was still hanging on, waiting for her compassionate hands, as if waiting for a blessing!

Marcia heard me mentally. Upon receiving my suggestions, she imagined Marita's body stretched out in the morgue and began to cry.

Even then, Mrs. Nogueira was not someone who would bend easily when it came to domestic and social matters. She collected herself very quickly, lest she feel sentimental. She had no intention of giving in to sentimentalism – she told herself, believing she was alone. She had to weigh the pros and cons.

Only a few minutes passed from grief to calculation.

In fact, she did feel sorrow for Marita and disgust for Claudio. But she reminded herself she was a mother. She had to think of her other daughter. Things were looking up for Marina. The Torreses were wealthy – perhaps very wealthy. Both girls had fought over Gilberto. After all was said and done, Marita's death might just be the solution to the problem. As soon as he recovered his self-respect, the two of them would come up with a good plan. They would say her death had been an accident and they would come up with a plausible story. She herself would say she had given Marita permission to stay overnight at the home of a sick relative, asking her to return as early as possible to bring them news about the case.

It was essential to create situations, to invent details. Marita's coworkers at the shop would want all the facts. The press would be interested, too. She had to be prepared to face reporters and photographers. She thought about the blue dress she usually wore when attending funerals and racked her brains trying to remember where on earth she had put her sunglasses.

Later that morning she would wake her husband up in order to come up with a plan. They would have a serious conversation. Until then she would make up a story that the public could swallow – everything for the sake of Marina's future and happiness. If the other one was dead, why should she worry? Her daughter, only her real daughter was what mattered now … And as soon as Marina got married … no more Claudio. Marcia did not feel useless, but she was tired of having to work so hard, having to put up with a husband she had despised for a long, long time. She would not be made a slave. She had received an invitation from Selma, a childhood friend, to share a very profitable business in Lapa. At the front of the building there was a coffee shop that sold appetizers and snacks, and at the back there were rooms to rent out.

I realized that Marcia was at a mental stand-still, wandering around in clandestine digressions, so I went back to Felix to get precise instructions about what to do.

Lying on the bed in the emergency room, Marita seemed to be in a coma.

Felix was assisted by two discarnate doctors who regularly worked in the hospital. Although he kept his composure, there was sadness on his face.

He greeted me patiently and listened to what I had to say.

Then, he told me to wait a few minutes. We would have to get more help.

Meanwhile, I examined the injured girl. Marita was unconscious, losing ground quickly. There was hardly any activity in her nervous system; she had anoxemia, detectable changes in her capillary vessels and injuries to her peritoneum. Her out-of-control sphincters released liquids and excrement that soaked her clothes.

Felix took all the necessary steps and asked his discarnate colleagues to stand in for us for a short time.

We set out for Claudio's apartment.

On the way, I noticed that Felix was making his body denser and was changing his appearance. This was something that I could only do after patient mental preparation, but Felix could do it with almost no effort at all. After a few moments, he had imposed a new vibratory rhythm on his spirit body.

The instructor had assumed the characteristics of an ordinary man.

Why the transformation?

"Andre," he answered, reading my thoughts, "no one can do everything, except God. You, yourself, are a doctor and you know that on certain occasions it is absolutely necessary to resort to an alternative form of medicine. On earth, it is sometimes necessary to use a dose of poison in order to help a saint. Marita is facing sudden physical decay and needs the help of somebody who loves her very much. The time has come for us to plead for assistance from those who, despite their love, have made her suffer."

My friend's voice was tinted with sadness; however, I was not able to ask him to explain his philosophy, because we had arrived at the Nogueiras' building. It was bathed in the rising sun.

We went up.

Just as I, myself, had done the day before, the instructor knocked on the half-closed door.

After repeated knocking, Moreira answered, looking half-asleep.

He could not see me since I had not had time for the necessary metamorphosis, but he delivered a series of insults at Felix, who accepted them humbly. When he finished, a bit disappointed at not getting any reaction that would feed his ire, Felix told him about the accident. He said he knew Moreira was interested in the girl's welfare, so he had come to ask for his help. He could see that Moreira was skeptical, so he asked him to go see if Marita had slept there that night.

Moreira turned and left, and then came back scratching his head. Yes, he would go, but he would not wake up the head of the family before seeing if the information was true.

With a sullen face, he accompanied Felix from Flamengo to the public hospital without uttering a word. But when he saw Marita's condition, he burst into tears, like a rock suddenly parting to reveal a fountain.

Moreira turned around and shot out of there like an arrow.

Felix, feeling somewhat comforted, explained that, apparently, Claudio would soon arrive at the hospital. From what he could tell, Marita had been granted a moratorium – she would last in her mangled body for perhaps fifteen to twenty more days at most – time for meditation, an invaluable preparatory measure before reentering the spirit realm … Her brain would be protected but would not recover – it was too badly damaged. In just a few hours, she would be able to think and hear normally, and would recover some feeling and sight. But she would not be able to speak. Considering her present state, she could easily remain in the physical world for quite a while yet, but the peritoneum had suffered irreparable contusions. Antibiotics would be useless, no matter how strong the dosage. But even so, Felix was grateful to the spirit supervisors that had won her that small amount of additional time. Her final hours would be invaluable to her. She would have the opportunity to prepare herself for the renewal, while, at the same time, Claudio, Marcia and Marina might reconsider their current course in life…

Moved, I shared his optimism.

After a little more than fifty minutes, Claudio arrived, accompanied by a doctor who was a friend of the family and had known Marita for a long time. Marcia had yielded to Moreira's pressure and had told her husband everything she knew.

The doctor had Claudio wait outside while he began examining the girl. After doing this, he made arrangements for her immediate transfer to another hospital that specialized in accidents in order to provide her with detailed treatment. He made the phone calls to prepare for her admittance and then ordered the first emergency measures to be taken, i.e. to get Marita and the room cleaned up because, even though she was in a coma, she still deserved the utmost respect.

But it must be said that nothing out of order was done. The girl's precarious condition demanded rest and quiet. It was best to examine her before making any move that might make her condition worse.

In fact, when they did start to move her, with Claudio and Moreira following several steps behind, her head dangled backwards, thus forcing the blood back in her throat, something that could choke her. Felix did his best to control the gurney bearers' hands, and as soon as she was situated in another bed, I gave her the deep magnetic assistance the circumstances demanded. I sat down so as to hold that broken body in my arms, enveloping it in my own breath in a procedure that we might call an "addition of strength," the results of which are extremely beneficial, especially when the individual, still retained in the physical body, is near the end of his or her endurance.

Meanwhile, Felix suggested that, in order to enable Moreira to watch what I was doing, I should make my body denser as I worked on Marita. Felix hoped that Moreira would offer to help me keep her breathing system working.

I prayed for success, and when Claudio and his "guest" entered, the vampirizer looked at me in astonishment.

The two of them staggered, worried and afflicted ...

Extraordinary emotion gripped my soul.

Claudio approached his adopted daughter's bed and burst into tears.

From what I could tell, he saw that moment as the right time to start doing a painful examination of his conscience.

Instinctively, he went back to his childhood and youth ... He remembered his first imprudent acts. Improprieties from the past took shape in his mind. He lined up in his imagination the sexual excesses of his life. Every young girl he had deceived, every woman whose weaknesses he had exploited, appeared on his mental screen as if they were asking what he had done to the daughter that life had given him ...

That man, who had stirred such conflicting emotions in me, and from whom, in my aversion, I would have preferred to keep my distance, now inspired a tenderness that only tears could express!

In front of the startled nurse, Claudio fell to his knees and so did Moreira ... Weeping convulsively, the father caressed the girl's disheveled hair, contemplated that face of wax that death seemed to be sculpting, gazed at her ecchymosis-swollen lips, breathed the unpleasant smell that came from her lungs, and, burying his head in the sheets, cried out in despair:

"Ah! My daughter! ... My child!"

Almost at the same time, Moreira bent his head, as if it were crushed by suffering. Both of them were now with their faces close to my knees, demonstrating the same surrender with which Marita was nestling in my lap.

I realized that Divine Providence, in its wise designs, had not brought me in contact with the victim only: her tormenters were also in need of love. Holding the unconscious girl against my chest, I patted Claudio and Moreira with my right hand and continued to pray ... The prayer cleared my thoughts and corrected the way I had seen things! ... Yes, while trying to console those two men, whom remorse had caused to kneel in unbearable pain, I thought about my own wrongs and I understood the purposes of life! ... No! ... They were not the rapists, the obsessors, the enemies, the tormenters I had detested just yesterday! ... They were my fellow men, my brothers!

2

Saddened but serene, Felix approached Claudio and gave him energies for his recovery. After helping him stand up, he left, saying he would come back later.

I didn't have to worry, he said kindly. We were in this together and he would send help. He would see to everything.

I answered, setting him at ease. I had grown very fond of that girl; after all, she was our daughter in spirit. No, I would not leave her alone during the phase of discarnation.

In the meantime, Claudio had gone in search of the specialist.

Moreira had been watching me from the moment he had arrived. He was now viewing me kindly, something that I made an effort to encourage.

Finally, he spoke to me. He mellowed his voice and said he recognized me. He complained that he had seen several discarnate brothers approach the door and make faces of disgust. They pointed scornfully at Marita, made shameful allusions, and traced figures in the air suggesting obscene pictures. One of them even approached him and asked who that woman was, who smelled like rotting meat.

I tried to console him. All that would pass. We were waiting for colleagues that would bring the resources needed to isolate the room.

To satisfy his questions, I explained that, without meaning to, I had witnessed the accident and had felt compassion for that girl, lying all alone on the asphalt.

He wanted details; however, afraid of being indiscrete, I promised him that as soon as there was an opportunity, I would get more information for both of us.

In an attempt to harmonize him with the requirements of the work ahead of us, I asked him if I could help out. I would be very happy if I could assist that young girl whose trial was now so humiliating. I had had some experience in hospitals and I might be useful.

Moreira was touched and agreed to the idea. Yes – he said – he was extremely devoted to her and he could see I had no ulterior motives in helping her. He could count on me. He talked about a reward. He knew ways in which he could be very useful to me. He would watch out for me and be a faithful friend.

Then, he curiously examined the procedure I was using to help Marita's breathing. He asked me to show him how to do it. He wanted to replace me. He did it so well and so humbly that within a few minutes, he was keeping the girl alive even better than I could have done.

I showed him everything I knew. He obeyed gently and held in his arms that mangled body that had been transformed into a burden full of pain, sprinkled with feces. Touched in the depths of his soul, the persecutor of yesterday embraced her with the dignity of a pious man helping a sister, using his own breath to reheat her lungs and to give her new energies.

I was deeply touched by this transformation and concluded that it is not always the actual lifeboat that saves those who are shipwrecked, but sometimes the piece of driftwood they would disdain in other circumstances.

I went out for a few minutes in search of Claudio, and I found him in the waiting area. He was using the telephone while waiting for the doctor.

Marcia's unmistakable voice could be heard from the other end of the line. Her husband was speaking, obviously traumatized. However, she maintained her usual mental nimbleness. She was happy to know her daughter was still alive but she would rather not discuss it anymore. If the doctor was already on the scene, her troubles at home did not have to be compounded.

Claudio went from merely informing her about the matter to pleading with her. It would be best if she could come to the hospital to mitigate the situation.

However, Marcia said she had commitments to keep. In fact, she was going out to buy materials for making various ornaments that Marina had ordered. She understood the fact that Marita might not make it, but she did not believe the incident was all that serious. Marita had always over-reacted; she enjoyed being outrageous. Besides, if she was as seriously hurt as Claudio said she was, he was there as her father, faithfully by her side. Thus, she, Marcia, would be spared from making any more sacrifices than those she already carried on her shoulders. She made a joke, using sarcasm to disguise her disappointment that Marita was not actually dead. If she would have died, it would have spared them more trouble. She reminded Claudio that Rio was not some rural town and that no patient should be given the luxury of having more than one person by one's bedside in a capital[21] that was bigger than Babylon. She said she was fed up with petty squabbles and quarrels between young lovers and that

---

21 At the time, Rio de Janeiro was still the capital of Brazil. – Tr.

she would rather take up knitting than bother with a daughter who was not really hers and who had always been irresponsible and oversensitive. She finished by asking him to try to keep the expenses down; that he should listen to the doctors and then bring Marita home as soon as possible.

Claudio, forlorn, insisted, painting a picture of the grievous scene. But Marcia ended the conversation by saying something that dashed his hopes:

"Well, Claudio, this is your problem, not mine."

Claudio dialed the Torres' number.

Marina had not returned yet.

Heartbroken, he called his boss's home, told him about the accident and requested a few days off from work at the bank. The manager put him at ease. He understood the emergency; he too was a father. Not only would he approve Claudio's request, but he was available if there was anything he could do to help.

Claudio returned to the room where Moreira was watching over the girl, and talked to the doctor on duty.

The doctor understood the man's anxiety and felt sorry for him, but it was still too early to be more specific. He would run some tests. He had ordered blood transfusions and antibiotics, and would see how Marita reacted. But he would also confer with a neurologist in case there were complications, considering the blow to her skull.

Claudio agreed and humbly asked permission to stay by her side. Cost was not an issue; he wanted her to have the best treatment possible.

The doctor promised to do all he could for her.

A few minutes later, Marita was wheeled into another room, where Claudio, Moreira and I could have more privacy. Those two males, who used to pick a fight over trifles, were now completely different, even submissive.

Marcia's husband's eyes were filled with tears. His heart was broken. The idea that his daughter had tried to commit suicide because of him was scorching his soul, as if a red-hot dagger had pierced his chest. He had avoided so many scandals, so many contrivances; but now, that battered body, ambushed by death, seemed like it might be the end of him. He felt defeated, to the point that he did not even care if he had to make a public confession of all the wrongs of his life ... Wrongs he thought had been completely forgotten in the folds of time now came to his mind demanding justice ... Especially Aracelia! ... Marita's mother, whom he had destroyed with sarcasm and ingratitude, now seemed to reach out to him through the tunnel of his conscience ... The image of that innocent country girl grew larger and larger in his mind. She complained; she accused him; she asked for her daughter; she wanted explanations!

Claudio thought he was going crazy.

If it were not for his resolution to see his prostrated daughter healthy again, he would shoot himself. He believed that suicide was the only release valve possible. He would do it, he reasoned sullenly. If Marita didn't make it, he would have no desire to go on living. He would close her eyes and then kill himself without mercy,

While these bitter thoughts were clouding Claudio's mind, Moreira had glued himself to Marita's lungs in a moving spectacle of patience and dedication. On my part, I could detect his sincere devotion and the purity of his purposes. The girl's damaged body was not repugnant to him. He embraced Marita with the tenderness of someone attending to a suffering daughter for whom all the care in the world is not enough ... From time to time, he wiped away his tears ... That spirit, whom I had known to be rough and vulgar, must have loved her deeply, because it is necessary to love someone with extreme tenderness to joyfully absorb her fetid breath and to caress her excrement-stained skin with the rapture of someone preserving a treasure that was immensely precious to the heart.

The silence was only broken from time to time by the activities of the nurse who came in to check on the I.V. or to administer injections prescribed by the doctor.

The day dragged on. It was 3:00 p.m. It was hot. To Claudio, the hours were like chains that he was dragging around in the prison of remorse. He felt lonelier and lonelier. He went back to the telephone and called Marina.

The girl answered. They talked.

Marcia had told her about the accident; however, she had hoped the unpleasant event was just a fright. No, she could not go to the hospital. Beatriz, whom she had always thought of as her mother, had worsened a great deal; she could die any minute now. Claudio would have to forgive her. However, she thought her sister would be happy knowing her father was watching over her. She couldn't ask for more than that.

Claudio went back to the room feeling completely beaten.

There was no one to give him a crumb of support; no one to understand his mental torment.

At 5:00 p.m., however, somebody showed up: an elderly gentleman that had been recommended by a helpful doctor.

Alone with Claudio, he introduced himself.

He was Salomao, the pharmacist.

He informed Claudio that he was a friend of Marita's. He had always appreciated her affability and politeness. Because his shop was next door to where the girl worked, they would sometimes have a cup of coffee together whenever he could not go home for lunch. He was shocked when he found out about the accident and had immediately decided to come and visit her, especially since he believed he was one of the last friends the girl had talked to the day before.

Realizing that Claudio was grateful but curious, Salomao told him everything he knew, detail by detail.

It was evident that some hidden disillusionment had motivated Marita's desperate act. He remembered perfectly well the tears she had unsuccessfully tried to hide. She must have taken the tranquilizers he had given her, but after some time, realizing they were harmless, she must have thrown herself in front of a car…

Claudio listened, in tears … Deep down, he accepted the possibility. There could be no doubt that his daughter had not survived the insult he had inflicted on her. This stranger only confirmed his suspicions. He could just imagine the horror and humiliation Marita had been through, leading her to decide to take her own life. He felt like the most despicable man alive, suffering remorse that whipped all the fibers of his conscience. He thanked the visitor, while trying to control his tears of pain. Claudio embraced the pharmacist in an impulse of sincerity, and added that he, Salomao, was Marita's true and maybe only friend; she had sought death but they would do all they could to keep her alive.

The compassionate pharmacist risked a suggestion.

He confessed that he was a Spiritist and he said that something called "passes," if combined with prayer, might benefit the unconscious girl. He said he did not know Claudio's family's religious principles, but he had a friend, Agostinho, whom they could talk to. Salomao reiterated the fact that he had faith in the power of prayer and spiritual protection. If Claudio would allow him, he would go and fetch the medium. Claudio accepted the offer humbly. He said he was all alone. It wouldn't be right to refuse help that was being offered so spontaneously.

He only said he felt he should ask permission from the hospital authorities first.

The doctor came to talk to them and listened to the request. Being a man of great experience as regards human suffering, he looked at Marita not only with the reasoning of a technician who is inspecting a machine on its way to dismantling for final inspection, but also with the sentiment of a loving father. He told Claudio he had the right to give his daughter any kind of religious assistance he wished, and provided he avoided breaking hospital rules outside of the room, he should consider himself at home.

Full of compassion, he himself was in favor of Salomao bringing the Spiritist to Marita's room. At 8:00 p.m., the pharmacist from Copacabana returned with a friend who was carrying a small packet containing a book.

Claudio was very surprised. That man, who greeted him kindly, was introduced as Agostinho, a regular and highly respected client at Claudio's bank. Although Claudio knew him as a successful businessman, he had never gotten to know him closely. However, if the visitor did recognize him, he did not let it show.

He turned his attention to the girl and asked about the details of the accident with the interest of someone listening to one of his own family.

He stood between Salomao and Claudio and prayed fervently. He asked for Christ's blessings on the injured girl as if presenting the invisible Jesus with a much loved daughter. Then, he administered longitudinal passes to Marita with the devotion of a father who was infusing her with his own energies.

I cooperated with him under the piercing look of Moreira, who made note of everything in his desire to learn.

The treatment, saturated with healing elements from the physical plane, did Marita a lot of good and her overall condition improved. The sphincter responsible for urination became more relaxed, the breathing more regular, and she fell into a calm sleep.

Claudio called for the nurse and asked her to send someone to change the bedding, while the three men talked in an adjacent room. When Agostinho was told that Claudio had never had any contact with religious principles, he offered Claudio the book he had brought with him: a copy of *The Gospel according to Spiritism*. He promised he would come back the next morning.

3

Back in Marita's room, Claudio was lost in thought, thinking, thinking...

Outside, the leaden evening sky, and with it silence, broken only by his daughter's labored breathing.

If Salomao had been the only unexpected intervener – he thought, preoccupied – he would not have considered the matter to be of much importance! That druggist, to whom he had entrusted the successes of the night, inspiring his gratitude and sympathy, did seem like a wonderful person; however, in his good-natured naiveté, he could very well have been misled in his beliefs ... Agostinho, on the other hand, had brought a jolt to his spirit. Being an educated, prosperous businessman, he would never let himself be misled ... Claudio knew about the man's keen mind and honesty. Furthermore, he surely must have had more important things to do with his time and attention.

What kind of doctrine was this – one that could induce a well-to-do gentleman to go into a hospital room and start praying, weeping with compassion for an injured girl that already had one foot in the grave? What principles compelled an educated, wealthy man to forget himself in order to help the unfortunate, to the extent of actually touching their fecal matter, imbued with the kind of love that only parents know about deep in their hearts?

Claudio looked at Marita sleeping peacefully and remembered the two selfless men that had brought her some comfort without asking any questions ... He had never had one bit of interest in religious teachings and usually treated the subject with contempt, but he now found himself beset by a lot of whys.

Downcast, Claudio longed for something ... Without the fluidic support of Moreira, who was dedicating all his energies to the girl in his arms, he thought about smoking a cigarette, but he reminded himself that a cigarette was not what he really needed at the moment.

He wanted to leave and run to Agostinho and Salomao to ask them about trust in God. He needed to know how they managed to have such faith. Both of them had succeeded in soothing the pain that was torturing his daughter ... And right now, he was wondering if he himself was not just as worthy of pity. Marita was resting in the sleep of victims, guarded in the inviolable peace of conscience, whereas he was tormenting himself in the waking state of a defendant! ... He realized he was sick deep in his soul, a shipwreck victim drowning in an eddy of despair ... He wanted to grab on to someone, something. Just a little ray of hope could keep him from the edge of a total fall! ... Loneliness suffocated him. He craved company.

I suggested that he read. He could open the book he had been given. It would talk to him silently and would be his friend. He should not decide to digest all its teachings in one go. He should consult passages here and there, collect ideas, select concepts.

He registered my thought, picked up the book and leafed through it. Even so, he tried to resist. He felt impotent, restless. He did not have the least bit of serenity to apply himself to the matter.

I insisted.

His nervous fingers opened the book to the Table of Contents. He glanced at the headings. Under Chapter XI he found the heading "Charity toward Criminals." Those words invaded his guilty mind like pincers of fire. He felt he had been found out by an invisible court of justice. "Yes!"– he told himself, disconsolate – "I've got to examine myself." In his own mind, he was a hardened criminal on the lam. Throughout each and every day, he had been seen and cherished under that roof as a loving father; but he knew he was nothing but a rapist, a filicide ... He bore the irremediable pain of having driven his dear daughter to madness and death! ... What kinds of condemnations would this book line up against him? He deserved to hear his own sentence pronounced in front of the victim that had succumbed under his merciless blow.

He looked for the right page and oh! What a surprise! The book did not condemn his life at all! He wept as he read and re-read those sentences that breathed gentleness and understanding. He found himself before an appeal to fraternity and compassion, not one that painted moral delinquents as beings from hell, and outside the orbit of Divine Love. The short passage asked for tolerance and ended by praying for those who have fallen in the abysses of wrongdoing.

Tears gushed from his eyes! ... Those words brought him back to his senses. He realized that the world and life ought to be bathed in profound mercy. He considered himself a murderer, yet here he was, reconsidering his own path with enough lucidity to analyze himself and to reflect ... That first contact with the truths of the spirit cracked the citadel of his atheism from top to bottom. With the longing of a man traveling across a vast desert, mortified with thirst, Claudio dove into the texts, from which clarifying, soothing ideas flowed like sublime torrents of pure water. He read about several topics ... He gained a quick understanding of reincarnation and the plurality of worlds; he pondered the wonders of charity and the marvels of faith through the immortal flames of Christianity that were being born right there, bringing warmth back to his soul!

When he looked at his watch, it was 2:00 a.m.

He had spent four hours immersed in the book without realizing it. He felt like a new man. His mind had cleared up, riddled with renewing thoughts that provoked burning questions. This was a doctrine that allowed him to feel and enquire freely, like a child in his mother's arms ... In fact – he reasoned – if God did not exist, if there was no afterlife, why did he feel so miserable? If everything in life was meant to end up in dust, what was driving him to suffer such mental agony with regard to the daughter who inspired so many conflicting feelings in him? He loved that poor girl so much! Why hadn't he been able to remain just a father to her, immune to the impulses of sex? What kinds of forces had compelled him to become Marita's tormenter? The idea of reincarnation cut across his mind like a lightning bolt. Both had lived in the past ... No doubt about it: they must have lived in the past, shackled to the domineering madness of passion, suffering and weeping together! His devotion to Marita was like the tip of an iceberg hiding the rest of its enormous bulk under the water ... At that moment, something told him down deep that he, Claudio, had brought her back to this world through paternity in order to guide her with cleanliness and selflessness! ... In the smile of a daughter, the wisdom of life had restored love to him so that he could right the wrong of the amorous tyranny he must have exerted in the past, and the ruthless passions that were burning in his heart in the present ... The realities of fate enhanced his thought, beautiful and diffused, like rays of sunshine breaking through the fog.

But even so, he did not excuse himself. He realized he had only increased his debts.

Glimpsing the realities of the Afterlife, he made an appeal to his friends who had already departed for it! ... He asked them to have pity on both himself and Marita! That they, in turn, might ask God to allow him to trade his life for hers ... He, a criminal father, would expiate his wrongs in the spirit world and then be born again in a deformed body as payment for his debts. He would ask to be afflicted in order to expunge the stains on his soul. However, he pleaded that his daughter be allowed to live and be happy! ... But if he did have to remain in this world, carrying the suffering and the torment of that moment, that they might let her stay in his arms just as she was – debilitated and mute! He was strong enough to bear her! ... He would be her shelter, her support! ... They should let her remain! They should give him the chance to transform, alongside her, all his caprices as an uncouth man into manifestations of pure love ... Somehow, he would find a way to nestle her in his heart. He would get her a wheelchair and push her anywhere she wanted to go. He would accept any obstacle without complaint; but he was begging Divine Providence to spare her from the scythe of death so that he could start his readjustment and reparation!

I embraced him, suggesting hope and trust. Who on earth was free of problems? How many others, right then, in other places, were not going through similar struggles? That burden assailing his thoughts was a traffic light on the road of destiny. It was invaluable to see remorse as the red light, demanding a halt. He should apply the brakes to the car of his desires and think ... think! All of us finally arrive at a day of reckoning with our own conscience. Claudio should not desert the torch that was now lighting his way. He should understand that God's law is not based on condemnation but on justice, and that God's justice is never applied without mercy. He should ponder the matter and conclude that if other imperfect men and women have succeeded in adding compassion to justice, why would God, who is Infinite Love, mete out justice without mercy? At that moment we were coming out of the darkness of the night ... Dawn was approaching, and with it the sun of a new day! ... He should bring all of his sentiments to the renewal that had just begun!

Moreira watched me embrace Claudio, and he looked at me anxiously, as if he were asking me about the thoughts I was suggesting. But before I let him resume his former place as Claudio's "counselor," I appealed to Claudio and encouraged him to begin his endeavor of reparation and readjustment.

The bank clerk did not hesitate.

Deeply moved, he got up, walked over to Marita's bedside and knelt down.

He confessed to himself that, for the first time in a long, long time, he could look at his daughter's face without the slightest hint of sexual fascination altering his sentiments.

His soul trembled, tormented.

He caressed her with a kind of tenderness that he had never experienced before, and let the tears run down his face while he prayed, whispering:

"Forgive me, my daughter! ... Forgive your father!"

The plea stuck in Claudio's sob-constricted throat.

Of course Marita did not respond; however, her father's caress had infused her with different energies, and both Moreira and I were surprised to hear her moan – a sign that she was returning to herself.

Full of hope, Claudio stood up. His caring act had filled him with sudden reverence; deep down he compared that newfound, pure love to a white lily blooming in a swamp.

More moans, imprecise, dolorous...

Claudio listened, filled with anxiousness. He would give anything to be able to understand those sounds of an unconscious child ... However, he guessed that they probably indicated unimaginable physical pain, a thought that threw Claudio into an agony of convulsive weeping. Moreira, the former obsessor, now a diligent servant, immediately got up and embraced Claudio to comfort him. But I noticed that now the two friends were both near and far apart at the same time – shoulder to shoulder, but opposite in thought. Moreira had indeed been influenced by this string of events, but not as much as Claudio. He demonstrated enormous caring for Marita; he was fighting for her, but down deep, he did not hide his purposes of continuing to control Claudio in his own interest. Realizing that his partner's heart had been touched by the edifying sentiments that the book had inspired, Moreira displayed his disappointment, like a pianist who has just discovered his favorite instrument is out of tune. Alarmed, he bombarded me with questions. I calmed him down, saying that Claudio's brain was not working properly at the moment, because he was greatly troubled. However, deep down, I knew that Claudio had taken a step forward and that his unhappy partner would have to rise to the same level if he wanted to continue enjoying Claudio's company.

Claudio's mind emerged morally tormented from those few hours of compulsory study like a landscape that had just been shaken by an earthquake. He had never experienced anything like it. Thus, Moreira was disgruntled, resentful and hurt.

Even so, he went back to the task of assisting the unconscious girl.

Just then, two aids – Arnulfo and Telmo – arrived; Felix had sent them to help us with the girl.

Both of them were friendly and spontaneous.

I introduced them to the surprised Moreira, whose spiritual condition they discerned immediately. However, with the kindness characteristic of benevolent hearts, they made every effort not to humiliate him with any dividing line of treatment. They surrounded him with optimism and gentleness, and treated him as an esteemed colleague. Only two days earlier, that brother, who played the role of "tough guy" in Flamengo, would not have accepted such friendship. But now, Marita was living suspended between two worlds… exhausted and afflicted with dyspnea.

For Marita's sake, Moreira was putting up with the changes, was holding back his impulses.

Dawn was yielding to daylight.

We approached Claudio.

It was crucial to make him lie down and get some sleep.

Moreira had a look of obvious displeasure on his face as he observed our care in giving soothing passes to Claudio, who acquiesced without complaint.

It is worth mentioning how relieved Claudio felt in response to our touch. He had just been through an unimaginable ordeal. He craved some rest and begged for the blessing of peace.

However, as Claudio's tense nerves relaxed and yielded to our gentle suggestion of sleep, Moreira observed everything with the growing annoyance of someone who was watching his house being shaken up, remodeled and changed without his having asked for it. He projected waves of bitterness and displeasure in his yellow-toothed smile. Everything around him was being turned upside down … between the friend, who was escaping his grasp, and the girl, whose physical body he had decided to preserve, he felt confused, out-of-sorts.

Realizing that he could not adopt a position of antagonism towards us due to the assistance we were giving Claudio, he worked even harder for the girl, whose deepest thoughts he was trying to read. Marita, in turn, because she had assimilated more energy, ended up recovering control of the brain centers that were still available to her. She recouped her sense of smell. She perceived, reasoned and heard with relative accuracy; however, she was still irreversibly hemiplegic, blind and mute. At first, she thought she had woken up in a coffin. She had heard many stories about "dead" people waking up in the grave. She had read accounts about such cases and she had seen several horror films. With an oppressed soul, she imagined that the same had happened to her and that she was lying in a coffin, in the silence of unbelievable afflictions … She tried to scream for help, but the thought came to her mind that she had forgotten how to articulate words. She knew she was thinking with her own brain, but she was no longer able to coordinate the movements required to speak. Despite everything, she realized she was conscious. She could feel and remember. She remembered the events that had inspired her to want to die. Marita was repentant. If life did continue after death, why provoke the premature death of the body? – she asked herself. She remembered the events in Lapa, her phone call to Gilberto from Cora's apartment, Salomao's pills, her sleeping near the sea, the stranger ready to assault her, her running to the street, her being hit by the car … And to top it all off, here she was … her mangled body feeling as if it were made of stone, her conscience active, her perceptions acute – but she was unable to communicate … She wanted desperately to get someone's attention, but she felt as if she had a lead collar around her throat. She became angry, to no avail. She trembled with impatience, astonishment, pain ... Suffering, revolt, petitions and questions faded unanswered deep inside her being. The harder she tried to cry in order to feel some relief, the more the tears stuck in her chest, with no outlet to relieve her agony. Her eyes and tongue seemed to be completely detached from her body.

Might she actually be dead – she asked in a mixture of perplexity and suffering – or not quite dead?

She heard the footsteps of the nurse on duty and her father's labored breathing, but she could not see them. In vain, she asked for an explanation for the nauseating smell that enveloped her.

After two hours of recondite anguish, which Moreira marked with acuity and accuracy, the girl calmed down mentally, and when I examined her inner thoughts, I noticed that, unfortunately, they were fixated on Marina.

Claudio's discarnate friend, who had always provided him with psychic support until now, and who now needed a moral base to ensure his own rebalance, found Marita's thoughts about her sister to be a verdant pasture.

I saw the danger but could do nothing to prevent it.

Moreira understood that he could no longer use Claudio's body as a puppet, so he analyzed Marita for ways to use her instead to feed his insanity.

For my part, I could not press the injured girl to stop her regrets. Any expenditure of energy beyond what was absolutely necessary to sustain her body could hasten her discarnation.

Unaware of the complications she was causing with this behavior, Aracelia's daughter reconstructed in her imagination all the problems she had had in her life. She blamed her sister for all her misfortunes and mentally pictured her as being her unforgiveable enemy ... Marina stealing Marcia's maternal love

... Marina robbing her of opportunities ... Marina stealing her affections, especially the chosen one of her youthful dreams...

The thoughts we directed at her were useless.

Moreira's influence, which encouraged Marita's accusations, was naturally stronger for someone who was trying to find sympathy and support.

That poor girl did not realize how powerful thoughts are. She did not know that, without indulgence and kindness, she was attracting only retaliation, and thus not only was she embroiling her family in harsh trials, she was also about to forfeit the invaluable work of recovery of that friend in need of love and light.

As he absorbed her unspoken thoughts, in which she exposed her innermost burdens, though unknown to him, Claudio's former assailant gradually recovered the brutality that used to mark his face.

He was losing his spiritual gains.

Under the pretext of helping Marita, he was reviving his instincts as avenger.

The look that had softened with compassion had regained the wild look of the mentally alienated. Every indication of a return to sanity and humaneness after seeing the mangled Marita had vanished.

It would be useless to try to bring him back to serenity. Absorbed in the complaints of the woman he considered as his beloved, he regained the fury of a wild beast thirsting for blood. In answer to our appeals for calmness and tolerance, he shouted, "No! No!"... No one was going to make him stop fighting for the tranquility of the woman he loved. He said that, until now, he had had no idea of the suffering her sister had imposed on her for her entire life, so he was bent on revenge.

Realizing he was abandoning the work he had so willingly undertaken, and that he was incapable of reflecting on the consequences of his desertion, I concluded that the former obsessor-turned-friend was being assailed by a fit of madness, and I wondered if brother Felix had not made a mistake when he prayed for Marita to stay longer in her broken body, so extensive was the damage Moreira could do from that moment on. I reprimanded myself ... No! I did not have the right to judge the crazed friend who had abandoned us as the morning sun rose in the sky. Brother Felix had known what he was doing, and of course, at another time in the past, I too had been insane and had failed.

It was my job to simply assist, to help.

I handed my duties over to Arnulfo and Telmo and set out for the Torres residence, the only place where I thought Moreira would go.

I went in.

Within the nearly-silent place, one would be hesitant even to whisper. The servants had tears in their eyes.

Beatriz was in a coma, waiting for death.

Pedro and other friends from the spirit plane surrounded her bed. A dedicated nurse was observing that woman who was about to dive into the great repose. Nemesio, Gilberto and Marina were sitting nearby.

I was surprised to find that Moreira had not arrived yet. But my surprise did not last long because, a few minutes later, Claudio's ex-companion, followed by four truculent, surly male spirits, entered the room disrespectfully. Without any concern for the dying woman, they approached Marina and shouted angrily:

"Murderer! ... Murderer!"

4

As a result of the aggression, Marina felt irrepressibly ill-at-ease. Her face paled. She felt suffocated. She registered all the symptoms of someone who had received a blow to the head. She threw her head backwards in the armchair and made an effort to hide what she was feeling, but it was useless. The Torreses – father and son – saw that she was fainting and rushed to help.

Nemesio said she must have fainted as a consequence of having stayed up all night without having slept at all the day before because she had been watching over Beatriz, whose body was being painfully consumed, little by little. Gilberto brought her a glass of water and then phoned the doctor.

On the spirit plane the impact was no less troubling.

Pedro gave me a concerned look, as if he were asking me to help him keep from exploding. He had met Moreira on our first visit to Flamengo; however, he did not know about the events that had been afflicting me since the day before yesterday. Judging from the disapproving look he gave me, he must have concluded that his daughter's bedroom had been invaded by discarnate wrongdoers for no reason. He could not understand the motives that drove Claudio's former "counselor" to revolt the way he did and recruit unfortunate colleagues to initiate an attack he regarded as an undertaking with the objective of meting out punishment and justice.

One of the discarnate women waiting to greet Beatriz after leaving her body came to me asking for help.

Moreira and his gang were spewing obscenities, offending the dignity of the room after having eluded the security outside the house. She did not expect me to confront them like an incarnate would. She accepted the newcomers as creditors deserving of our utmost pity. Even so, Mrs. Torres was saying her last prayers and she needed peace and quiet.

With certain therapeutic methods, it is impossible to reestablish organic normality without removing the focus of infection, and in this case, the focal point of disharmony was Marina.

If Marina left, she would take the agents of disorder with her.

I approached the pity-worthy girl and urged her to leave. She needed some rest. She should not be stubborn but accept my suggestion for her own good.

She obeyed, although reluctantly.

Marina asked her friends to excuse her; she would wait for the doctor in another part of the house. I followed her.

The gang, however, intercepted me and Moreira questioned me. He wanted to know why I was trying to help someone he hated. He asked angrily if I did not know Marina very well, if I had never witnessed her debauchery with both father and son at the same time, and why I was so interested in a woman he called a minx – beautiful on the outside but sordid on the inside.

Moreira mocked my unwillingness to talk. He slanderously referred to the woman who had asked me to get him out of there, and said that he was not a coward who disturbed the dying. He asked me insolently why the venerable spirits and friends, whom he called "those women," expected him to leave when they allowed Marina to breathe freely in the same room. He emphasized the fact that just because he was frank and tough, he did not consider himself to be any worse than her.

He showered me with complaints full of bile.

He challenged me to explain my point of view. Using words that might endanger the trust he had honored me with since the day before, I risked reminding him that, in spite of it all, Marina was Claudio's daughter and Marita's sister, and we both owed them our warmest affection. Any harm to Marina would be disastrous for both Claudio and Marita. It was not my business to show favoritism towards her by criticizing any corrective measures he might take regarding her, but I was a friend of the Nogueiras' and could not let anyone hurt her.

He smiled and said that my comments did make some sense; that he would promise to lessen his revenge but that he would not stop completely.

He dismissed his four collaborators and told them to wait for him out on the patio. Then he followed me, holding onto Marina in a rough manner.

With no idea she was in the company of spirits, Marina entered the room, left the door ajar, lay down on the bed, and closed her eyes.

She relaxed.

She longed to sleep, to rest ... But she could not.

Moreira, insensitive, aimed to make me give up any sympathy I might have for the defenseless girl. He informed me that he was going to submit her to an interrogation about Marita so that I could hear her silent testimony and be able to judge for myself.

I prayed for Marina to give answers that would ennoble the interrogation, but my hopes were dashed at the very start.

Having promoted himself to the status of judge, Marita's undesirable patron struck with a pejorative insult in the girl's ears and asked her for her opinion about her hospitalized sister. He insisted that she disclose what she thought about that suicide.

Although feeling weak and thinking it was her own idea, Marina turned her attention to her sister, and presuming that she was talking only to herself, she allowed the thoughts to swarm in her brain without the brakes of self-criticism.

Yes, she did feel sorry for Marita – she admitted, calculatedly – but she was grateful to fate for having gotten her out of the way. Of course, she would never have had the courage to drive Marita to suicide; nevertheless, if Marita, herself, had decided to leave this world, thus clearing the way for her sister, she, Marina, felt relieved. Gilberto had told her about a phone call he had received two nights ago. He had given her his impressions. It had not been a prank. From what they could tell, Marita had imitated Marina's voice and asked questions … Convinced that the young man did not love her, she had preferred to die. Gilberto was very clear. Based on the phone conversation, which he disclosed in the smallest detail, Marita had probed his feelings with the aim of getting an indirect confirmation of his love for her. But disillusioned by what she had heard, she had decided to kill herself. In light of it all, she, Marina, had nothing to regret. If the young Torres loved her as much as she loved him, and if the other had decided to "go away," that was no reason for her to torment herself. A few weeks earlier, Gilberto himself had asked her about her sister's oddities. In his opinion Marita was neurotic and unbalanced because she had never known her real father. Nemesio's son believed she suffered from syphilis in the brain, and that she was not fit for marriage. After a short pause in her train of thought, like someone who turns off a light only to turn it on again, switching scenarios, Marina went on thinking, remembering...

She had phoned home that night and Marcia had told her that Marita had not died yet. However, the doctor had informed her mother confidentially that medicine did not have the means to help Marita recover and that her death was now just a matter of days. The doctor had recommended that special attention be given to Claudio, who was crushed with anguish. He had also suggested that she not tell her husband what he had just disclosed to her about Marita, stating that he had only spoken freely to her because she seemed to be calmer in the face of the ordeal; that in her position as a mother, she should try to avoid strong emotions so that she could support her family in the crisis they would have to face at any moment now. Marina's thoughts wounded Moreira in his deepest fibers.

The doctor's diagnosis was like a shot to the head.

He had not accepted the idea of losing Marita on the physical plane. Unconsciously, she had fluidic resources that were compatible with his own, providing him with feelings of euphoria and physical strength. He extracted from her the mental stimuli that reinforced his masculinity as much as the stimuli he got from Claudio in order to live on earth like any other human being.

Between frustration and rebelliousness, he called Marina a dirty name and justified to me why he had the right to punish her. Outraged and childish, he screamed at me that both of us could see how Marina rejoiced at her sister's tragedy; that I could not deny how cold she was; that I should back him up when the time came; that I should be his witness.

Marina, however, continued thinking and considering, as if she were spontaneously adding margin notes to the theme suggested by Moreira.

She did love Gilberto. Only him. She would find a way to rid herself of the older Torres. The more the time passed, the more she was convinced that she belonged to the younger one. She dreamed of marrying him, of being his wife and the mother of his children.

However, when the image of a future home appeared in her imagination, Moreira threw himself at her and screamed:

"Never! ... You shall never be happy! ... You killed your sister! ... Murderer! Murderer!"

Faced with this assault – my protection and interference on her behalf was not advisable at that moment – the girl was overcome by a strange feeling of uneasiness.

Those accusations struck her deep inside, as if someone were trespassing on her thought.

She gasped in discomfort.

She started to think about Marita but from a different perspective, making comparisons. She uselessly argued with herself in an attempt to confute the remorse that had invaded her conscience. She felt she was in conflict with herself. She moaned uneasily. She had no idea she was in a battle with an invisible Intelligence that was demanding justification for her behavior. As her adversary hammered away at her brain with accusations – which she accepted because she knew she was guilty – Marina began to lose her footing. Her reasoning became fuzzy and she mobilized all her energies so as not to pass out; she was afraid of going crazy.

The enemy had challenged the fortress, exploiting the cracks in the walls. The fortress would have endured, invincible, if it had been intact; however, the cracks were there, and the enemy shot arrows of curses and sarcasm through them, generating psychosis and invoking death.

I worked in silence, calling upon mental resources to help the victim break free. However, even though the girl was skillful enough to live amongst incarnates without committing herself on the surface of the circumstances, she was completely ignorant of any ennobling knowledge she might use to leave the pathway she was on and adopt a new direction. My efforts were futile.

Marina was at the mercy of the power that was sapping her mental resources, and felt defeated.

From indifference regarding her sister's accident, she went to oppression, and then fear.

At the touch of the inquisitor rummaging through her brain, she began to imagine that, actually, Marita would never have thought of suicide if she had found in her sister an honest and kind companion.

She remembered the night when she had seen Gilberto for the first time. He was coming out of a movie theater with her sister, protecting her from the rain. Such sweetness in those eyes; so much caring in those arms ... She thought she had found a younger Nemesio. Although committed to Torres, the father, she thought she could find in the son the youthful attributes that were lacking in the older man ... Whether just a whim or true affection, she had fallen in love with the young man and had courted him openly. She had entwined him with her gifts of intelligence until she had lit in his enthusiastic soul the desire to share her dreams and emotions. She had invited him out and had captured his heart. She had planted in him the need for her and she had made him a dependent, a slave. She had manipulated him completely – something her sincere but inexperienced sister had not had the courage to do – even though she knew about their commitment because he himself had disclosed it to her. Seeing that he was chained to the other, she outdid herself in the processes of seduction. She flattered him; she imposed herself on him; she ensnared him, like a spider spinning the silky web it is going to use to capture the insect it plans to devour.

Facing the sentence of this unexpected judge, she craved tranquility. She meticulously analyzed her attitudes and came to the surprising conclusion that she had only hurt herself. Remorse was like an invisible dagger piercing her skull. A flood of tears welled up from her chest to her eyes, like streams of water that the drill can extract from the subsoil only after it pierces the deepest layers.

The doctor, assisted personally by the owner of the house, found her in a fit of tears. Despite feeling apprehensive, he consoled her and lifted her spirits. He said she was feeling exhausted. He praised her for her punctuality and her devotion as Beatriz's caretaker. He prescribed tranquilizers. She should get some rest and be sure to take care of herself.

Marina, however, knew that her conscience was in a panic and that any attempt to make her deny her inner tribunal would be useless. When the doctor left, she began crying convulsively again in front of Nemesio, who, terribly concerned, shut the door and approached her with the intention of comforting both her and himself.

I felt embarrassed in light of that demonstration of tenderness, when actually there was no mutual affection between them, and I was concerned about Moreira, who watched them in scorn and hurled offensive comments at the pair.

Nemesio begged the girl to take care of herself and rest up a bit. She should be patient and both of them would be happy. It was only a matter of a few days before he would go to Flamengo personally in order to make the final arrangements for the wedding. He was counting on her and wanted to make her happy. Enchanted, he kissed her wet face, as if he wanted to absorb her tears, while the girl, clearly disturbed, looked at him askance in a mixture of pity and repulsion.

I invited Moreira to leave with me, but mercilessly, he asked me if I lacked the courage to get to know Marina as well as he did; and because I wanted to defend her, he added that he was not there as a tormenter. Sarcastically, he suggested that I should not accuse him, because he was about as guilty for Marina's indisposition as a scalpel would be guilty for removing a tumor.

I asked him, for Claudio's sake, to help us protect the girl; after all, she was just a recruit in the war against evil, although she considered herself to be very experienced.

Why couldn't we stand watch at the door? A time might come when we might need her help. Although he said that he had never indulged in intrigue, he had no desire to be a cover for criminals and agreed to leave. Outside the room, however, since I made a reference to hypnosis when it comes to the emotions, and since I commented on the need to be patient when dealing with persons with sexual problems, he laughed and said scornfully that it was useless for me to use polite terms for obscene situations, which, for him, had their own names. He warned me that when the father left, the son would come and that I would lose face anyway.

In fact, when Nemesio left, the young man, tired from having stayed up all night, came in our direction and entered the room.

Moreira gave me a significant look, but before he digressed into criticism, someone showed up with enough sympathy and compassion to divert our attention.

It was brother Felix.

Just by looking at him, I could see he had already been informed about everything that was happening. Nevertheless, he opened his arms to Moreira like a father that has found a long-lost son. Our friend, who had returned to his sentimental imbalance, realized that he had just been infused with regenerative fluids, and he remembered the first time the benefactor had asked him to help protect Marita. His heart softened.

Felix did not show a trace of disapproval at his desertion and appealed to him with absolute trust:

"Ah! My friend, my friend! ... Our Marita!..."

And faced with Moreira's questions, Felix, who was treating him as if he were his equal, explained that the girl was getting worse. Dreadful pain was mortifying her body. She was exhausted, afflicted. Since the moment Moreira had left her, everything indicated that the poor girl was losing ground quickly. The suffering child needed him, was waiting for him in order to feel some relief.

Those sincere words had a profound impact on Claudio's former obsessor. He rose to the call and went with us back to the hospital, where we could see that the girl was in a deplorable state.

Four hours had passed, modifying our work schedule.

I realized that what Felix had asked of Moreira was not just a compassionate artifice. Although Marita was being helped by Telmo's infusion of energies, she had difficulties absorbing them.

Without meaning to criticize anyone, I must say that the two of them lacked the harmony needed to be the cog in the gearwheel. Telmo, full of energies, supporting Marita, was like a valuable new pair of shoes for sick feet. When he gave up his place to the newcomer, I could almost immediately sense some relief. Marita adjusted herself automatically to the care that Moreira was offering her. But even then, peritonitis had already set in.

The girl's suffering had increased.

Aracelia's daughter moaned under the anxious eyes of Claudio, who was observing her, tormented with inner suffering.

But now, the former obsessor found things to be very different. Tortured by physical pain, Marita could do nothing but think about her own torment, bruised, sweaty, disheveled ... And her physical suffering, which transfused all her impulses into a moan that she could not articulate, elicited in Moreira feelings of sympathy and compassion.

5

We continued to witness Claudio's increasing inner renewal. He had met with Agostinho a few times and had acquired more resources related to Spiritist education. The next day, as the sun was setting, Marita rested under the care of Moreira, who felt comforted by the good results of his efforts. He could see that the girl was more in tune with his fluidic support and he felt exhilarated.

Divine Providence was blessing the inexperienced "farmer," offering him the joy of seeing the promising sprouts of the first seeds of good that he was planting.

Marita's spirit body was incredibly sensitive due to the physical damage, and if Moreira left the girl for only a few minutes, she would start to moan in terrible pain. However, she would calm down again as soon as her supporter returned.

Moreira felt useful; he was proud of himself. He looked for reasons to talk to us and exchange opinions. He asked how he might learn to be more effective. He had acquired an interest in working. He was like a man who, in vain, had wanted to be a father for a long time, and having found a child, had managed to occupy the empty space in his heart with her.

Claudio, in turn, did not restrict himself to working on his own transformation only. He tried doubly hard to give his daughter all the care and assistance he possibly could.

The next morning, the doctor friend brought a neurologist to see Marita. There was a discussion about the possibility of changing the treatment. It would entail transferring the patient to a hospital in Botafogo; however, the peritonitis made it inadvisable to move her too soon. Thus, it was agreed that she would receive high dosages of antibiotics until the hoped-for improvement made the transfer possible.

The girl's father did not spare any effort or discourage any means that might help her, whatever the cost.

When night came, brother Felix came to us and, after congratulating Moreira for the good job he was doing, informed us that Beatriz had finally discarnated.

At long last, Nemesio's wife had left her cancer-devastated body.

After the instructor had checked the stability of the procedures in play, he asked me to accompany him to the Torreses.

I did so.

On the way, Felix confided in me discreetly.

He was concerned about Marina. It was absolutely essential to protect her against the incipient obsession.

Moreira may have left her, but the troublemakers and vampirizers he had hired were still in the inner courtyard: gratuitous, unfortunate persecutors who would inevitably attract others to disturb the girl's remorse-damaged mind.

The terms brother Felix used and the inflexion in his voice reinforced the greatness of his soul. He did not see Marcia's daughter as the corrupted young woman whom, without any malice, we would not hesitate to regard as a prostitute, nor did he condemn her for her recondite ideas. He referred to her as if he were talking about good soil that its negligent owner had made useful only for vipers. From his own point of view, Marina was a child of God, deserving respect and tenderness. He had confidence in her and had hopes for her future.

But before the circumstances required that I make some comment, we arrived at the home of the family that death had visited.

We went in carefully.

Brightly-lit chandeliers illuminated the small group that had come for the wake.

Here and there, conventional, unfeeling phrases were flung at the ears of the deceased woman's husband and son.

Nemesio and Gilberto did not reflect very much sadness on their tired and impassive faces. The prolonged disease had exhausted too much of their strength for them to care much about social niceties, even the simplest ones. Worn out from the sleepless nights, they did not hide their relief. They referred to the deceased as a tormented traveler who should have dropped anchor in the port of final solace a long time ago.

The garment abandoned by that kind and venerable soul was receiving special attention so that it could be put on display in the expensive coffin, while Beatriz's spirit, though unconscious, rested in the arms of loving sisters under the tender, emotional care of Pedro and other family members.

Brother Felix assumed command and gave instructions.

Beatriz had prepared herself laboriously for that moment. She would be taken right away to an assistance institution on the spirit plane above Rio itself until she recovered her energies to continue the journey in the spirit world.

Everything was going according to plan.

However, when Beatriz's sad physical remains were finally brought into the wake, Marina broke into tears of compunction. She wept, touched with sincere and inexplicable grief. She seemed to be the only person in that polite social gathering who truly loved the pious woman that had silently and humbly turned the last page of her existence in that place favored by fortune. When she viewed the dead body, she fell to her knees in copious tears. She envied that woman whose last complacent smile was stamped with serenity, as if she was happy to leave Marina in the place that she, Beatriz, had occupied for so many years at the side of a husband who had always deceived her.

"Ah! Mrs. Torres! ... Mrs. Torres!"...

The tear-filled words escaped from that young chest as if they wanted to make a long confession.

I approached the girl in order to help her, but Felix thought that getting it off her chest would do her good.

Exhausted by insomnia and worn out by the obsessors draining her energies, Marina was afraid.

She contemplated Beatriz's spiritless body through her tears, reflecting on the secrets of death and the problems of life...

If the soul did survive the body – she thought anxiously – surely Mrs. Torres could now see her as she really was. She would see her not as the willing, dedicated caretaker, but as the woman who was controlling her husband and her son.

She was frightened. She begged for her understanding, her forgiveness.

If it could speak, what would that silent mouth say to her after knowing the truth?!

However, at that very moment, Beatriz was being taken to an institution for recovery and was inaccessible to the complications of terrestrial society. In her stead was Marina's own remorse, which had increased in her imagination, accusing … accusing…

The girl's pain provoked sympathy among those present and it gave both Nemesio and Gilberto a new reason to be attracted to her. Witnessing the girl's pungent tears, they both looked at her tenderly and expressed gratefulness in their eyes, each desiring in her the ideal partner for his next marriage, without the least bit of suspicion about the other's convictions.

That night I truly noticed Beatriz's absence in the home environment.

The departure of Pedro's daughter and the spirit friends who used to come to visit her had left the place completely robbed of any resources that might guarantee order.

After some time, discarnate vagabonds had free access to the place.

The level of the thoughts at the wake degenerated into libertine conversation. Not even the dignity deserved by death was respected. Humorous stories broke out, supplemented by the jocularity of the storytellers. One of the guests enthusiastically commented on the disgusting shows he had attended on a recent trip abroad. This aroused the interest of the vampirizers who were listening in on the descriptions, seduced by the temptation to repeat them in their own version.

Finally, not content with the expensive liqueurs kept in the family liquor cabinet for so long, incarnate and discarnate alcoholics compelled Nemesio to order wine and whisky, which was quickly gulped down by thirsty throats.

Brother Felix had anticipated this disrespect and asked us to apply anesthetizing resources to the discarnate matron to keep her insulated from the shameless feast held in the name of loving solidarity with the deceased.

Beatriz's last spirit friends left discretely and we ourselves had no choice but to abandon the house in the middle of the night after assisting Marina, relegating Beatriz's body to the thick clouds of alcoholic fumes that contaminated the entire residence, making the air difficult to breathe.

Only the next day, after the funeral, did I leave the hospital for the Torres residence. Marina was still there.

Mother and daughter called each other to discuss the new situation. Marcia thought Marina should come home, but Nemesio wanted her to stay and take care of his place. He even phoned Marcia to ask her permission. He needed Marina to manage the household staff. A few more weeks and everything would be resolved satisfactorily.

Mrs. Nogueira, honored by his polite request, did not hesitate to trust him and happily agreed.

Everything he said to her indicated a future alliance between the Nogueiras and the Torreses by means of Marina's marriage to Gilberto.

However, Marina was being robbed of her energies by the vampirizers Moreira had introduced to her. She had shut herself in her room and remained in bed, wasting away. She was pained by the disloyalty she had cultivated regarding Beatriz and she felt guilty for the tragedy that had ruined Marita, whom she did not have the courage to go see. She had always seen herself victorious in every match, but she now felt defeated, like a player taken out of the game due to her ineptitude. She wept. She heard voices. She could swear she was being persecuted by strange shadows. She avoided everybody and was tense, nervous ... Whenever she was with Nemesio or Gilberto, she would burst into tears, which advice could not remove and medicine could not sedate.

After five days of real concern, Nemesio phoned Marcia and asked if he could meet with Claudio in Flamengo the next morning. When she told him that the head of the Nogueira family could not leave the hospital, Nemesio insisted on paying her a visit. Marina was disheartened. He wanted to take her to Petropolis for a change of atmosphere and a new environment. The girl had fallen into prostration because of her sacrifice in meeting the demands of his deceased wife. He wanted to reward her for her dedication with a few days in the climate of the sierras, but first he wanted to consult the family to make plans.

Marcia wanted to demonstrate family respectability and asked if Gilberto would be going along, as if she were afraid of becoming an accomplice in an undesirable and premature relationship between the young couple. However, Nemesio was too much in love with the girl to grasp the subtlety of Claudio's wife's intention, which was to come across as a strict guardian of domestic virtue. Mrs. Nogueira expected to have Gilberto as a son-in-law, and being completely unaware of the intimacy between Marina and Gilberto's father, she did not realize the full extent of the effusive assurance of moral guarantee that Nemesio was mechanically offering her in asking her to trust him.

She needn't worry. The girl would be going only with him and a governess. Nobody else.

Marcia agreed and thanked him.

Even so, a visit by Nemesio was set for the next day.

When the time came, I followed Nemesio to Flamengo, like someone who studies a dangerous ingredient before adding it to the medicine.

Marcia had not omitted anything required by good manners concerning the Torres' period of mourning.

Discreet decorations in the living room, blue hydrangeas and purple coffee cups and saucers.

Nemesio was pleasantly surprised. His hostess was wearing a dress made of soft translucent cotton. He could not tell if she was a second edition of Marina or vice versa.

After they were seated comfortably, the conversation began with an exchange of reciprocal feelings. Condolences for Beatriz's passing, sorrow for the accident in Copacabana. Marita's condition; Marina's exhaustion. Claudio's devotion to the hospitalized girl. Praise for family members. Comments on the difficulties of life.

Marcia, like a good host, commented on all the topics with the best of her intelligence. Radiant optimism. Refined, good manners.

Nemesio, enchanted, smoked and smiled, admiring her personality.

At a certain moment, the conversation turned to the trip to Petropolis and the tone of the dialogue became livelier between the one the visitor expected to become his mother-in-law and the one the hostess did not expect to become her son-in-law.

"You can rest assured," said Torres, euphorically, "Marina will travel only with me; everything will be in order. Believe me, a change of climate is the indicated therapy. The poor girl deserves a good rest; she's been working too hard."

"I have no objections," answered Marina's mother, noticing the light in those piercing eyes investigating her reactions. "But … I am a mother, you know. Also, my husband is very busy at the moment with our other daughter, who, in spite of being adopted, is still a piece of our heart … A trip, so soon…"

"Ah, nothing to worry about; after all, I'm not a child anymore."

"No, but you know … my daughter's staying at your place was OK while your wife was alive in bed, but now … I know that Marina wouldn't be in the company of strangers. To us, you're not only the head of the firm where she works. To her, you're also a friend, a protector, a father!"

"Oh, I'm a lot more than that..."

Marcia shuddered. What did Nemesio mean by that, considering the sentences she had intentionally pronounced in such a way so as to make them sound reticent? She expected him to offer her some indication that there would be a wedding ceremony for Marina and Gilberto in the near future. Without meaning to, she remembered Claudio's suspicions. Could the outings and the invitations for entertainment made to Marina by the rich real estate agent have the shameful meaning her husband conferred on them? Or were they just means of consoling a poor man? "Oh, I'm a lot more than that!" Those words, pronounced with so much tenderness, swept through her brain. They woke her up to a reality that had never even dawned on her before. Even so, she refused to believe it. Impossible! Impossible that Marina...

In a flash she used all her feminine curiosity to examine the rich businessman from top to bottom. Too human not to evaluate her participation in the game without knowing what she had to do to defend her own interests, Marcia found in the widower, whom she had seen as old and patriarchal, a remarkable handsomeness that would impress any inexperienced girl. She had met Gilberto and regarded him as a fine young man; however, she concluded that the father could beat the son in any game of seduction. She, who was proud of her vast experiences in the realm of love, was now afraid ... She wanted to say something and come up with a brilliant way out, but she choked. Those captivating eyes; the elegance of that mature and circumspect "Beau Brummel"[22], disturbed her.

22 George Bryan (England, 1778-1840) better known as Beau Brummel was the most famous of the dashing young men of the Regency. http://histclo.com/bio/b/bio-brum.html. – Tr.

She trembled, disconcerted ...

Nemesio smiled, interpreting her emotion as the happiness of a mother who is assured of her daughter's future.

"You don't have a thing to worry about," he said. "Marina is the depositary of all my respect. Rest assured that during these two months of daily contact, she has enjoyed absolute freedom in my household, where she reigns completely. I'm sure you are a woman of the times we are living in, without limitations or prejudice. So, you won't be angry to know that, in my home, Marina does what she wants, spends as much as she wants and sleeps wherever she wants, without anybody disturbing her."

Marcia listened to Nemesio with deference and concluded that he liked her free, uninhibited daughter. However, she still did not understand what Nemesio had in mind when he commented on the freedom Marina enjoyed. She could not figure out in which situation the gentleman wanted Marina to be freest, if by his side or by his son's ... She was smart enough not to risk any conclusion that might ruin her future advantages, so she collected herself, smiled slyly and replied:

"Well, I don't have a daughter who's dating in the times of the martyrs; still, I would like you to be a bit more explicit."

And then, leaving her almost speechless with astonishment, Nemesio depicting the sweetness of a boy, actually confessed his romance with Marina. He said he loved her daughter and wanted to marry her. True, he was in mourning, but in a few weeks social conventions would have ended. He asked Marcia to keep the secret from her husband for now. He also said he had surrendered to her friendly manners and had opened his heart, asking for her help.

Before the look of shock in her eyes – which he interpreted as motherly joy – he mentioned part of the fortune he had amassed. He listed six of his best apartments, which were rented out under excellent terms; he pointed out his real estate business, whose profits were satisfactorily large, although he also managed other people's capital at very low interest rates for larger projects.

Mrs. Nogueira was floored, completely stunned.

She did not know what was worse: the outrageousness of the situation or Marina's sagacity. She discovered that she had been outsmarted.

In a fraction of a second, she wondered about Gilberto's position. How would he feel about losing out to his father?

Marcia was experienced, although sometimes she came to conclusions too late regarding her husband and daughter when it came to tendencies and behavior; but she was not fooled by the implications Nemesio was trying to hide with his pleasant talk. The impassioned inflection, with which the widower spoke each sentence, when the flowers on his wife's grave were not yet withered, made any other interpretation unnecessary. That man was talking about her daughter, not with the expectations of an innocent admirer, but with the certainty of an established lover.

What had Marina been up to while staying at the Torreses? – Marcia wondered, troubled. If Marina had enticed Nemesio, luring his spirit into the web of delusion, what had been her attitude towards Gilberto, changing the road he was on? But, realizing that Nemesio's qualities, plus all the money he possessed, were not something to toss out the window, Marcia listened to everything with a complacent smile on her face.

When she was just about to say something, the phone rang.

It came as a relief: a providential interruption that changed her mind and gave her time to analyze the situation.

It was the family doctor, who had confidential news.

In keeping with what she had asked of him days earlier, he told her that Marita had worsened. If Marcia wanted to see her before she died, she should do so right now. Claudio did not grasp the seriousness of the problem and still believed Marita would recover. However, he, an experienced doctor, did not harbor any hope. He mentioned the peritonitis, the kidney problems, the cachexia[23], the wounds produced by the contusions...

Marcia thanked him and turned pale to the point that Nemesio had to rush to her aid. She gave him the news and he offered to take her to her daughter's bedside. He explained that if she accepted, not only would he be happy to accompany her but he could also take the opportunity to visit Marita and personally greet Claudio, whom he already considered a friend and part of the family.

Scared and anxious, Marcia accepted, and soon both of them were in the car and on their way to the hospital, looking like an elegant happy couple going to make a ceremonial visit.

---

23 Weight loss, wasting of muscle, loss of appetite, and general debility that can occur during a chronic disease. (The American Heritage® Dictionary of the English Language, Fourth Edition, 2000, Houghton Mifflin). – Tr.

6

I accompanied Nemesio and Marcia to the hospital with the objective of continuing my task.

As the car sped along, Mrs. Nogueira observed Nemesio's seriousness and robust frame. She reprimanded herself for thinking thoughts that she ought not to be thinking. As she studied that gallant figure, she wondered why Marina had preferred the son over the father, when the latter was a kindly, wealthy gentleman who could offer her financial independence and social status.

From time to time, she glanced at his profile more closely and concluded that young people were not logical.

A few minutes later we entered the hospital. The pair was met by the doctor with whom Marcia had spoken on the phone a short time before.

The kindly doctor informed Marcia that he had warned Claudio that the worst was about to happen, but Marcia changed the subject so that Nemesio would not think that this was her first visit. She commented on the temperature outside, the details of the surroundings, and made other small talk. The doctor did not realize he was being used, and answered her calculated questions, unwitting playing along.

Consequently, when they went into Marita's room, Nemesio was convinced he was accompanying a living symbol of motherly love.

Claudio looked worn out. He greeted the newcomers modestly and respectfully. At first, awkwardness; then, resignation. He was suffering too much to quarrel and he had learned too much during those painfully difficult days to start complaining. Moreover, when he saw Nemesio, he gave him the look of a troubled man asking another for sympathy and help. He was embraced by Nemesio after Marcia introduced him. He felt like a student who was being tested.

Torres, whom he knew so well, albeit at a distance, seemed different now. He knew that he used to show off Marina on idle nights out, and that on several occasions he had stifled the urge to hit Nemesio when, humiliated, he had had to leave nightclubs to avoid feeling disrespected. However, now he was imbued with different feelings as he contemplated Nemesio's face. He saw himself as being put to a test of tolerance and understanding. In a split second, he recalled the Christian-Spiritist principles that were changing him on the inside. With Marita lying in a hospital bed, he looked at Nemesio and Marcia and concluded that he did not have the right to judge that man who was exploiting his family. He automatically remembered Jesus and the lesson of casting the first stone ... He quickly compared himself to Nemesio and realized he was worse than him ... Nemesio had been having fun with a girl who granted him some liberties, another man's daughter. He, himself, however, had not hesitated to abuse his own daughter after having deceived her in an abominable way. What right did he have to criticize, when his own victim was lying right there?

Obviously – he concluded instantly – friends from the spirit world had brought him this detested businessman in order to test his inner renewal. And he also had the obligation – he concluded humbly – to analyze his own reactions and classify himself according to what he was in the depths of his conscience.

During that split second trial, he no longer saw his wife as the cordial enemy of so many years. According to the new concepts he had begun to nourish, that face, covered with too much makeup, masked a discontented heart, whose tragedies he himself had caused. He had dashed all her dreams right after they had gotten married. He remembered how he had been disgusted and cruel towards his wife – a candid, spontaneous girl at the time – at seeing her lose her figure when she was pregnant with Marina, and how he had foisted his primitive instincts on Aracelia. Ever since the shock of finding herself forced to raise two girls instead of one, Marcia's real personality had vanished. She lost her balance. And he, instead of regenerating himself and rescuing her, had never stopped hunting for exploits. How could he criticize Marcia when he should be criticizing himself instead? There was nothing keeping him from avoiding this self-evaluation by indulging in trivial talk; nevertheless, he knew he could not escape his own soul. It would be more honest to probe himself and learn to tolerate himself … He noticed that Nemesio and Marcia were expecting him to say something. Then, in order to make them feel less uncomfortable – rather than to avoid self-criticism – he looked at his disfigured daughter, still inside her physical body solely due to Moreira's energies combined with intravenous feeding, and addressed Nemesio in a voice of profound suffering:

"As you can see, our child isn't doing well at all."

The two visitors were stunned at seeing that still-breathing corpse.

Marcia felt overcome with astonishment mixed with pity, but she controlled her emotions.

Torres, in turn, clenched and unclenched his fingers in a gesture of anxiety. The emaciated girl reminded him of what Beatriz had looked like. He automatically took a step back, looking for Marina's father in order to express his sympathy. He found Claudio holding a handkerchief to his face, trying unsuccessfully to hold back the tears that ran freely down his unshaved chin.

Mrs. Nogueira played hostess.

Although she felt shaken, not only because of Marita's decline but also because of her husband's demonstration of unexpected sensitivity, she collected herself enough to speak with self-assurance.

Respecting her husband's grief, she doused the truths she had heard from the doctor, recapitulated her own version of the accident – the one she had told her friends – and apologized for the traumatized shape Claudio was in. She confessed politely that she, too, was deeply hurt; however, seeing Claudio subdued by suffering, she did not have any choice but to collect herself and take control of the situation.

Her husband, weeping helplessly, understood she was lying so as to impress Nemesio and that she was choosing well-thought-out expressions in such a way that he would think that she had barely left Marita's bedside. But Claudio did not contradict her.

He limited himself to weeping silently. Instead of being indignant as was usually the case when she was lying, he pitied himself this time. He saw himself as a traveler who had strewn barbs along the path by which he would inevitably be compelled to return...

Confirming this impression, Marcia stood up, and overcoming the repugnance caused by the dreadful smell coming from the bed, she arranged her unconscious daughter's pillows, said a few words of caring, and noticing Nemesio's discomfort in that room that exhaled the disgusting smell of urine, she said it was time to leave.

It would not be fair to keep Mr. Torres any longer, she said. As for herself, she told Claudio to wait for her; she would come back later.

Goodbyes and displays of solidarity.

Brother Felix had been present and had accompanied the meeting in all its details. He said that if I had returned to the hospital in order to be of service, I should go back to the Torres residence for the same reason in order to help Marina, whose obsessive process had grown worse. However – he added – it would be profitable to follow the two visitors as well so as to study their reactions with the objective of being helpful.

I got into the car for the return trip.

Nemesio composed himself, chose the longest route and drove very slowly.

Claudio's grief had surprised him. Compared to Claudio, he was very strong, even though he had seen the death of his own wife just a few days ago. He had not broken down, whereas Claudio had melted at the bedside of an adopted child, whose only need was the tranquility of a morgue.

From time to time he would shoot a look at Marcia, thinking he understood her better now. The mother of the girl he intended to marry was perfectly comparable to her in beauty and intelligence; she could not be happy with that sobbing man.

The astute businessman returned to his own traits. Little by little he forgot all about Marita and the grieving bank clerk, whom he regarded as a sissy, and began to praise the enchantment of the day, as if he wanted to awaken in Marcia the conviction that in that car she was under the protection of an understanding, strong companion who could ensure her complete well-being. He asked her if she frequented the most famous Carioca[24] spots in Rio. He mentioned the scrumptious lunches in Paineiras[25], the picnics at Pedra do Conde[26], the beaches in Copacabana, and the incomparable view from Pico da Tijuca[27] on sunny days, when binoculars seemed to bring the Restinga da Marambaia[28] right up to one's eyes...

Marcia had been to all those places and knew them like the back of her hand; even so, she feigned ignorance. From personal experience, she knew that men like Nemesio preferred meek, fragile women who helplessly turn to them for protection. She told him that she had never been to any of them, except Sugar Loaf, which she had visited on a brief tour when the girls were still little. Saying that she was inexperienced with regard to romantic things, she added that she had gotten married very young, and ever since then her life had been a torment amid brooms and pans, with the obligation of having to put up with a sniveling husband – something Nemesio himself could verify. He could also see the suffering of a woman chained to an unhappy marriage, as was made clear from the way the whimpering Claudio had greeted them without a single word of cordiality or friendliness.

Nemesio loved such descriptions. He laughed. He talked about psychoses. He mentioned distinguished neurologists.

Marcia smiled maliciously, looked at him for a long time, and said it was too late for treatments; that for a long time now, she and Claudio had lived separately, even though under the same roof.

---

24 Carioca is a term used to refer to people born in Rio de Janeiro or to places frequented by them. – Tr.

25 A road located in Tijuca National Park. – Tr.

26 A mountain in Tijuca Forest. – Tr.

27 The highest spot in Tijuca National Park. – Tr.

28 An 81km sandbank located in Rio and managed by the Brazilian Navy. – Tr.

She was used to suffering – she declared with a sigh.

Nemesio understood the insistence of those looks and felt recondite satisfaction at finding himself wooed.

He did not dislike the presence of his future mother-in-law. If it had not been for Marina – he thought – he would not hesitate to attract her to a more intimate relationship. Spending the whole morning in the company of that fine-looking, intelligent woman had been a tonic for him. He had forgotten himself, had amused himself. But even so, he did not think it was advisable to be hasty. He took out his pocket watch, saw that it was only five minutes till noon, and invited Marcia to lunch. He knew an excellent restaurant in Catete.[29]

Mrs. Nogueira accepted. The meal was a happy occasion.

The guest made an effort to anticipate the host's preferences in order to share in his favorite dishes. Soberly, she stuck to mineral water and ate very little from the menu. In compensation, she thought a lot and talked as much as possible with the clear intention of captivating him. At a certain moment, she thought about the risks Marina was being exposed to, and smoothing her voice, she hinted it was time to leave. She said she did not want that happy meeting to end without thanking him for his devotion to her daughter. Moreover, she asked his permission to remind him that the girl was too young, and that she feared for her inexperience…

Flattered, Nemesio reiterated his confidence in Marina, but did not forget to make a significant gesture to Marcia, adding that, although he would be keeping her daughter in his home, he did not want his mother-in-law to forget his dedication as a true friend. Claudio's wife picked up on the hidden meaning and coquettishly answered that, as a selfless mother, she wished her daughter all the happiness that the world had denied her.

---

29 A middle-class district in Rio de Janeiro. – Tr.

Between the two of them, their emotional contract was perfectly clear, although the terms of the agreement were written between the lines: allusions, sighs and reticence...

After Gilberto's father said goodbye to Marcia in Flamengo, he got in his car, but could not get Marcia's image out of his head. He tried to free himself of it by imposing Marina's image on it. Consequently, when he entered his house, he decided to go see Marina immediately.

He went to his bedroom, put on his pajamas and slippers, and dreamily went softly to Marina's room with the intention of surprising her, to communicate his latest feelings to her, and most importantly, to rid himself of the thoughts Marcia had aroused in him.

He turned the doorknob and opened the door without a sound. However, he had to make an effort not to collapse, garroted with stupefaction. Gilberto and the girl were kissing in a passionate embrace. Because his back was to the door, Gilberto could not see his father. But Marina was facing the door. She saw Nemesio wince, ashen, and fainted.

Everything happened very fast.

Nemesio turned around and like a beaten dog, slinked off, almost choking. Somehow, he managed to get to his bedroom and threw himself on his bed, stricken with pain.

Conflicting thoughts swept through his head. How to interpret this painful enigma? Was Gilberto taking advantage of the weakened girl or was she dividing herself between the two? He tried to stand up, but it was as if he had been hit by a stone deep inside his heart. His chest ached; he was bathed in cold sweat and he could not breathe.

After about a quarter of an hour, Gilberto, unaware of the volcano of tears his father was struggling to hide, came to his room and told him that Marina had worsened after having fainted. She had come back to consciousness obviously possessed. She was screaming, crying, biting and hurting herself.

Nemesio looked at his son with wounded eyes and asked him to do what was necessary. Gilberto should call the doctor and also Marina's mother in Flamengo, insisting that she come. Nemesio made a huge effort to explain that he himself had arrived home feeling gloomy for some reason.

I rushed to assist Marina and realized that the obsession had taken place. The vampirizers that Moreira had brought had been joined by others. The defenseless girl was completely under their control. The shock she had received when Nemesio entered had destroyed her last reserves of resistance. Marina was under the yoke of the discarnate criminals and lay hypnotized, beaten...

A short time later, Marcia was beside her daughter, who had become demented and unrecognizable.

The doctor said she should be taken to the hospital immediately, a decision Nemesio approved with the indifference of someone who is just doing his duty. To unburden her conscience, Marcia called Claudio with the news. In order to soften it, she explained that Marina had been working too hard and was mentally exhausted. The doctor had prescribed a short stay in an institution. As a responsible mother, she had no objections to this, but she would like to have his opinion first.

Claudio agreed and Marcia quickly entrusted Marina to a well-known psychiatric hospital, whose doors the girl crossed, inspiring pity and compassion.

Returning to the Torres' beautiful home two days after, I found Gilberto feeling confused and unhappy, but more dedicated to the girl than ever. Nemesio, on the other hand, realized that his old notion of love had been a passing fancy, and only forty eight hours after the incident, he was in Flamengo exchanging confidences with Marcia about the new facts. The two of them were enjoying total intimacy. They had found reasons to excuse what they called "youthful madness" as they consoled each other.

7

Exactly two weeks after the accident in Copacabana, Marita was ready to discarnate.

Moreira inspired pity. Those blessed days of learning and suffering had changed him on the inside. Realizing that the girl had reached the final stages of organic breakdown, he wept desperately.

Marita was disengaging herself from the corporeal world little by little. Not even the warmth of that generous friend lending her a sort of supplementary lung could hold her back any longer.

Although she was lying still, she felt lucid, profoundly lucid. The light in her eyes had nearly gone out; however, the magnetic support she had been receiving uninterruptedly opened her spiritual sight.

Over the past two days, Marita had managed a great deal of recovery. She could hear the conversations between Claudio and the doctors or nurses extremely well, and she could also hear Agostinho and Salomao's prayers and comments while she was receiving passes.

When she first felt Claudio's hands cleaning her body, she became desperate and clamored to herself that she was not comfortable with such humiliation ... She emitted thoughts of rebelliousness against fate for having connected her in such a way to a man she hated so much. However, as she perceived his reverent tenderness while he cleaned the fetid excretions stuck to her wounded skin, she ended up planting a new sentiment in her heart. She softened; she became transfigured. She heard him talking about God, and sometimes she felt his fingers grazing her forehead as he prayed ... On one of these moving occasions, as she was trying to grasp the reason for Claudio's transformation, Felix approached. He caressed her disheveled hair paternally and, with the conviction of someone who was focusing all of his available energies on influencing her to adopt the right attitude, he said:

"Child, forgive him; forgive!"

Deeply touched, she registered the unknown voice and remembered the mother who had left her at birth.

Yes – she decided – only motherly love would come back from the grave to guide her burning heart to the fount of forgiveness.

Forgive – she said to herself – what else could she do as she faced death? Yes, she should leave this world forgetting insults and injuries ... She saw herself in her armor of bones like a chick inside the egg. The slightest tap or brief movement would break the egg and she would have to leave, although she didn't know where she would go ... So, why not leave quenching the flames that were scorching her sentiments?

Marita pondered those hands as they uncovered her, wiping her wet skin and dressing her again with tenderness only seen in mothers when they touch their sick children, and she concluded she had to forgive and forget.

She actually felt sorry for her thoughtless father. Forgive him, yes! ... She thought about that with the joy of someone who had just received a blessing ... Now he was respecting her, cleaning her, praying ... He would go on living on the earth, maybe carrying bitter remorse, whilst she would travel to places she had never known, trusting in that voice that had driven her troubled spirit to the peace of forgiveness ... She recalled his tears on the night when he had declared his insane passion for her, and she was touched with understanding. A poor father who had never found refuge in his own home! ... Could a man like that, stranded at home like a miserable dog, have a normal mind? Who could say but that he had approached her like a sick man in need of some unknown medicine to soothe the storm of his sentiments? Most likely, the assault she had suffered at Crescina's was the product of an insane mind and not of a normal man ... Why not forgive the father that had been out of his mind? ... She reconstructed in her memory his gestures of tenderness and love as they played together when she was a child. Claudio had been her only friend ... Whenever she cried, she would climb into his lap, looking for the comfort of the mother she never had. She spent a long time visualizing him on the screen of her imagination, once again holding her in his arms so that she could enjoy watching the animals in the zoo ... Mentally, she tasted the ice cream cones he bought for her on summer afternoons ... She remembered, remembered ... No, no! – shouted her conscience – her father was not perverse; he was good ... How could she refuse to show him compassion if Marcia always neglected him and Marina avoided his presence? Surely, he must have suffered a lot before surrendering to mental disturbance ... How could she not forgive the madness of one night in a benefactor of twenty years? Why not die blessing such dedication? How could she condemn him as he stayed at her bedside, patient and selfless, tolerating her? ... She recalled her adoptive mother; she imagined herself in front of her sister, and she desired, in spirit, to make things right with them ... Who could say that Marcia and Marina had not been under the effect of hidden imbalances? Who could be absolutely sure they were not ill? At that moment, as she was making amends with Claudio, she also longed to reconcile with the two women. She forgave them for all their lack of understanding and, in return, deep down, she asked to be forgiven for all the problems she might have unwittingly caused them! ... Gilberto was also included in that parade of memories. His image appeared in her head enveloped in the sweet vibrations of the dream that had been the light of her life! ... She could never hate the one she still loved so much! ... Gilberto must have had his reasons for leaving her, and in those final, serious reflections he appeared to her full of tenderness and dressed in the handsomeness of a beloved and virtuous partner!

After having expressed all these thoughts, Marita felt lighter, almost happy!

She tried to move, to cry out to her father that she considered him to be a good man; that she had no reason at all to accuse him; that what had happened at Crescina's had been nothing but a deplorable mistake; that she herself was about to die, but she wanted him to continue living and being a good person! ... However, the mere idea of moving her body made her feel as if she were shackled to a statue. She could not feel a thing in her stiff arms and legs; she had no voice in her throat, which seemed to be made of stone; nonetheless, so great and so heroic was the effort of her renewed soul that tears rolled down her half dead eyes.

During that solemn moment of peace, Marita began to vaguely perceive voices and forms from the spirit plane. She felt happy and frightened at the same time, as if she were waking up in a light that was piercing the mist.

When Claudio noticed her tear-soaked face, he was hopeful and called for the doctor.

Mightn't it imply a bit of improvement?

But circumspect, the doctor shook his head and asked for more time to examine the patient before he could say for sure. Deep inside, he knew the girl was in a pre-agonic, disturbed, delirious condition.

On the day of Marita's discarnation, the doctor told Claudio that the girl would last only a few hours more. As far as medical science was concerned, everything was about to end, but Claudio, being such a loving father, should pray according to the type of faith he cultivated in his heart, and ask for strength.

Claudio looked down and thanked the doctor humbly.

He phoned Agostinho and Salomao to give them the news.

Claudio's two new friends arrived that evening.

He asked them to pray for him; he wanted to be worthy of the faith he had embraced. For the first time, he asked to be given magnetic passes. He bowed his head and turned the palms of his hands upward to receive them, imitating the gesture of a poor child begging for a handout.

The elderly pharmacist and the businessman comforted him. It would not be right to keep the suffering girl in a decayed, irreparable body any longer. However, when they left, both men were choked up with emotion.

At 9:00 p.m., more devastated than ever, Claudio asked to be left alone with his daughter so that he could say goodbye. No one denied him that favor, asked with such humility.

Alone with her, Claudio began to reflect ... He recomposed the past, imagining the roads on which he had passed by ruins that he had abandoned forever. However, as he looked at the dying girl in light of the purified love he had begun to devote to her, he imagined the two of them together in the distant future … Between the past, which inspired only disgust, and the future, in spiritual communion with his beloved daughter, Claudio felt crushed, all alone.

I was touched in the deepest fibers of my soul as I contemplated that man, bent over under the weight of moral suffering, trying to escape his memories in order to pray ... The unarticulated cries arising from a chest filled with anguish, appealing to God in the silence of the room, were like canticles of pain suffocated by tears!

At 11:00 p.m., brother Felix and other friends, including Pedro and Percilia, joined me.

Discreet expectation was on everyone's faces, except for Moreira, who was beside himself in tears.

The instructor gently helped him up and told him that his work was done. He should no longer vitalize those lungs that death had begun to stiffen. Our sad friend obeyed in convulsive weeping.

Felix placed his hands on that disheveled head and sent a burst of energy into it.

Marita showed unexpected mental agility.

She believed she was coming back to life; that she was being born again. She could hear the sounds around her with extreme auditory acuity.

The benefactor approached Claudio and whispered something in his ear. Of course, he was telling him to say goodbye.

Unaware of the fact that he was being touched by a spirit mentor, he was infused with sudden courage. He stood up, took two steps forward, and knelt down beside the dying girl ... He placed his head on the motionless body, but intense emotion betrayed his energies. Tears shook his limbs like a storm shaking the branches of a tree about to fall.

Marita perceived his gasping, sobbing chest and wanted to hug him, but her arms felt like they were chained to the bed.

Completely supported by Felix's magnetic emissions, Claudio felt more animated. He picked up the copy of *The Gospel according to Spiritism* from the nearby chair and said in a trembling voice:

"Daughter of my heart: if you can, listen to your father, I beg you! ... Please, forgive me! ... I don't know if you know that I am different now ... I have met Jesus, my child, and now I know that God is merciful and that nobody dies – nobody ... I know that justice is within us, that we suffer for the wrongs we have committed, but that God does not refuse us the opportunity to redeem them! ... I understand the harm I did to you; I am a criminal, nothing else ... My daughter, think of the remorse I shall bear for the rest of my life! ... You know that now I must walk alone, bearing the loneliness I deserve ... Wherever you are, pity your father! ... Trust in Jesus and the good spirits! ... They know you didn't commit suicide; they know I am a murderer ... Ah, my child! Think about that sad, sad word! ... Murderer! Help me wash this stain from my conscience! Pray for me to Christ's messengers so that I may have the strength to do what I have to do!"

Claudio paused briefly when he saw Marita's face covered with tears, and he yearned to see her regain enough consciousness to realize he had changed. He was inwardly certain she had been lucid enough to hear him and had blessed his vows of spiritual growth. Anxious but hopeful, certain that he was being heard and understood, he continued:

"Despite everything, my dear child, do not feel sad because of my plea! ... I may be a defendant but I do have hope! See, I have found Jesus' revelation in this book!"

Then, with trembling hands, in a gesture of pious trust, he put the book in her stiff right hand.

Marita, now awake, felt the volume on her rigid fingers and responded by crying even more intensely.

Claudio felt encouraged by that manifestation of intelligence and raised his voice, begging her to listen to what he had to say...

He stated that he knew he was in the presence of spirit friends who could testify to his sincerity, and certain that he was committing his own soul with his affirmations, he opened himself up to his daughter. Right there in front of her, he confessed all the wrongs for which he accused himself. He told her Aracelia's story. He swore he had not known she was his daughter and that he had only found out through Marcia, because, irresponsible as he had been in his youth, he wrongly believed Aracelia was having affairs with several men. He explained that Marcia had called him back to reality on that horrible night at Crescina's. He described how he had been depressed, tormented by remorse ever since seeing her prostrated in bed, begging her to forgive him for inducing her thoughts to commit suicide ... He told her he had read and learned a lot about reincarnation since his first day at the hospital, and he was convinced that both of them were connected through several existences. He said his passion must have been the result of the carelessness and cruelty still living in his heart ... But – he continued – right there, in light of all her suffering, which was an unappealable sentence of pain, he promised to regenerate himself no matter how harsh the readjustment ... At the end of this long exposition – which Marita heard contritely, sentence by sentence – Claudio took the book from her small hand and burst into convulsive weeping again.

"I've been praying and God has had mercy on me, a criminal" he went on ... "But if Infinite Kindness will grant me just one more request, bless me my dear; give me a sign of benevolence before you leave … If you are listening to the defendant that I am, accompany me in this desire … Pray, too! … Ask God for a little strength. Move a finger, just one finger so that I will know that you have forgiven your father! … Don't leave me in uncertainty, now that I am about to start my life again, handed over to the consequences of my wrongs!"

Registering her father's pleas, which pierced her soul, Marita wanted with all her heart to grant his request…

Forgiveness! … Forgiveness! … The word resounded in her spirit like a canticle coming down from heaven and reverberating on the walls all around! … Forgiveness! … Those eleven letters, arranged in the form of sounds, were like the music of eternity performed in the firmament on trumpets made of stars, whose soft accents soothed her heart!

The poor girl concentrated all her energies on a thought full of faith in and gratitude to God, and she prayed mentally: "Forgiveness, O Lord! … Forgiveness for my father; forgiveness for me! … Forgiveness for all those who have erred! … Forgiveness for all those who have fallen!"

Her perceptions were sharpened and she felt as if she were bathed in ineffable joy … She could see Claudio distinctly now; she saw Moreira in tears; and turning her attention serenely around the bed, she saw all of us. Felix silently applied magnetic fluids to a particular area of her brain, and in astonishment, Claudio saw her right hand rise … In agony but grateful, he avidly held those small cold fingers and wanted to say, "Thank you, God," but his throat was choked with tears. It was Felix's voice that I heard, gathering us all in a prayer:

"O Lord Jesus! We thank you for the happiness you have given us with this lesson in suffering during these days of toil and expectation!

"Thank you, O Lord, for these hours of afflictions that have cleared up our souls, and for the minutes of pains that have awakened our consciences! Thank you for these two weeks of tears, which have done for us what we could not have done in half a century of hope!

"And now, as we show you our gratitude and praise, we ask still more! ... In your mercy, bless this sister who is saying goodbye, and bless this companion who is staying behind. Change their pain into renewal and their bitterness into jubilation! ... Accept their tears as a prayer to you as they wait for your peace along their way!

"However, O Master, we do not ask you to show mercy only to them, our beloved friends, whom we consider the children of our very own soul! ... We beg for your support for all those who have slipped on the deceit of misguided sexuality, whereas you have offered us this instrument to be a shining star of love, assuring us of the joy of living and guaranteeing us the means of existence!

"Allow us, O Lord, to bring before you those who earthly conventions so often forget to name when they speak to your heart.

"Bless those who have gotten lost in madness or misfortune in the name of the love they have never known!

"Help our sisters imprisoned in prostitution, for all of them were born for the happiness of a home, and correct with your magnanimity those who pushed them into the corruption of their reproductive forces. Protect the victims of abortion, violently torn from the maternal womb in brothels or in places covered in impunity, and correct, under your support, the mothers who did not hesitate to asphyxiate or destroy their developing bodies. Restore those creatures, sacrificed by their beloved's desertion, who found no other recourse but suicide or madness to hide the mental torture that pushed them beyond their endurance. Show your compassion to all those whose love was scorned, transforming them into ruthless, smiling tormenters. Protect those who were born maladjusted, in a condition of sex reversal, coping with difficult tasks or enduring regenerating inhibitions. Rescue those who reincarnated into such trials without the strength to stick to the obligations they assumed, thus wasting away their lives in debauchery. Safeguard all children who have been abused, and renew with your generosity all rapists who unconsciously made themselves beasts. Shelter those who discarnated prematurely due to the blows of homicide in tragedies involving misery and despair. And lastly, help those who have become their suffering tormenters, tortured by remorse, whether in freedom filled with anguish or in the small cells of prisons!

"O Master, guide to the upright path men and women, our brothers and sisters, who, dominated by obsession or betrayed by their own weaknesses, have failed to keep their vows of conjugal faithfulness. Rebalance those who make nighttime a pasture for insanity. Comfort those who exhibit deformities and diseases as a result of passionate excesses or wrongs committed in this or other lifetimes. Rehabilitate the insane minds of those who exploit the horrible darkness of licentiousness. Regenerate the wild thoughts of those who abuse youth, getting them addicted to drugs. Sustain those who, before their reincarnation, asked for the tears of celibacy and received them as an expiatory means to purge the sexual distortions to which they became addicted in past lives, and who so often succumb to starvation and discouragement in their own home under the contempt of insensitive family members, to whose happiness they have dedicated all their youth!

"O Lord, also extend your merciful hand over upright, ennobled hearts! Awaken those who live within legal unions in compliance with earthly organizations and enlighten those who live in homes infused with the dignity they deserve so that they may treat with humaneness and compassion those who cannot yet abide by their principles or imitate their good examples! … Illuminate the sentiments of women sanctified by sacrifice and toil so that they may not reject others who have not yet won respectful motherhood and who, so many times, bear the brutality of their sons in brothels! Sensitize the reasoning of men who have aged honestly so that they may not forsake unfortunate, lost young people!

"Dear Lord, do not allow virtue to become a fire in the torment of the fallen, nor let honesty become ice in hearts!

"You, who came down to the alleys of the world to heal the sick, know that all those who journey in this world, tormented by a lack of the nourishment of love or maddened by sexual deviations, are sick, unhappy children of God in need of your hands!

"Inspire us in our relationships with one another and clear our minds so that we may know to be grateful for your kindness, forever!"

When Felix finished, the room was illuminated by a light coming from his chest area. However, it was not only us, his wards, who were deeply touched by intense emotion in our innermost being! … All the discarnate entities who worked in that hospital, even those connected with other religious persuasions, gathered in that room discreetly and attentively … Ignorant, vampirized spirits who were wandering around nearby rushed to join us, attracted by the streams of solar light that the room radiated in all directions and, a short distance away, many of them bowed their heads reverently.

In the middle of the night, that room in that venerable healing institution on Resende Street was like a glowing heart made of concrete studded with sparkling stars of love!

Claudio heard nothing, but touched by the balsamic vibrations of the environment, he wept quietly as he felt the icy hand glued to his relaxing its pressure of goodbye. Heartbroken, he gazed at his daughter's face and noticed that the paleness of death was drawing its last smile on it ... He stood up and carefully closed those exhausted eyelids, wetting them with his own tears. Beside him, Moreira could not suppress his own violent sobs.

Telmo was applying anesthetizing passes to the girl, and a discarnate doctor that had joined our group cut the last bonds that still held the captive soul to the lifeless body.

When he saw that Marita was free and sheltered in Felix's arms like a tired, sleeping child, Moreira, in the affliction and humbleness of those who completely deny themselves in order to help the ones they love, asked, brokenhearted:

"Brother Felix, what am I to do now, useless as I am?"

"Moreira," replied the instructor, blessing him with his eyes, "we are one big family here. Very soon you will have what you need to return to Marita's side, but right now she only asks for peace and rest. We, on the other hand, are asking for your help! Marina is suffering ... We must free her. We are counting on you as our brother and friend!"

Claudio's former obsessor, anxious to show his submission, knelt down and bowed his head, confused at realizing that Felix was asking him to remedy a situation that he, Moreira, had made worse. In tears, he promised to fulfil his obligation. All he wanted now – he stressed – was to learn, help, devote himself to the good, to work and serve...

*****

Fortunate inhabitants of earth! When you pass by the beds of those who are going through a prolonged death, banish from your mind the idea of hastening it!

Around those mangled bodies and behind those sealed lips, benefactors from the spirit plane are taking measures, performing noble tasks, saying prayers or holding out friendly arms.

Until now, you have not known the value of a few minutes of reconsideration for earthly travelers who, before returning to the shelter of the home, aspire to evaluate the paths they have trod.

If you do not feel capable of offering them a word of consolation or the support of a prayer, just leave them be! ... Their tears are pearls of hope with which the lights of other dawns moisten their faces! ... Those groans coming from their chests and reaching their lips, as if they were sobs imprisoned inside the heart, are nearly always songs of joy before the immortality that shines on them from the Beyond!

Comrades of the world – you whose sight is still limited by the cage of flesh – in the name of your dearest sentiments, offer consolation and silence, sympathy and veneration to those who are approaching the grave! They are not the tormented mummies that your eyes see, destined for the tombstone that will decay into dust ... They are children of heaven, preparing to return to their homeland, about to cross the river of Truth, whose banks you, too, shall reach one day!...

*****

At sunset, Agostinho and Salomao followed Claudio and his daughter's body to Caju Cemetery.

A simple ceremony consecrated by prayer.

On the way back, Claudio, downcast, said goodbye to his friends when they reached Cinelandia, and took a taxi to Flamengo.

He reached the building, went up to his apartment and, craving company, opened the door. He combed the place room by room and felt a chill in his body and soul...

There was nobody there.

8

In satisfaction of Felix's recommendation that I help with Marina and Claudio, I stayed in Flamengo with our disconsolate friend.

Left to himself without human consolation, Claudio pondered and understood. He had read a lot. He had had several conversations with Agostinho and Salomao. He could not deny the truth. Thanks to the mercy of Divine Goodness, he had found faith again; nevertheless, Divine Justice could not spare him the loneliness that he himself had planted.

His heart was heavy from missing the daughter that the grave had concealed. Those two weeks at the hospital had united them in spirit forever. At Marita's side, he had received the light of renewal. It pained him to think that he could not feel the joy of carrying her, supporting her, helping her any longer …

Depressed, he sat down and wept.

It was late and Marcia had not come home.

He phoned Justa's neighbors. They contacted her and she came right away. Claudio told her about Marita's discarnation and she regretted not having been informed in time to attend the funeral. She explained that Marcia had gone to Petropolis and she did not know when she would be back. Marcia had complained about being exhausted after having taken Marina to the institution for treatment. She had told Justa that she planned to spend a few days in the sierras in order to recover her strength. According to their arrangement, Justa was supposed to go to the apartment in the mornings and take the afternoons off.

Claudio inquired about the institution where Marina was being treated, but the maid replied truthfully that she did not know. Marcia had given her no information about it whatsoever. Moreover, without meaning to worry him, she, herself, thought Marcia looked exhausted. She seemed on edge; not well at all.

Claudio thanked her and consulted the phone book.

He tried unsuccessfully to get in touch with a well-known institution in Santa Teresa[30]. Claudio kept trying, and after six attempts he finally got what he was looking for. A kindly nurse, with whom Marcia had left her address, answered from an institution in Botafogo, informing him that Marina was one of their patients. Visits, however, even by family members, were not allowed. The girl was going through a crisis and was being assisted by doctors.

Even as her father, he would have to talk to the administration before trying to visit the girl in person.

Claudio sat down in an armchair in order to think. The only option remaining was to call the Torres residence. Surely, Gilberto could explain things. However, the young man's image loomed in his imagination like a scalpel about to slice open a mental wound. Claudio remembered the meeting in Lido, when he had betrayed Gilberto's good faith. He felt ashamed of himself. He pondered and pondered. He examined himself

---

30 A neighborhood located on top of Santa Teresa Hill in Rio. – Tr.

coolly and concluded that if he really wanted to be a new person, he should not try to escape the consequences of his past wrongs.

Once his mind was made up, he did not hesitate.

He used the phone with little hope of finding Gilberto at home, since it was already past 9:00 p.m. However, the young man answered.

Notwithstanding feeling terribly awkward, Claudio expressed his condolences to Gilberto for his mother's passing and informed him that Marita had died also.

Gilberto seemed depressed, tormented.

Nemesio's son confessed that he had not heard about the extent of the accident or Marita's death. Probably, due to the difficult times the family had been going through with Beatriz's slow death and Marina's nervous breakdown a few days later, Marcia and Marina had not had the opportunity to inform him about the seriousness of the situation. He regretted the accident and expressed his condolences. He had always regarded Marita as a sister of the heart. When asked by Claudio, he explained that Marina had had fits of rage. The family doctor suspected premature dementia, but he had refused to treat her personally. He had referred the problem to psychiatrists.

The dialogue continued.

Gilberto said he had made a few decisions the past few days. When they had both met in Copacabana, yes, he had decided to marry Marina as soon as possible and enjoy the tranquility of a home; but his father, very worried at seeing the girl in such a state, albeit grateful for everything she had done for the family, had convinced Gilberto to change his plans. Nemesio, who was out of town to get some rest, had been very candid about the subject. He said he would not approve the marriage, because he did not think Marina was capable of handling the responsibilities of married life. Moreover, he had mentioned "certain things" and had advised the young man to leave Rio. He would send him monetary support in some other city, where he could recommence the education he had interrupted. Nevertheless, he, Gilberto, had seen things differently, and in light of his father's impositions, had felt depressed, defeated.

Claudio humbly accepted these arguments and brought up the fact that Gilberto was still very young, that he should not go against his father's advice, and that he should continue to think things over since marriage, for anyone, involves freedom and awareness ... Claudio's remarks were so sensible and comforting that Gilberto felt inwardly pacified and was better able to understand his father. He felt changed because of that unexpected kindness. It was like he was listening to an older, nicer Claudio ... Deeply touched, he thanked Claudio and even asked him not to abandon him. He realized he was on his own now. His father was kind and generous, but he was a businessman. He always had a lot of things on his mind. Gilberto felt he needed someone who could inspire him and lend him a helping hand. He would love to meet with Claudio more often.

The young man perceived that Claudio was speaking to him in tears, thanking him for such kind words. It was as if Gilberto was instilling newfound confidence in that man whom he had met days earlier but had not fully understood.

Claudio meekly asked about Marcia. It was likely that when she had left for Petropolis, she had given Gilberto a number where she could be reached. Gilberto confirmed this. Gilberto was supposed to look after Marina. If the girl got worse, she would be grateful if he would call her immediately. She had explained that the reason she was passing this duty to him and not her husband was due to the fact that Claudio was busy at the hospital.

Armed with this information, Claudio thanked him again and hung up. He started to ponder things again. Judging from the tone of the conversation, the young man had changed completely. Every word he had said had been carefully calculated. Formal, disenchanted. And what did he mean by those two words: *certain things?* He, Claudio, felt like a new man; however, his past experience was the basis of his impressive transformation. He knew that Marina was risking a two-fold danger in this love triangle. He was sure something very serious must have happened. He was mature enough to know that either the father or the son had been caught red-handed doing something that the other did not like. He deduced that Marina had broken down, thinking she could escape from herself. He thought about her and pitied her. After all, he had not become a believer in order to judge. He wanted to understand, to serve. He now understood that obsession was the cause behind these tragedies. And he, himself, who had never helped his daughter develop her inner life, had no right to complain. He thought and thought, and a little after 10:00 p.m., he called his wife.

Marcia answered.

When Claudio questioned her, she said she was resting with friends. When she found out about Marita's death, she confessed she was relieved. She had hoped the girl would not make it, all mangled as she had seen her. She made some unpleasant, mocking comments.

Judging from her tone of voice, her husband realized she was having one of her worst days. There was sarcasm in every syllable. Her irritation was obvious.

Claudio very meekly apologized. He did not mean to interrupt her trip. Even so, he could not help worrying about Marina. If possible, he would be grateful if she would tell him the best way to visit her right away. He asked her the name of her doctors. He wanted to get their opinion.

His words flowed so smoothly along the phone line that she changed her attitude. She softened her voice. She would have to ask her friends for that information. She would be back in a few minutes.

A short time later, Marcia came back and said she would leave for Rio the next morning so that they could talk. She had "certain matters" to discuss with him, but wanted to do it face to face. He should wait for her in Flamengo. She would arrive early by car with the sole objective of talking to him. Then, she would return immediately to the hotel in the sierras.

In fact, the next day, before 9:00 a.m., right after she had given Justa instructions about domestic chores, the bank clerk found himself facing his wife.

Marcia looked as if she was returning from a different country altogether. She was wearing a lot of jewelry; she was smiling. Her unusual hairdo reinforced her natural elegance and made her look much younger. Her makeup matched her new pink dress. She looked even taller due to her high heels, like a slender young crane walking carefree in an open field. She flashed colors, exuded perfume.

Nevertheless, the human flower she had turned into could not hide from me the worms that were devouring it. Marcia was the hostess of a small cortege of discarnate vampirizers that were altering her mind.

Even to me, accustomed as I was to seeing her as a difficult woman but well-adjusted to her place in society, she looked almost unrecognizable.

Her voice had a metallic tone and her eyes were colder.

When she came in, she greeted her husband and Justa with the gestures of a complacent caretaker.

Claudio was frightened. He was unable to understand what was happening. They were going through the ordeal of having lost one daughter, and seeing the other one very sick ... On the other hand, Marcia had told him over the phone that she was exhausted, so how could she be on such a festive excursion? He instinctively remembered Gilberto being concerned about "certain things" and Marcia saying she wanted to discuss "certain matters." Feeling apprehensive, Claudio wondered what secrets lay hidden from his heart.

The new arrival sat down, crossed her legs with juvenile coquetry, and with no more ado, explained why she had returned in such a hurry.

Claudio asked about Marina.

Marcia, clearly interested in other matters, summed up as best she could the story of the infirmity. She named the psychiatrist handling the case; she alluded to the care that surrounded the girl at the institution, and she praised the generosity of Mr. Torres, who had not hesitated to spend as much as necessary for the girl's treatment. She commented broadly on the praiseworthiness of Beatriz's widower, whose greatness of soul – she said enthusiastically – she was only now beginning to discover. And lastly, she proposed making arrangements to transfer Marina to an asylum in Sao Paulo, where she would receive the right treatment for a few months. All Claudio had to do was agree. Nemesio would pay for everything as a token of his firm's gratitude for the work Marina had done.

Claudio listened, humbly, and then argued that maybe the situation was not that serious; that the word "months" scared him. He believed that if Marina received the right medicine not only for the body but for the soul, she would recover in less time.

He argued rationally. He demonstrated in a natural way that it would not be right to abandon Marina, and that financial support meant a great deal now, especially since the care required by Marita had exhausted all his savings; but he did agree that his troubled daughter demanded their love and devotion.

After making judicious comments, which Marcia listened to impatiently, he looked at her expectantly and asked her to join him in a fresh start. A life of harmony, of reciprocal growth. With all sincerity, he entrusted her with all the different projects he had planned during those days of struggle, from which he had emerged transformed. Claudio bared his soul to her. He had become a Christian Spiritist. He felt like a new man. He shared with her the fact that between him and the past, faith had risen as a barrier of light. He longed for the blessing of a home and the tranquility of a family ... He promised to adopt upright behavior and to be a faithful husband. He would not try to impose his ideas on her, but he longed to show how much he loved her ... He said that, since yesterday, he had been praying to Jesus to inspire him as to how to reveal himself openly to her so that she could forgive and understand him. God had granted them a future. He would make up for all the wrongs he had committed and was ready to prove his fidelity and affection.

Marcia, however, jumped to her feet, put her hands on her waist, and with a laugh of derision, said sarcastically:

"Well, I'll be! ... After growing old, the devil becomes a saint! ... Always the same old story!"

And she added with an air of mockery:

"This is just what I need! You, a Spiritist! ... I might have known! ... I swear you must have gotten involved in this folly while at the hospital. The way you talked when Nemesio and I were in the room! Your behavior towards Marita! ... Well, well! ... Who could have hypnotized you like that?"

Claudio realized that all hope of reconciling with Marcia in order to experience a respectable home had vanished, and feeling attacked in the faith he had begun to treasure, he replied, clearly hurt:

"But do you even know what Spiritism is?"

Marcia, obsessed, and with the attitude of someone who had long sought to leave the road she had been walking in order to go in a new direction, replied ironically:

"Perfectly well. Yes, I do know what it is! When Aracelia died, I discussed it with some friends, but after some time I gave it up. Spiritism is a movement of people who want to seat dogs on benches and pick stars as if they were oranges! ... What nonsense! ... We are all miscreants in this world! ... I am; you are; everybody else is! ... Spiritists are like dogs trying to sit in the armchair of false virtue. Utter nonsense! We all have to walk with our feet on the ground."

"I don't see it that way."

"Well, if you have a different opinion, and if everything you have said is true, it's too bad, but the change has come too late! ... I've come from Petropolis just to tell you it's all over between us ... Now, my old man, you can get a life and I'll get one for myself."

She continued, alleging that, after suffering for so many years in that apartment she called "my cage," she would make the right kind of nest. She would only wait for Marina to get better in order to ask for a legal separation. If he, Claudio, did not sign the papers, he would have to leave the apartment. She said she was sick of it all. She wanted freedom, peace, distance...

Claudio listened, downcast.

He recalled what Agostinho and Salomao had taught him; he remembered Marita; he reconstructed the texts he had read.

Yes – he concluded mentally – this broken marriage was his work. He was reaping what he had sown. One of his daughters was dead; the other was sick, and his wife was obsessed ... Thorns for those who planted them. He looked at the sarcasm-filled Marcia and realized that they were like two castaways on a world voyage, but with the difference that he had accepted rescue by the lifesaver of faith, whereas she had chosen to sink into the unknown. He patiently put up with her accusations for a few bitter minutes until his "old man" resurfaced.

It's impossible to bear such abuse – he told himself. The restorative doctrine he had embraced was not meant to create unworthy men. It was a doctrine of understanding and benevolence, but also one of cleanliness and respectability. He did not think he was capable of being insulted in such a way without fighting back. He became indignant. He wanted to retaliate, to shout at her, to hit her ... But when he raised his hand to slap her, the notion of responsibility suddenly woke up ... He remembered the hospital and saw again in his imagination that small, icy hand that had waved goodbye in a gesture of forgiveness ... His discarnated daughter's submissive, cold fingers were in his hand, reminding him that he should forgive just as he had been forgiven ... A sudden calmness invaded his heart and he started to weep.

Marcia was delighted. She emphasized the fact that she would not be missed by a husband who had become a weakling, a coward and crybaby. She said that, judging from that cowardly spectacle, she had decided she could not count on Marina ever being cured. She would put her foot down. She would have nothing more to do with that house. She summoned Justa, and pointing her finger at him, said she would send someone to fetch all her belongings for them to be taken to Selma's, a childhood friend living in Lapa. Swearing angrily, she slammed the door behind her without another word to Claudio, who remained in the room, crushed with suffering.

Claudio stayed home for a few more hours in order to recover. That afternoon he sought out Salomao in Copacabana. He felt better upon seeing him. They conversed for a while. Right there in the pharmacy, he phoned the psychiatrist indicated by Marcia.

The specialist listened politely. Yes, he would do everything needed so that Claudio could see his daughter the next day.

Claudio thanked the doctor and after hanging up, he asked Salomao if he might have a minute with him in private. When they were alone, he asked his friend if he would pray for his other daughter, Marina, whom he suspected was obsessed. He described the problem succinctly.

Salomao comforted him. He had several friends who specialized in disobsession. He would ask them for their help along with the benefactors who, on the spirit plane, supervised their endeavors. As for him, he would devote himself to the case in full confidentiality. Noticing that Claudio's face revealed a heart afflicted with anguish, Salomao invited him to have a cup of coffee. They sat in a quiet spot, exchanging confidences, observations, plans and hopes. They would share spiritual activities and would be brothers in work and thought.

Claudio felt relieved and returned to Flamengo. The next morning, he went to the institution in Botafogo.

At the prearranged time, he entered Marina's room.

He was shocked to see how decimated she was. She had lost a lot of weight. Her face was completely different. On the outside, she seemed alienated from herself; however, her eyes revealed a soul aflame with anguish.

I was deeply touched, not only when I embraced her, but when I saw Moreira close by, doing what he had promised he would.

While this friend, elevated to the condition of caretaker, welcomed me warmly, Marina threw herself into her father's arms in an explosion of tears.

They sat down.

The nurse left them alone and Marina asked about her mother. Why hadn't she come to see her? Why did she despise her so much? Why? Why?

Claudio struggled to calm her down, and he did it so well that the girl, astonished, became a bit more lucid. Her father talked to her in a tone she had never heard before. He probed her innermost fibers, soothing, adjusting ... He told her about forces that were imponderable to most people, and he mentioned discarnate intelligences who attach themselves to troubled individuals, making their imbalances worse. He persuaded her to follow the doctors' orders, and he said that he had been initiated into the joys of prayer since the accident that had struck Marita, whose discarnation he brought up with loving caution. In due time, he would pass on to her everything his friends had taught him about reincarnation, reparative suffering, obsession and communication with spirits. They would study together, and he added: "Even if Marcia didn't like it." She, Marina, should be patient, calm and inspire confidence in those who were treating her. He wanted her to confide in him, a father renewed by faith, what concerned her most. He was there to encourage her, to understand her. He needed her to open up, unburden herself so that he would know where to start. She should not hold anything back; she had nothing to fear. He wanted to see her healthy and happy. All these words were expressed full of caring and illuminated with so much love that the girl held on to him with even more devotion, like someone who managed to grab an unexpected root while sliding down in a deadly fall ... She asked if he had ever heard strange voices or seen things nobody else could see. Claudio assured her that he would explain such phenomena as soon as she recovered, but he insisted that she should give him all the information he needed so that he could help her.

Imploring him not to condemn her, and feeling encouraged by his kindly smile, she described all the feminine artifices she had used to seduce Nemesio Torres. He, a mature man; she, almost a child. She was proud to see him as both her boss and her vassal. At first, there were happy outings, a lot of money, and reciprocal caresses, which she accepted much more because she was proud of being able to impress him rather than because she was actually attracted to him. She told him how Nemesio, at first captive, began to enslave her. She mentioned the night when he had gotten her drunk on purpose, and she had woken up in his arms in some unknown house in Sao Conrado ... Ever since then, she had been his lover. At his insistence, she had helped with Beatriz so that he could always have her at hand ... He had fallen in love with her and had told her this many times. He longed to marry her as soon as he became a widower. But Gilberto had entered the picture, and despite fighting against it, she could not help herself. Ever since she first saw him, she knew he was the man of her dreams ... Painting her emotions live, with all the shades of realism that her delirium produced on the words, Marina confessed she had deliberately seduced Gilberto away from Marita. To get revenge on Nemesio, she did exactly what he had done. One night at a party, she encouraged Gilberto to drink too much whisky and when he became excited, she took him to her room at the Torreses under the pretext that he needed to sleep it off. She gave herself to him without any notion of carefulness or reproach ... When he woke up, she made him believe he was responsible for her future ... That is how she began to skillfully divide herself between one and the other, although her indifference towards Nemesio had turned into a strong aversion. The more she communicated with the son, the more she detested the father, until Beatriz's death precipitated events. Realizing that her boss was bent on marrying her, she had become obsessed with his son to the point of being caught red-handed by Nemesio in a very embarrassing situation.

Claudio listened, contrite.

He had the impression that he was only now getting to know his family for the first time in his life. Still wounded by what Marcia had said, he did not know which of the wounds pained his soul more – those that his insensitive wife had opened up in his spirit, or those in the fabric of his heart caused by his suffering daughter's secrets. Nevertheless, he embraced Marina even more tenderly, and feeling encouraged, she told him she wanted to leave Nemesio and marry Gilberto, be his wife, understand him, and make him happy.

Claudio promised to cooperate, although emphasizing the need for her health to improve first.

However, the painful report was not over yet.

The cup had to be drained to the dregs.

In sentences interrupted with sobs, Marina told her father that Nemesio had visited her in that same place four days ago. He had taken advantage of her situation and stated that he would, by no means, give her up to Gilberto; that he would wait for her to recover in order to prepare everything for his second marriage; that he would confirm all his promises to her in order to raise her to the status of his wife and to benefit her entire family if she would abandon his son, whom he planned to send to the south of the country ... But since she told Nemesio very clearly that she would never leave Gilberto, begging him to forgive her and asking him to see her as his daughter, he had become furious and had threatened her ... If she left him, he would kill her. She had cried and begged for compassion saying that she did not have the courage to go on pretending ... She loved Gilberto and wanted to be cured in order to live with him and for him ... Nemesio had laughed in scorn and reiterated the fact that he would make her pay for her thoughtlessness; that he would never allow her to be happy with that son he had begun to hate; and that, in order to humiliate her, he had seduced a very willing Marcia, and had decided to take her to Petropolis instead of her.

Claudio wanted very much to believe Marina was delirious but the memory of his disturbed wife confirmed her story. As for me, I had confirmation from Moreira. In a few words, he told me that, after Beatriz's discarnation, a gang of disturbed spirits had captured Nemesio for the purpose of exploiting his sexual energies.

Claudio realized how serious the situation was. However, at the end of the visit, he comforted his daughter, promising to help her find peace and hope for her tormented mind. He recommended work, trust, patience and self-control so that she could recover faster, and he reassured her he would talk to Marcia and the two Torreses so that her plans for future happiness would materialize harmoniously.

Marina said goodbye to her father with a smile of comfort, already showing visible signs of improvement. But when he was back out on the street, Claudio started to pray; he could foresee that he was on the verge of painful, bitterer trials; he pressed his right hand against his afflicted chest, as if he had brought from the visit thorns of fire that burned his soul.

9

Pedro and I set out for the recovery institute that Felix headed in the spirit realm.

On the way, I was happy to see that Pedro felt more peaceful and cheerful. He watched Beatriz's recuperation, nourishing new joys. His eyes were bright with dreams for the future.

He shared with me the surprises his daughter experienced when she had first arrived on the higher plane: affections from other times; dear family members arriving from far away to congratulate her. Beatriz had just concluded a noble endeavor, one among many other admirable undertakings whose importance can only be evaluated in the homeland of the spirits: the endeavor of inner renewal obtained at the price of untold sacrifices. Tears shed in silence and unknown suffering had won peace and light for her. An unknown woman in the physical world, seemingly enslaved to a husband and a son who did not appreciate her, she had achieved sublime, inner victories, thus storing up inalienable riches for immortality. Of course she had not come back after having reached angelic glory, but as far as was possible, considering the circumstances into which she had reincarnated, she had come back triumphant.

I rejoiced, too, at what I heard, and I did my utmost to avoid being asked about the Torres family, who, in my opinion, were still incapable of enjoying the merits of the selfless missionary who had served them. I was afraid of dimming the mirror of optimism on which my friend's hopes were reflected. And maybe for the same reason, Pedro did not ask me anything about his son-in-law and his grandson, who, without their maternal guardian, were now on their own.

We arrived at the institute *Almas Irmãs*[31], the name given to it by its founders, who built it for the purpose of assisting spirits in need of sexual reeducation after discarnation. The institute consisted of several constructions showing simple, harmonious lines, and occupying an area of four square kilometers of buildings, streets, parks and gardens. A veritable city in itself.

One could breathe tranquility and joy.

On the narrow pathways of soothing green, flowers touched by the breeze looked like nods of welcome.

Smiling faces greeted us amid circumspect faces that nodded at us in acknowledgement.

We were pleased at seeing patients of all ages and both sexes.

One group of buildings suggested a university campus.

But rather than meeting examples of psychopathy connected with sexual disturbances, the persons who welcomed us affectionately looked wholesome.

Pedro, who had arrived there a few days earlier, satisfied my curiosity by explaining that the guild responsible for the institute had enormous space reserved for the patients. However, he advised me to change any previous preconception I might have had regarding the type of work being done there. Those who were truly mentally imbalanced as a consequence of

---

31 Literally, "Fraternal Souls" – Tr.

emotional delusions brought from earth were confined to and treated in mental wards after having broken away from demented phalanxes in the darker lower zones of the spirit world. He added that many of those that had greeted us so serenely were survivors of intense dramas of passion. But now, lucid and peaceable, they were just like human personalities who had overcome crises of insanity after having yielded to mental imbalance.

His explanations were suddenly interrupted, because we had arrived at the place where we were to meet with Felix, who had been informed of our presence beforehand.

The instructor had said it would be impossible to meet with us at the time. He would be waiting for us in his own residence later. Nevertheless, he had a wonderful surprise for us. Belino Andrade, a friend whom I had not seen for ten years, and who had been my close partner in a number of activities, was there, waiting to show us around.

He embraced us fraternally, and continuing with the explanations that Pedro had started, he told us that Almas Irmãs was a school-hospital of the utmost importance for candidates who wished to reincarnate. Most of its patients or students came from purgatorial regions after having ridded themselves of the most immediate consequences of the vices and vile passions they had cherished on the physical plane. They were rigorously examined and had to meet all the selection criteria while still living in that place of expiatory anguish. Only after having been deemed worthy were they allowed to enter that outpost of recovery for longer or shorter stays involving meditation and study, researching the causes and observing the effects of their failures in the area of affections.

While we enjoyed a pleasant walk, Belino explained that all of them, after having been sufficiently instructed, are sent back to the terrestrial domicile, where they reincarnate into the same environment where they failed, and, as far as possible, into the same blood families that had harmed them or had suffered their harm.

While at Almas Irmãs, they received the award of knowledge; on earth they were to apply it by means of the difficulties and temptations of material life, thus showing they had assimilated the virtues they acquired while here.

As Belino showed us charming squares or called our attention to various aspects of the landscape, he compared the objectives of the institution to those of centers of higher learning in the world that confer academic titles for the right to practice a specialized profession. He compared the terrestrial arena to the sphere of practice in which graduated students are driven to experiences and responsibilities that determine merit or demerit. At the institution, the mind was recomposed; it learned and recovered, was restored and renewed, but almost always for the purpose of returning to the world in order to incorporate what it learned. He added that, except for compulsory reincarnations for pressing reasons, the issue of returning required specific considerations and adequate preparation. For that reason, many of the spirits at Almas Irmãs were reincarnating with pre-established domestic plans so as to host, with their own genetic resources, fellow spirits that were in tune with them. From the institute, the latter, who were to be future sons and daughters, guarded and defended their future parents until they themselves could reincarnate. Thus they formed entire families undergoing spiritual growth and redemptive trials that spiritually represented the institute's work on earth, much as is the case with many similar institutions and a great number of other associations dedicated to the regeneration and the progress of the soul in the spheres of spiritual activity that surround the earth.

In other words, that spiritual school-hospital acted as an advanced outpost of constructive spirituality, keeping permanent contact with human life.

All reincarnate individualities connected with Almas Irmãs have files containing the entire history of what they are accomplishing during their reincarnation. These files indicate not only the balance of the credits earned but also the debts acquired. This balance can be examined at any time so as to provide them with the help they deserve, depending on the loyalty they demonstrate in keeping the obligations they undertook and according to their willingness to contribute to the general good.

I asked Belino if he knew the overall average rate of success for that community, and he said that, yes, he did, that in the eighty-two years of its existence, Almas Irmãs, which had an oscillating population of five to six thousand souls, showed that, out of one hundred students, eighteen were victorious regarding their reincarnation commitments; twenty-two had grown spiritually; twenty-six had barely grown and thirty-four had acquired even worse debts.

In answer to my question as to whether or not the ones who failed were readmitted, he said that no one on earth can evaluate the expectations, the love, the effort and the sacrifice with which discarnate friends cheer for the triumph or partial improvement of their loved ones in the material world, nor can they imagine the desolation that assails their souls when they are not able to welcome them back, even if their spiritual growth was very small. He said that complete failures automatically go to the lower regions, where they may stay for a long time due to mental imbalance or debauchery, although they never lose the devotion of friends domiciled here, and who intercede for them from spirit colonies dedicated to various kinds of assistance. However, he did know of cases involving re-admittance after such disasters. On the other hand, he praised the rewards given to the victors. The learners who are rewarded for having shown substantial assimilation of the resources offered by the institution are honored with wonderful opportunities to work in higher echelons, according to their requests.

We arrived at a group of buildings that Belino said were places for various instructional activities.

We began our inspiring visit.

The classes impressed us due to their content, and the teachers due to their kindness. Sexuality, as the central theme, warranted the greatest respect.

The students studied pictures and drawings showing the implements of sex with the loving interest of those who feel moved by the maternal lap, and with the attention of those who are grateful for the divine concessions.

Everyone greeted us warmly but did not let our presence affect their dedication; nevertheless, I must emphasize the emotion I felt at observing the increasing veneration with which sex was praised in the various teaching facilities, and studied and revered in several study groups. Subjects were taught in specialized courses: Sex and Love; Sex and Marriage; Sex and Motherhood; Sex and Sexual Urges; Sex and Balance; Sex and Medicine; Sex and Spiritual Growth; Sex and the Law; and other categories.

Belino said that all the courses were frequented by a great number of students, and when asked which of them had the largest enrollment, he replied that "Sex and Motherhood" and "Sex and the Law" were at the top of the list. The former was attended by hundreds of individuals who are going back to earth specifically for readjustments in the home, and the latter attracted an enormous number of conscious spirits who study the best way to bear certain inhibitions in order to correct deplorable habits while incarnate. Many of these students would leave reports in the institute's files regarding the sentences they drew up for themselves before facing the trials they deemed necessary for the level of spiritual growth and happiness they wanted to reach.

Belino's explanations became more and more interesting, and I was pondering the extent of the endeavors of the spirit city[32] in which I had been living for fifteen years, without even coming close to getting acquainted with its full range of learning and assistance, when we reached the director's residence.

Felix, accompanied by brother Regis, whom he introduced as his eventual replacement, greeted us warmly.

I was surprised.

Felix did not look like the person who made himself smaller when he worked with us in Rio. There, revered and loved, he was the distinguished dignitary of higher knowledge, to whom Nosso Lar's administration had delegated enormous responsibilities. Director and commander, father and brother.

The atmosphere in the office where we met radiated simplicity without carelessness, comfort without luxury.

Behind the plain armchair in which he was sitting, there was a large canvas on which a gifted artist had painted the portrait of a noble lady praying in the lower regions. The venerable woman was stretching her arms upward to the leaden sky, which filtered reverberations of light as if responding to her pleas. Around her, swarms of greatly disturbed spirits – some comforted, others awe-struck – were groveling on the ground.

Noticing our surprise, Felix explained that the picture portrayed the image of a magnanimous servant of Christ. She may have been unknown to incarnates, but she was consecrated in the spirit world to helping hearts immersed in the darkness.

32 The spirit author is referring to Nosso Lar (Portuguese for *Our Home*) – a service-colony in the spirit realm. See *Nosso Lar*, by the same author, psychographed by Francisco Candido Xavier, International Spiritist Council.

She visited the caves of extreme suffering sometimes alone and sometimes accompanied by teams of collaborators, providing comfort and support ... She adopted discarnate criminals as children of her soul. She infused them with the ideal of regeneration, uplifting and instructing them. From time to time, he, Felix, would go to visit her in the caring shelter, which, even today, the selfless educator supports with her love in the dark regions. Felix continued by saying that in that shelter there are often more than one thousand lodgers on a revolving basis, since the benefactor is constantly sending certain ones to beneficent schools to prepare them for reincarnation on the earth or for internships in other places. Felix said that he owed her – sister Damiana – his first contact with the truth eighty years ago. He had personally ordered the painting as a reminder in times of important decisions, responsibilities and duties, of the mire in which he had once been immersed and from which he had been rescued by that missionary, elevated in the spirit world to serve unfortunate souls.

Pedro, however, changed the subject by talking about how pleased we were after our visit to the classrooms, and the discussion returned to matters related to sexuality, which were addressed so uniquely in Almas Irmãs.

Regis explained that he, too, had been surprised at first by the place's deep respect involving sexual studies, in contrast to the careless way that, with only a few exceptions, earthly political, religious and social authorities usually deal with the subject. And he emphasized, with humor, that we humans are contradictory when incarnate, because we are always ready to fix a malfunctioning light socket but we want to deny God the right to help and rehabilitate his children going through emotional disturbances.

Our host, commenting on the ideas we were proposing, explained in summary that in the higher realms sex was not considered solely as a morphological mark for the physical body, distinguishing between male and female, a unilateral definition that, on earth, was still accompanied by tyrannical attitudes and demands inherited from the lower nature. Among discarnate spirits, starting with those of average evolution, sex was seen as a divine attribute of the human individuality in the same way as intelligence, sentiments and reasoning, along with other faculties that were less-used in the human experience. The more evolved the individual, the more he or she realizes that the use of sex requires discernment due to the responsibilities it implies. Any sexual link installed in the emotive field produces systems of vibratory compensation, and the partner who harms the other to the point of causing subsequent moral damage must answer to Divine Justice. All sexual abuse that damages consciences demands correction, as does any misuse of the intelligence. A man or woman who abandons his or her partner for no good reason, thus generating sexual excesses in the victim, creates a karmic debt, for no one causes harm to another without entangling him or herself in it. He predicted that the earth, inspired by science, will gradually renew principles and concepts, guidelines and legislation concerning sex, and this will put the problem of sexual relations in its proper place. He reiterated the fact that, on the earth, sexual matters are treated based on the physical features that distinguish men from women. However, he stated that this idea does not define the complete reality, because behind such traits there is an immortal spirit that may be thousands of years old, bearing a number of complex experiences, which forces science to declare that, at present, complete masculinity or femininity are non-existent in the human personality from the psychological point of view. Men and women, in spirit, present a higher or lower percentage of male or female characteristics in each individual, a fact that does not guarantee the potential for normal inner behavior for all of them, according to the concept of what is "normal," which the majority has established for the social environment.

Pedro asked about homosexuality, and Felix explained that countless spirits reincarnate in an inverted condition, either for expiatory purposes or for specific endeavors that demand strict discipline from those who accept or ask for them. He also explained that men and women may reincarnate as homosexuals or intersexuals[33] in the same way that they may retake a deformed physical body or one that is inhibited in a particular area of manifestation. He added that the soul reincarnates into this or that situation in order to grow and perfect itself but never for bad purposes. This leads us to believe that wrongdoings, whatever they may be and in whatever situation, are always our own responsibility. In light of this, he added that in the courts of Divine Justice and in all the districts of the Higher Realms, human personalities labeled as abnormal have the right to watch-care as much as any others who enjoy the blessing of an existence ensured by the benefits of normality, according to human opinion. We should also remember that the wrongs committed by persons with psyches deemed abnormal are evaluated according to the same criteria applied to the wrongs of those who are normal. Furthermore, he remarked that, in many cases, the excesses practiced by supposedly normal persons are much worse because they are less justifiable in light of all the prerogatives and privileges they enjoy in the stable environment of the majority.

---

33 Having both male and female anatomical characteristics, including in varying degrees reproductive organs and secondary sexual characteristics, as a result of an abnormality of the sex chromosomes or a hormonal imbalance during embryogenesis. (American Heritage Dictionary of the English Language, 4th ed.,2009).–Tr.

And in answer to my question about earthly preconceptions and prejudices regarding the matter, Felix said that human beings cannot suddenly change the moral laws by which they are governed, or else humankind would fall into licentiousness. The spirits who are still ignorant or animalized, and who, for now, represent the majority of humankind in all the countries on earth, are invariably bent on usurping premature freedoms to convert the sublime values of love into criminality and debauchery. He added, however, that in the world of the future, reincarnate brothers and sisters in conditions judged as being normal or abnormal will be treated on equal footing and on the same level of human dignity. This will repair the injustices that have been committed for centuries against those who are born with anomalous particularities, suffering the persecution and cruelty of human society, which prevents or makes it very difficult for them to perform their tasks in the physical existence, if it does not render them hypocritical beings with the need to lie constanly in order to live under the sun that Divine Goodness makes shine for the benefit of all.

The conversation was truly fascinating, but a colleague arrived to inform us that Beatriz was ready to see us.

We went inside.

Felix introduced us to two women who shared his home with him. Sara and Priscilla had been his sisters on earth. Both were extremely affable.

Felix told us that, at first, he lived there with close coworkers, but over the past few years, he had succeeded in getting his sisters, who were working in other sectors, transferred to Almas Irmãs so that they could work together in preparation for the future. They were the last three of the family whose members, almost all of them, were living again in the physical realm. Sara joked in good humor that she would be following them soon.

Stopping from time to time to examine all the details of the large courtyard we were crossing, Felix told us that the institute has residential areas, as well as buildings for administration, teaching, maintenance, and temporary hospitalization. The residential areas accommodate entire families, couples, spirits bound to each other by emotional ties, and groups of researchers who visit each other or are visited by friends from other organizations or other shores, going on spiritually constructive or recreational excursions, as well as attending artistic or assistance-related enterprises, not to mention routine duties.

In answer to our questions, Felix said that Marita was there too. She was interned in a rest area for convalescents. However, he did not encourage us to visit her right away, because she was deeply traumatized, although calm. Her premature discarnation had caused a lot of harm. Nevertheless, he had asked friendly guides to grant her the possibility of returning very soon to the family environment of Rio so as not to waste measures put into place for the redemption of her past. Marita's premature discarnation had been a serious blow to the plan drawn up for her in Almas Irmãs years earlier. Nevertheless, he still hoped the damage could be repaired by sending her back to her loved ones by means of an emergency reincarnation. That way, she would be able to take advantage of the opportunity and the atmosphere of service, like a worker who switches machines without leaving the workshop. The procedure for the emergency return had been planned out since yesterday by the competent authorities. That is why he did not think it appropriate to interest her in matters capable of distracting her from the domestic stronghold.

Pedro mentioned the theory, defended by some religious thinkers, that holds that the date for the spirit's discarnation is pre-determined, to which Felix replied:

"We shouldn't totally discredit religious teachings. There are plans and occasions that are foreseen with relative accuracy regarding the death of the physical vehicle; however, the interested parties usually change them, thereby improving or worsening their situation. Time is like the credit that a bank loans or takes away, depending on the acts and attitudes of the debtor. So, we have to remember that the consciousness is free to think and act in both the physical and spirit realms, even if it is chained to the consequences of a blameworthy past."

And smiling, he concluded:

"Every day is a day to create one's destiny or reconstruct it since we are all responsible consciousnesses."

At that moment we entered the room of the newly-discarnate woman, who was receiving special attention from Sara and Priscilla.

Beatriz looked much younger.

Her face was still circumspect as always, but her eyes shone with the youthful brightness of someone who is recovering long-forgotten hopes.

Pedro approached her. We talked. She said she was delighted and grateful to her two care-takers. She spoke as if she were in the home of unknown persons, unaware of all the attention she had received from Felix before being delivered from her wasted body.

The conversation glided along on the skates of reciprocal tenderness. She, feeling gratitude; her hostesses, feeling pleased.

Several topics were brought up. We noticed that Felix was trying hard to distract Beatriz by diverting her thought, which was chained to her old home. All of us were making an effort to induce her to constructive forgetfulness; however, when she realized we were about to leave, the woman's kindly soul made itself obvious by reminding Pedro that she had not yet gotten any information about her mother, who had returned to the spirit world years before her. She also asked whether she could be favored with a visit to her family on earth as soon as possible. A hardworking disciple in that renewing atmosphere, Beatriz's eyes were wet with tears as she begged us to forgive her attachment to what she had left behind. But this was easy to understand – she stated with humbleness and greatness of soul – because she believed she had been immensely fortunate amongst all the fortunate women in the world, having by her side a husband who, in her opinion, was one of the most loyal partners in the world and the father of the best of sons...

The night was getting late.

Pedro comforted Beatriz, encouraging her hopes, and while we were saying goodbye in order to get some rest, I reflected on the transformation of the friend who had learned to place love above all his repressed bitterness, to smile affectionately at a trusting daughter, and to postpone the truth until the right time.

10

Before leaving for a rest, I spoke with Felix, who approved my request to continue assisting Claudio and his daughter.

The instructor was well-informed about the case, but said he would like to have a few more details. He listened to me with a worried look and concluded that Claudio and Marina's problems had come to a head. It was necessary to support and help them. Considering the commitments in which they were entangled, it was almost impossible to tell what might happen.

The benefactor seemed calm as he spoke, but it was easy to tell he was suffering. From time to time, tears came to his eyes, but as a model of courage, he did not allow them to flow.

Nevertheless, controlling his emotions, he suggested measures and articulated plans of action. I should embark on a new stage of assisting Marina in Botafogo. He considered Moreira to be a diligent coworker, whom time would make very valuable someday. However, he considered the task of shielding the girl from the vampirizers too complex for Moreira to handle on his own because their numbers had increased due to Marcia's unexpected attitude in encouraging Nemesio to embark on an adventure that reeked of madness. Thus, he asked me to join Moreira, to encourage Marina, to open my arms to Claudio, and to help Marcia and the two Torreses as much as possible when the conditions allowed for it. He promised he would monitor us, trusting in the Blessing of the Lord, who foresees everything and provides everything at just the right time.

I understood. Felix was suffering in silence. He was weeping inside.

In keeping with his instructions, I returned to Rio the next day. However, before I set out, due to my interest in sex and penology, as I reflected on the obscure infirmities swarming the earth, Felix took me to a small building situated in the center of the institution. It was called *Casa da Providência*[34]. It was Almas Irmãs' courthouse, where two judges examined requests by members of the community regarding brothers and sisters now incarnate in the physical sphere.

Dozens of persons were coming and going. To start with, Felix, always greeted with reverence by all of them, explained that in this courthouse they only organized processes for assistance and correction related to brothers and sisters that were about to reincarnate and those that were already on the physical plane but still spiritually connected to the interests of the institute. Rebirths, tormented infancies, childhood accidents, teenage rebelliousness, sexual dramas, unstable homes, legal separations, family abandonments, certain instances of suicide, as well as diseases and obsessions resulting from sexual abuses, in addition to a great many other themes related to the subject, were examined according to the pleas and complaints handed over for the pronouncements of justice. Casa da Providencia only decided cases connected with Almas Irmãs. However, the vast majority of such cases

---

34 Literally "House of Providence" – Tr.

had implications for other areas. In such cases, matters were discussed here first, and then sent to higher courts. Even then, the two judges and he, Felix – who, due to his position, had to study every case one by one – did not reach a final decision by themselves. At weekly meetings, a council composed of ten instructors, six colleagues and four sisters with enough merit before the colony's Governor, gave their opinion about all the recommendations and acts, confirming or disapproving them so as to prevent arbitrary decisions. Maybe because of his humility, he stated that many cases were decided much more on the judges' and colleagues' opinions than on his – one more reason for him to respect them. Furthermore, Felix explained that more than half the cases went straight to the authorities in the Ministry of Regeneration and Assistance, who, by the way, came to a final decision very quickly.

Inside the courthouse, we went down the corridors to the central office.

Felix, who was there only for my sake, did not allow himself to impetuously enter the public hearing room where all the complainants and litigants were gathered. Some of them might try to make personal appeals to him directly, hoping in vain to put pressure on the judges, an inappropriate situation to be avoided.

We went into another room, where the instructor gave me the satisfaction of being introduced to judge Amantino, who was working with the help of five assistants. It was a wonderful atmosphere where supervisors and subordinates worked together, cordially united by reciprocal respect.

Felix's arrival caused a loving commotion, which he immediately subdued by telling them he was just passing by. He was there for just a moment. He said that I could come back later when I had enough time to immerse myself in studying.

The five assistants went back to work. Amantino, however, seemed to be willing to spare a few minutes with us. It would be impolite not to accept his offer.

We sat down.

More to comply with the judge's kindness than to rush into analyzing the mechanics of the place – something that would require thorough consideration – I asked him about the percentage of souls that come back from their reincarnation completely blameless, according to the conclusions of that temple of justice. The judge answered good-heartedly that we had begun the interview by asking an unpredicted question. He said that the records indicated that in nearly eighty years, the average of complete blamelessness was not more than five out of a thousand, despite the fact that from time to time there were outstanding records of many who returned after having accomplished more than ninety percent of what they set out to accomplish, something that in Almas Irmãs was considered a high degree of merit.

Anticipating more questions, Amantino said that, despite the equity of the judgments, the force of the record of all the wrongs and defections of the reincarnate spirits prevails so that justice is preserved. Nevertheless, the limits of tolerance observed in the Higher Realms are much broader because the judges and instructors do not base their findings exclusively on the records, but also on the principles of human understanding dwelling in their consciences. And based on his or her own conscience, the executor of the law is fully aware of the difficulties faced by individuals who wish to undergo full corrective measures in the maze of their own sentiments, which are almost always still tainted by the shadow of primitive animality.

I took advantage of the subject and asked about divorce in general.

Amantino complied. Knowing that all earthly marriages between two people of a respectable level of evolution are based on pre-established plans, either for the benefit of all or as legitimate trials, the higher realms make divorce as hard as possible using all the means available. However, in many cases it is allowed or even recommended; otherwise, justice would be reduced to the condition of prepotency against victims of social cruelties that laws on earth cannot repair or foresee for now. After the problem surfaces, the one responsible for the rupture of the union's trust and stability automatically becomes the defendant. By means of resources used by the Higher Realms, the victim is influenced to be generous and benevolent so that the couple's service plans are not interrupted. This is always important for the community and includes both incarnate and discarnate spirits, whose benefits are reciprocal in terms of humility and benevolence for any of its members. For that reason, they arrive at our Spiritual Homeland as worthy children of God; great women and great men, justifiably considered great before Providence if they bear without complaint the infidelity and violence of their partner, forgetting insults and injuries for the love of the tasks the Designs of the Lord placed in their hearts and their hands as a result of the moral support given to their family or the continuation of good deeds. Those who display this kind of behavior dignify all the spiritual groups they are connected to, and it does not matter if they come from this or that religion, from this or that world environment. They are welcomed with garlands as true heroes for having embraced without fighting back those who hurt their souls, without withholding their presence and love. However, those who display an obvious inability to forgive offenses, although their lack of inner greatness is pitied, are also helped with their desire to separate. Their debts are postponed until sometime in the future and the changes required of them are conceded to them. At that point, both partners continue to receive the spiritual help they require, according to each one's merits and needs, and both are given freedom and respect as regards changing partners and pathways, along with the natural responsibilities that result from their decisions.

This happens – Amantino continued – because Divine Providence tells us to praise the virtues of those who love unselfishly, without forgetting the deference owed to those who live an upright life but suffer harm in their marriage. The Executors of the Universal Laws, acting in God's name, do not approve of enslaving anybody, and at any spot in the universe, the objective is always to uplift free and responsible consciences capable of rising, revered and dignified, to Supreme Wisdom and Supreme Love, even if it takes choosing multi-millenary experiences of suffering and illusion.

Impressed, I asked about the morals in countries where men are allowed to have many wives. Amantino explained that polygamy, even if apparently legal, is an animal heritage that will disappear someday, and that if we have reached a level of development inspired by Christ's teachings, we mustn't forget that, according to the Gospel, one man is enough for one woman and vice-versa. He added that there are difficult trials and circumstances in which one partner is called on to abstain from sex in the interests of the peace and spiritual growth of those who surround him or her, and such a situation cannot be changed without altering or worsening one's moral debts.

I asked him if Casa da Providencia provided help according to the extent of the wrongs committed. He countered good-humoredly that help always comes according to the extent of the "rights." The more upright the incarnate spirit is in carrying out its duties, the more help it will receive on those dark days when it slips into folly. Before any request for help on such occasion is granted, it is examined by a safe accountancy using the file that belongs to the candidate for whom the request is made. "Rights" are credited; wrongs are debited. After both are tallied, it is possible to tell how much help is possible or advisable regarding the average amount of help attributable to each individual petition. However, he emphasized that, by means of this clear application of the law, many requests for assistance are automatically transformed into corrective measures. If the candidate has more debits than credits, the assistance assumes the form of a correction, which sometimes angers the requester in that it is not possible to change the course of justice. Consequently, all prayers, or even mere vibrations of happiness and gratitude felt by all the incarnates or discarnates who have benefitted from their request act like bonuses and guarantees that entail a very important meaning for each one, whether there or somewhere else – Amantino emphasized convincingly. Whether or not one believes in immortality, every person is an eternal soul. For that reason, regardless of one's will, the laws of creation record the good and the bad practiced by every spirit, returning a harvest based on what was sown. When we work on our moral improvement one step at a time, and when we realize that physical existence is a learning experience for the soul, entailing rights and wrongs, the individuality on whatever plane of life, is, with rare exceptions, judged and sustained, before anything else, according to the level of his or her usefulness for the common good. This – the judge pointed out – is the general principle of nature. The productive tree attracts the orchardman's immediate attention. The useful animal receives special care from its owner. Thus, it is perfectly right to expect that the more value the person has for the common good on earth or elsewhere, the more devotion he or she will receive from the Higher Realms.

We could not argue. All his thoughts were expressed clearly and spontaneously.

I expressed my desire to learn how the hearings were held. However, since Felix was opposed to changing the task at hand, Amantino suggested that we hear at least one case right in that room so that I could have a sample of how things worked.

Felix agreed but asked for two sentinels to guard the entrance.

I thought my friend's demand was a bit odd, considering the simplicity I had grown accustomed to venerating; however, I was about to be amazed by the unexpected.

When the door opened, a forlorn looking woman came in.

When she saw Felix, she forgot about Amantino's authority, rushed up to the instructor and fell down on her knees in front of him.

Felix motioned to the guards and asked them to stand her on her feet.

Only then did I realize that the mentor had prepared beforehand to reject any manifestation of idolatry, avoiding the flattery he could not stand.

Despite being a bit embarrassed, the newcomer was forced to stand up to speak, upheld by the guards.

"Instructor, have mercy on us!" the woman cried out, handing over her documents. "I prayed for protection for my daughter, but look what happened! ... An asylum ... an asylum! Can a mother's heart agree to this? Impossible ... impossible!"

The instructor read the papers and argued:

"Jovelina, let's be strong and reasonable. The verdict is fair."

"Fair? Don't you know my daughter?"

"Yes, I do." Felix answered with an indefinable sad look on his face. "Iria Veletri ... I remember when she left thirty-six years ago ... She got married when she was eighteen and then left her husband, an upright man, when she was twenty-six, just because he could not afford her desire for unbridled luxury. In their eight years of marriage, she never came close to honoring her commitments. She had six abortions ... Abandoning her home and sinking into promiscuity, she was indirectly invited many times under the inspiration of friends on the spirit plane to rid herself of dissolute habits and become a respectable mother of children, who, despite being born from suffering, would become, over time, guardians and selfless companions ... We made several attempts ... Iria, however, aborted every one of her fetuses ... Six abortions so far and she has not done one thing that might recommend that she remain in the world. Her file does not contain the least gesture of kindness towards anyone ... She has freely handed herself over to the vampirizers that are consuming all her energies ... And Casa da Providencia could not oppose her will to live obsessed like this so that she would not continue to make her womb a lair of death."

And looking at the woman with sadness in his eyes, he surrounded her with paternal kindness and finished:

"Ah! Jovelina, Jovelina! ... How many of us here have beloved children in asylums on earth ... But an asylum is also a shelter provided by Divine Providence so that we may purge our wrongs ... Go back to your duties and honor your daughter by working and serving more ... Your motherly love will be for our Iria a light that chases away the darkness!"

The petitioner looked in his eyes, which spoke of recondite mental suffering, and thanked him, choked with anguish by humbly kissing his right hand.

The room recovered its proper atmosphere, but the incident did not stimulate any comments.

I parted from my new friends and when we had taken a few steps outside the building, I said goodbye to Felix also.

A few hours later, I entered the institution in Botafogo. Marina, under Moreira's care, was sleeping uneasily.

11

While in the mental hospital, Marina needed care and someone to keep an eye on her. Behind the scene of her struggle, Moreira and I did our best to provide for those needs. In the physical world, Claudio and Salomao combined their efforts, ensuring cooperation.

The combination of medicine and spiritual support was working smoothly.

Nevertheless, things were becoming more and more complicated.

After five weeks in the climate of the sierras, Nemesio and Marcia had returned to Rio, somewhat changed by the venture. Marcia was interested in a permanent relationship, but Nemesio was hesitant. When she had asked him to support her legal separation, he had withdrawn in a hurry. He was frightened, not of social gossip but of himself. A month away from work, in the arms of a woman he had not expected, had really unnerved him. It was not that Marcia had lost the charm with which she had seduced him, but that he feared for himself being with her. Sometimes when they went out, he would call her "Marina." He would wake up in the middle of the night thinking he was with the girl whom he had accepted as his fiancée. He would dream of being with her again as if they were teenagers, and in his sleep he would offer Marina declarations of love, like the ones he had made when Beatriz was dying in bed.

We went to him several times to rescue him from such crises by using magnetic resources, and we noted his relief when he realized that Marcia, experienced and maternal, knew how to tolerate and understand him.

Claudio's wife, in turn, meant to win his heart, but she was aware of the obstacle. It was obvious to her that Nemesio had the girl constantly on his mind. He loved her daughter and he belonged to her via his soul, although he had never failed to show Marcia respect and tenderness. At first, Marcia wanted to scream. Then, she calculated, as usual, and concluded that she was not involved in a love affair but in a business deal, the advantages of which she did not mean to lose. Deep down it did not matter to her if Nemesio did love the girl. She only wanted to capture him, to gain his wealth and his trust. With this purpose in mind, she meant to do whatever was necessary: orders obeyed, favorite dishes, stimulants at the right time, slippers in hand...

When Marcia asked him to marry her in another country where divorce was legal, Nemesio promised to do it. But when they returned to Rio, he asked her to stay at Selma's, the friend who lived in Lapa. It was because of Gilberto. It was important that they not get married right away, at least until he could make all the arrangements to move Gilberto to a city in the south where he would look after his father's commercial interests. Marcia would have to wait. And wait she did, despite the fact that both of them were constantly together. Outings, dinners, entertainment, nights out on the town...

Gilberto, however, seemed downhearted, depressed. A child without a guide; a mariner without a compass. Without the least incentive to work, and without the anchor of an ideal to rule his sentiments, he was wasting his father's money. Binges and whisky. Many times, while drunk, he would talk about suicide because Marina was so far away. He felt defeated, unfortunate. Here and there, through friends, he heard offensive comments about his father and Marcia, but he still had enough integrity left to reject what he considered to be gossip and slander. He knew his father was resting and he knew that Marcia was in need of the same. And in their defense, he would shout angrily, almost always drunk and encouraged by alcoholic discarnates that maneuvered him as easily as if they were holding a drink in their own hands.

However, in the midst of this downfall, Felix was reconstructing the situation…

After two months of treatment, Marina returned to Flamengo, safeguarded by her father's love.

She grasped her new situation in a matter of hours.

She had lost her mother's support and she knew very well the obstacles she would have to overcome to re-enter her profession. Patients who had recovered had told her how difficult it was for former mental patients to get a job.

At first, she nourished complexes; she suffered.

Nevertheless, she had discovered a father whose greatness of heart she had not known about until then and a faith that had renewed her hopes.

Claudio surrounded her with tenderness and kindness. The apartment was full of gifts and flowers. Spiritist books, sometimes read in tears, inspired her with consoling certainty regarding the truths and promises made by Christ, whom she had accepted as the master of her soul. She welcomed Salomao's friendship as if she were his daughter, and she considered herself as one of those whom Claudio called his spiritual family. She became interested in working for a charity dedicated to helping destitute children, along with a group of women devoted to helping unfortunate women. And when Claudio invited her to join him in weekly home Gospel sessions, she gladly accepted the suggestion and asked Claudio to bring Justa, a widow who was alone, to live with them. The former maid was delighted and was promoted to housekeeper, with the security of a happy family member.

The apartment was perfectly peaceful, although Moreira and I remained ready to defend the place.

Conversations and readings, endeavors and plans arose as flowers of hope, and from time to time, Felix, delighted, would come to take part in our joys and prayers.

Regarding Nemesio and Marcia – total silence. Father and daughter tried hard to forget them, whereas Gilberto…

Friends requested their help and compassion for him. The young man was sinking fast. Defeated, depressed; drinking binges, disorderliness. If Claudio and Marina could do nothing to protect him, maybe they could have him hospitalized, at least.

How could they deny him their help?

Claudio noticed that Marina still loved the young man dearly, ardently, and decided to respect her decisions regarding him.

After a few serious discussions concerning what Marina had suggested, the bank clerk decided on a good time to meet Gilberto at a barbeque house in Leme. They shared a snack and Claudio invited him for dinner the next day. Marina and he would be waiting for him. Torres' son smiled and promised to be there.

Six months had passed since Claudio's transformation, and evenings in May caressed Rio with refreshing breezes coming in from the sea.

Gilberto arrived on time, sad but sober. Before they all sat down to eat, he talked about banalities, sufferings, failures. He declared himself to be a loser; he was depressed. Little by little, however, he realized he was in the company of two hearts that wished him well and he began speaking more positively.

His host took part in the conversation with the prudence of a father, and the girl expressed herself with confidence, showing in her eyes that her love and hopes had not died.

The guest felt better. He felt he was immersed in a shower of balsamic energies. He imagined returning to his old home; he thought about the mother, whom death had taken away, and he wept...

Before that explosion of tears, Claudio, as moved as Moreira and I were, put his hand on Gilberto's shoulder and asked why he had forsaken their friendship.

Gilberto unburdened himself and said his father had had a serious conversation with him. He had denounced Marina as a misguided young woman. He informed Gilberto that he, Nemesio, had enjoyed her love. He described intimate facts about her and told him she had chosen a path of immorality; that she was not the woman he should marry. Nemesio had constrained and threatened him, and had finally insisted that he give up marrying her because she was ill ... Gilberto had subsequently avoided her for those reasons, although he still loved her. Even so, he had no intention of reconciling with her due to his father's accusations.

Marina, downcast, neither confirmed the allegations nor defended herself. She limited herself to crying discreetly, whereas Claudio tried to reconcile the two unhappy hearts.

Moreira, who had passionately assumed the girl's defense, lost his temper. He regressed to his former insolence and shouted out that even though he had been studying the Gospel for six months, he found it very difficult not to summon his old gang of friends and punish the old Don Juan.

Apprehensive, I asked him to please keep still for the sake of the good we were there to do.

Moreira was astonished at my incisive tone of voice. I explained to him that unfortunate brothers in the vicinity might have heard his intentions, and if any of them sympathized with the idea, he could be sure they would head for the Torres residence and look for a way to get in.

I used the opportunity to pass on to him warnings that had been extremely valuable for me during my earliest experiences as a discarnate man undergoing reeducation.

I told him that I had learned from various benefactors that evil does not deserve any other consideration beyond that which may lead to its correction. However, if we cannot keep it from reaching our heart as a sentiment, we should at least not think about it; but if we do not have the resources needed to immediately put it out of our minds, we can at least avoid talking about it so that the already-articulated unfortunate idea does not become a living agent of destruction that acts because of us and independent of us. I stressed the fact that the atmosphere in the apartment was free of undesirable influences; however, he, Moreira, had spoken overtly and other spirits nearby, who may be interested in our return to mental cruelty, might have registered his suggestion.

Gilberto said goodbye and left.

Moreira felt like a student that realizes he has made a mistake, and asked me what we should do. I had no doubt. I explained that we were now living in the spirit world, where thoughts and words take on a much stronger force of expression and action than in the physical world, and that we had no choice but to follow Torres' son in order to surmise any danger and try to neutralize it.

My friend, troubled for the first time in a long time, left the Claudio home and accompanied me.

Both of us got into the car, facing the self-absorbed young man.

Gilberto entered the apartment thinking about the now-changed Marina ... Her hair done with simplicity; her face not overly made up; her manners and sensible words. Also, he remembered Claudio informing him, but without complaining, that lately Marcia was always out of town "resting up." The atmosphere in the apartment exuded tranquility. All of this was new to him, a new sensation ... He was troubled, regretful for having been so candid, and did not know if he had been jealous or just impolite.

Instinctively, he headed for the room that Marina had occupied and where he had seen her faint in Nemesio's arms.

He wanted to remember, to think things over...

We followed him on the soft carpet, but when he turned the door knob quietly, as if he did not want to awaken from a dream, he was astonished as he peered through the slightly opened door and saw his father and Marcia kissing. And around them, our spirit vision identified a mob of disturbed friends that Moreira had unwittingly summoned ... Those vampirizers had registered his indirect call and were hard at work, transforming the middle-aged couple's simple impulses of fondness into lustful rapture.

Nemesio, with his back to the door, was seen without seeing, just as had happened to Gilberto, himself, a few months earlier, and just as had happened to Marina. Marcia, facing the door, saw Gilberto and the look of utter astonishment on his face.

The boy turned and left without a word, smitten with grief. Doubt crushed him. His father, his idol, had suddenly toppled over. Did Nemesio really have good reason to separate him from the girl he still loved?

On my part, I had to do something for the repentant Moreira. He approached the gang, who now complicated his life – although they believed they were pleasing him – with a mixture of revulsion and patience.

I stepped in and asked for peace. We should all respect Nemesio and his companion. We had no right to scorn or condemn them.

The gang left and Moreira turned his attention to Marcia, who, too astute to cause problems, had not fainted as her daughter had. Thinking rationally, she coolly disentangled herself from Nemesio and stroked his hair, explaining she had come all the way from Lapa just to see him because she had been troubled at seeing him indisposed the day before. She did not want to harm his health. She helped him lie down on his bed, from which he had evidently gotten up in order to greet her, and after giving him some loving advice, she left, saying she had matters to discuss with the maids.

Out in the hallway, she asked herself how she should handle the problem. Although she was calm and collected when it came to preserving her own interests, she was still a mother and had to think of her daughter. Was it right to embitter Marina by poisoning Gilberto's spirit? Was there anything she could do for Marina to encourage them to make up? Wouldn't it be completely demoralizing to let the boy think she was a woman without scruples, since they might be mother-in-law and son-in-law someday?

Moreira took advantage of those few minutes of reconsideration, respectfully embraced her and asked her to be compassionate. She should help Marina by supporting Gilberto. She should go to the young man while she had the chance. She should talk to him and try to reconcile the young couple.

Feeling moved, I myself approached her and asked her to intervene. She could help. She did not plan to reconcile with Claudio. She really did want a separation. Why not do something just and charitable for her sick daughter by leading the young man away from the moral decadence he had succumbed to, and towards a dignified marriage? She had welcomed Marina into her motherly arms; she had sung lullabies to her in infancy; she had guided her in childhood, and she had prepared her sentiments for happiness ... How could she abandon her at a time when destiny had given her every resource needed to extend her hands to her? Under the impact of these arguments – which she assimilated as thoughts – Claudio's wife remembered the past and wept. At that moment, her sentiments were as pure as they had been on that night, when, full of indignation and pain, she defended Marita at Crescina's "place." Between conscience and heart, there was no room for cold calculation. She did not hesitate. She went to Gilberto's room and entered unceremoniously as a mother assisting her son; she sat down on the edge of the bed where he was lying prostrate and spoke to him, her eyes full of tears. She began by asking him to forgive her. Next, she asked permission to confess that she and Nemesio had loved one another for quite a while. And in an impulse of kindness that raised our opinion of her, she lied for Marina's sake ... She told Gilberto that she and Claudio had broken up a long time ago and that she could not stand to be around him, unfortunately. She added that she had become intimate with Nemesio even before Beatriz's death, and that they met regularly in clandestine places. She emphasized, with a studied inflection in order to impress him, that she had made the unfortunate mistake of allowing Marina to become Beatriz's nurse, since from then on, she had enough reasons to believe that Nemesio coveted her daughter. When she realized she was right, she had become jealous ... However, she respected Beatriz's spiritual greatness and had had the strength to wait for her death before taking any measures. With that obstacle out of the way, she had resolved to leave Claudio for good, to the point of not troubling herself with the sick girl and going with Nemesio to Petropolis, where they stayed together in a delightful hideaway. She continued justifying, justifying ... Now that he had caught her in his father's arms, she begged for his forgiveness as a son, whose respect she would do her very best to preserve. She would not be returning to Flamengo. She would get a legal separation from Claudio somehow and would share Nemesio's life somehow for as long as he let her ... Even so, she was a mother and she was asking this for Marina. If he did love her, he should not treat her with indifference or spite, especially at a time like this, when she was recovering from a serious mental ailment. He should look after Marina and do for her what she, Marcia, could not do anymore...

Mrs. Nogueira finished, sincerely moved, and we were truly touched at seeing what miracles understanding and kindness can work for a young heart. His eyes shining with happiness, Gilberto got off the bed and fell on his knees before that woman who had calmed his soul with the charitable version he needed to reconstruct his pathway.

In tears of joy, Gilberto kissed Marcia's hands and thanked her for the warm words of filial love. Yes, he knew – he told her – that although his father was a kind person, he must have obeyed the suggestions of spite in order to separate him from his chosen one. He would go to Marina and promise to forget the past so as not to wound the maternal dignity with which she, Marcia, had manifested the loftiness of her sentiments after having found herself caught between the passion of being a wife and the devotion of being a mother. He added that he had been with Marina that very afternoon. He had noticed her sincerity and sadness. He had been rude and had wounded her heart, but he would rush to Flamengo immediately and make up with her. As for the future, he had no reason to be at odds with Claudio; however, since the legal separation was imminent, he would do his very best to help his father and Marcia get married in a country where divorce was legal.

It was only a matter of minutes from the conversation with Marcia to the telephone, and from the phone to a new meeting with Marina.

With the young couple together again, Claudio was ecstatic and rejoiced with prayers of gratitude.

Moreira and I sent word to brother Felix, who came the following evening to share our prayers of joy.

After embracing Claudio and the two sweethearts, who left for Copacabana in search of Salomao, Felix, Moreira and I left for Lapa.

Marcia was sitting on a sofa and smoking a cigarette, musing ... she was waiting for Nemesio to pick her up. They would be having dinner in Cinelandia and then would go to a movie. Felix, magnanimous as always, ignored the cigarette smoke and kissed her on the forehead with tears in his eyes.

We did not have the spiritual stature needed to read his sublime thoughts. We could only see that he was enraptured as he contemplated her, as if he wanted to thank her for her unexpected act of selflessness. Before leaving, he exclaimed:

"Praise be to God!"

Starting the following day, the relationship between father and son went sour. Nemesio, perplexed; Gilberto, aloof. A few weeks later, after Nemesio found out that Gilberto and Marina were together again, he traveled with Marcia to the south, with the intention of finding employment for his son in Porto Alegre amongst old friends from his youth. The couple stayed there for several weeks, and when they returned, they brought with them an extensive work and study plan, which Gilberto, after discussing it with his father, politely rejected, despite all the advantages being offered to him.

As we listened to the closed-room dialog, we could feel the respectful tenderness with which the young man spoke to his father, imploring his help. He asked him to be so kind as to not transfer him, but let him stay in Rio. He begged his father to forgive him if he disappointed him, but he was all grown up now and he wanted to marry Marina, whom he had reconciled with; that ever since he was a boy, he had worked with his father at the real estate agency. So now, he expected his father's blessing.

Nemesio listened, resentful, furious. To him, Marina and Gilberto together again was an unsupportable example of moral bankruptcy. He had never loved her as much as he did at that moment, when all of his hopes vanished. He considered himself finished, beaten. He had gradually lost interest in Marcia, although he continued seeing her. To him, Marina meant youthfulness, euphoria, enthusiasm, spontaneity. And now, just when he was plotting how to recoup her love, his son was stepping in to thwart his plans.

When he was sure that Gilberto had finished, he struck the table with a heavy ruler, and blind with a rage that encircled him like a mane of fire, he shouted:

"Never! ... You shall never marry that..."

And he spewed forth swear words and insults, which Gilberto listened to, stunned and hurt. Even so, after that tirade of offenses, and responding to the name-calling and intimations, he said he would bear all the consequences but would not betray the commitment he had made to himself.

Nemesio, totally out of control, attacked his son and slapped his face.

Gilberto spun on his heels and fell to the floor, only to get up and fall again under another heavy blow. Nemesio, like a beast out of its cage, kicked him hard and shouted:

"Get out! Out! ... I never want to see you again!"

We followed the speechless young man, who reached the street using a handkerchief to stop a trickle of blood coming from one side of his mouth.

Forty minutes later, a bus deposited us in Flamengo.

The Nogueiras were just finishing their lunch, and before going to the bank, Gilberto arrived and gave Claudio and Marina the bad news.

The wounded trio understood the full gravity of the situation. Nonetheless, Claudio offered to help. He would do his best to get Gilberto a job at the bank. He considered the director to be a friend. He would ask him for the favor ... Gilberto should forget all his grievances and regard Nemesio as a man with an ill soul.

Gilberto recalled Marcia's secrets, felt sorry for Claudio and began weeping. That man, much more harmed than he himself had been by his authoritarian father, that man with a stricken heart was pleading benevolence for his own tormenter.

Marina, whose understanding of life had matured, also exhorted him to forgive and forget. And as proof that she really had changed, after treating Gilberto's lip, she suggested that Claudio take him immediately to see the bank director. They should not miss the opportunity. It was no use mourning the inevitable. She tried being good-humored and lent a comical aspect to the drama, looking ahead to the future. She came up with light-hearted comments about the problem, as if she were using wreaths of flowers to decorate a room bristling with thorns. In this way she managed to convince the weeping and laughing young man to have a bite to eat before leaving.

Claudio's boss welcomed the applicant very graciously; however, he did not have an immediate opening. He would have to wait for about a month. Applicants were not accepted without having passed special tests, but he promised to talk to those above him. He believed it might be possible to hire him as a temp.

Gilberto thanked him.

Alone with his benefactor, he referred humbly to the problem of housing.

After all, he had been kicked out of his home.

Claudio calmed him down.

Of course, it would not do for him to stay with Marina and him in Flamengo, although he thought there would be nothing morally wrong with it. But they had to immunize Nemesio against any new attack of rage. He knew about a boarding house for earnest students, and he asked Gilberto not to refuse his financial help. He should stay there and wait for his call. Afterwards, he could pay any small debts he might have acquired. He shouldn't be ashamed of himself. He patted the young man on the back and said that they were now like father and son, and consequently, money between them should be common property.

Gilberto, although visibly embarrassed, accepted.

A few hours later, knowing Nemesio would be at work, Gilberto hired a truck to go to his home to collect the belongings he thought would be indispensable, advising the dedicated Torres' housekeeper that he was leaving home in order to try his luck working with Marina's father for a while.

The news produced immediate results.

After doing all we could for Claudio's troubled spirit, we watched as Nemesio entered the bank all out of breath the next day at 2:00 p.m. Surrounded by a horde of rambunctious spirits, he asked to see Claudio in private. An employee motioned and Claudio came to meet Nemesio, but sensing that he was about to be put to a test of infinite tolerance, he met with Nemesio in the lobby.

The visitor started by demanding an explanation about his son and emphasizing the fact that he would not let Claudio influence him.

Claudio mobilized all his reserves of humility and replied calmly that Gilberto only regarded him as a friend and was doing nothing against his free will; that he, Claudio, did not feel authorized to answer for him; that...

But Pedro's son-in-law interrupted and roared:

"Oh, shut up, you blockhead! ... You nobody! ... You idiot! ... Bonehead Spiritist!...

Nemesio punched Claudio right in the face and started strangling him while the victim tried in vain to protect himself.

The attack was very quick.

Before the onlookers could recover from their shock, Claudio was lying on the floor, and it was only because a few of them intervened that Nemesio was kept from kicking him while down. Forcefully restrained, he shouted insults, encouraged by the unfortunate spirits.

Claudio got up and was ready to strike back. He was angry and dazed. His chest ached with accumulated pain. He would get his revenge. That audacious businessman would feel his retaliation. He was going to smash him like a worm. But all of a sudden as he was about to pummel his enemy Marita's image surfaced in his mind. That small, cold hand, which had risen in death to bless him, was in his! The face of the girl that had been hit by a car appeared in his memory as if to ask him if he had forgotten his vow to be a better person. He had promised her he would change and be a different man ... He could not break his promise. He remembered her suffering, her body covered in dolorous wounds. Had he not been responsible? Had not Divine Providence been greatly merciful by allowing his wrong to go unnoticed? Had he not been forgiven by the daughter he loved? What would she say to him from the Beyond if, unlike her, he did not forgive the criminal that had seduced his older daughter and stolen his wife? He had embraced principles that prescribed clarity of reason so that he might learn to combine kindness and discernment, justice and charity ... It was his duty to see his enemies as infirm spirits, in need of help and benevolence. How could he condemn someone for something that he himself was guilty of? Was not his spirit in debt amidst failures and temptations?

Claudio dropped his hands to his side, and listening to the sarcastic comments of Nemesio, who was leaving in a rage, constrained by people who were calling for police intervention, he leaned against the wall, under the sympathetic eyes of the bystanders. He did not try to hide the thick, bitter tears that ran down his clean shaven chin.

The bank director arrived on the scene as the aggressor reached the curb and asked what all the commotion was about.

One of the employees nodded towards his offended colleague, explained the assault and concluded:

"Of course he didn't fight back, because now he's religious, a Spiritist."

The director was impressed. Wishing to defuse the atmosphere of indignation, he asked the doorman:

"Who is that caveman?"

An elder lady who was there with checkbook in hand replied:

"I know him. He's Nemesio Torres, the owner of lots and more lots of land."

"The shark!" exclaimed the director with a tone of scorn. "What kind of a place does he think this is?"

And looking around at the dumbfounded clients, he protested:

"People! This is Rio! ... Rio! ... Why do we let criminals like this run free? This is a matter for the police, a rope, the cavalry, jail…"

He accidentally backed into Claudio. He turned, composed himself, patted him on the back and led him into another room. There, he listened to his subordinate's story about his daughter and the young man he had introduced him to the day before. Between indignation and pity, the director said that Gilberto was hired, adding that his salary would be provisional until his position was duly legalized.

As the wedding date approached, Gilberto was employed and highly regarded by all.

Nemesio, on the other hand, was upset and unhappy, and invited Marcia on a six-month trip to Europe. They would travel Portugal, Spain, France, and Italy, and would stay a while longer in Switzerland. He felt he had been cheated by fate ever since Beatriz's death. He was unlucky, thwarted. He longed for change, renewal.

Marcia, who had stopped all phone calls to the family since Petropolis, did not waste any time in writing a post card to Marina, telling her the news. She confessed she was hopeful, delighted. She would be accompanying the one whom she did not hesitate to call "her future husband," and she promised to send news from each city they visited.

Marina read the message discreetly and did not tell either Claudio or her fiancé about the trip. They would have to find out about it through mutual friends.

The couple's absence gave the trio a blessed hiatus, full of joy and tranquility from beginning to end.

The Flamengo apartment had become a hive of light and peace. And while Moreira watched over Marina with unconditional fidelity, I went back to my studies and experiences together with Felix, although I lovingly kept track of my friends in Rio as they prepared for the happy event.

Gilberto and Marina's wedding took place exactly one year to the day after Marita's death. The ceremony was marked with flowers and prayers, embraces and promises.

The couple's happiness also reached us at Almas Irmãs, where a small team of friends joined us in a prayer for the safety of the two newlyweds, who were accepting new responsibilities and new struggles.

However, I was displeased to notice Marita's absence. Beatriz, herself, had participated in the joyful vows, although she knew nothing about her husband's whereabouts.

Felix saw my disapproval regarding what I imagined to be an omission, and explained that the girl was ready to reincarnate and deserved special care; that he had been allowed to make some changes to the regenerative process of the Nogueira-Torres group. Due to her sister's interference, Marita had not managed to marry Gilberto; however, she would return to live with the couple as their daughter so that the amount of time granted to the group for their common existence on the physical plane would be taken advantage of using all the resources possible, no matter how small they might be. Of course it was neither a strictly organized nor compulsory reincarnation for judicious reasons. However, it was an urgent measure that she would feel compelled to accept for her own benefit. Consequently, she would return to Rio with us for the first time after nearly eleven months of internment in a rest home, where she had lived only with longings and memories of the past as an inductive measure. She would embrace only the people she wanted to, and would do only what she felt like so that her impulse to reincarnate would become stronger. Felix understood that Gilberto would be the central theme of her emotional compensations, so he emphasized the fact that all our efforts on the occasion would be concentrated on him. It would be necessary for Marita, unaware of the marriage, to meet him when he was alone because her resentment from having lived together with her sister still pained her memory like an open wound. And, considering the fact that they would meet again later as mother and daughter in vibratory conflict in order to purge reciprocal wrongs and aversions from the remote past, it was indispensable for the reincarnating girl to be asleep for physical birth under the impression of complete euphoria.

Accepting the logic of these explanations, a few days later I was informed about the date chosen for the trip.

When the time came, Felix shared with me that he was not only sending two coworkers to prepare the environment regarding Beatriz's son, but that he was also going to use that opportunity since he knew Gilberto was studying in the evening with a group of friends in Gloria for the next entrance exam, which would settle him into his position at the bank.

As agreed, we left with Marita, calculating the time needed to find Gilberto away from home, and predicting that his study group would finish sometime after midnight, according to our instructions.

The plan was carried out with barely any variations in the timeframe.

We were encouraging Marita's joy as she descended with us over Guanabara Bay. From afar, we could see the contrast in the lights between Leme Hill and the Urca residential area, and further still, Botafogo Beach ... A few minutes more and we were on Beira Mar Avenue. As we touched down in Flamengo, the girl's exclamations of joy increased at seeing again the city that held her love.

As we stood in front of the gentle waters, assimilating the nutritive energies of nature, we were informed by our helpers that Gilberto had gotten out of his car on an adjacent street corner.

Without delay we led Marita there. When she saw him, she almost fainted with happiness and called to him anxiously:

"Gilberto! Gilberto!"

The young man did not hear her voice with his physical ears, of course, but he did register Marita's presence in the form of a memory. He suddenly recalled the girl he still believed to be Claudio's adopted daughter and walked off in the opposite direction to the one he would normally take. However, he stopped after a few moments in order to reflect and contemplate the bay turned silvery by the moonlight ... Yes, lying on that sand he had sworn his eternal love and had planned the future...

My God! – he thought – how life has changed!

Embraced by the discarnate girl, he looked at her image in his mind and wiped away the tears.

Felix, however, removed her gently and asked her what she wanted most.

"To live with him and for him!"

This answer reached us like a cry of hope hidden behind sobs.

Addressing her paternally, the instructor, who had expected no other answer, said he thought it would be best if we returned to the apartment. He would do all he could to guarantee her reincarnation. She should be at peace about it. She would live with Gilberto and receive his dedication. Nevertheless, he advised her against being too excited about it because it would not be good for either of them. They would be together soon enough.

The girl obeyed but looked at us with teary, questioning eyes. I noticed the presence of Marcia and Marina in her mind, but she removed their images and asked whether she could see Claudio again, emphasizing the fact that he had been her last friend just before she died.

Felix agreed gladly.

A few more blocks and we were at the apartment. The ever vigilant Moreira greeted us at the door. He was visibly moved when he recognized Marita, but he did not try to talk to her, obeying a gesture by Felix, who wanted to spare any distractions.

Tormented and trembling, the girl, with our help, entered Claudio's bedroom and oh! What a surprise! Claudio, in spirit, near his sleeping body, looked as if he had been waiting for her visit, because he held out his arms and cried out in thrilled exaltation:

"Dear daughter! ... My child!"

The girl remembered the scenes she had imagined while in the hospital; the torture of time passing slowly; the prayers that soothed her bitterness; the unwavering devotion of that father who had been redeemed by suffering; and she knelt down in front of him looking for his lap, as she used to do in her childhood.

Claudio, perplexed, could not see us. He was concentrating exclusively on the vision, which was having an unparalleled effect on him. He hesitantly touched the untied hair he had stroked so many times in the hospital, and he remembered Marita in her childhood, when she would come home from school. He asked her:

"Daughter of my heart, why are you crying?"

Marita looked at him pleadingly and begged:

"Father, don't worry so! ... I'm happy, but I want Gilberto; I want to come back to earth! ... I want to live with you again in Rio!"

Revealing his pure love, Claudio held her in his arms trembling with joy, and raising his eyes to the ceiling with the eagerness of someone who wanted to break through the concrete to talk to Jesus, he pleaded in tears:

"O Lord, this is the beloved daughter whom you taught me to love with the purest love! ... She wants to return to the world to be with us again! ... Master, in your infinite kindness, give her a new body, a new life! ... O Lord, you know that she lost all of her childhood dreams because of me ... If it is possible, dear Jesus, let me give her my life now! Lord, allow me to offer the daughter of my soul everything I have! O Jesus, Jesus!"

Felix felt that such excessive emotion might be harmful to Claudio, so he took Marita in his arms and asked me to stay behind to help Claudio back into his languishing physical body.

The instructor left, carrying Marita paternally, while Moreira and I helped Claudio recover his physical body. After comforting passes, Claudio woke up weeping convulsively, remembering in detail what had happened.

After a few minutes, we heard footsteps in the living room. Gilberto came in quietly. His father-in-law meant to call him to tell him about the incident, but he assimilated our exhortation to silence so as to collaborate with the future.

Yes – he agreed, as if talking to himself – the truth of life mustn't dawn on most men, except by means of vague dreams, so as not to confuse their nascent reasoning, just as God's Universe mustn't shine on creatures on earth, except as stars, like drops of light in the darkness, in order not to overwhelm their smallness ...

Nevertheless, the certainty that Marita would reincarnate illuminated his mind and warmed his heart.

12

Marina had just completed the fifth month of her pregnancy. Living with her husband and father, along with the devoted Justa, who cared for her like a mother would, Marina's life was pure happiness, despite the natural physical constraints.

Claudio lovingly followed the development. Deep down he was sure that Marita was once again part of the family, about to reincarnate into a new cradle. Every night, prayers for the tranquility of the spirit that was returning, and prayers for the happiness of his children. Monthly visits to the doctor, thus lending assistance to his daughter. Comforting passes to the mother-to-be. Gifts for the baby...

We admired his patience and tenderness as he read aloud informative articles written by gynecologists and pediatricians, calming and instructing Marina while she knitted clothes.

At the same time, Gilberto was happy in anticipation of an heir.

They wondered about the baby's sex, planned achievements, thought about the future. Justa reminded them about the story of the man who carried a basket of eggs, dreaming of the farms that would come to him from the improbable chicks.

Everybody laughed.

From our side, guarding Marita as best we could during the reincarnation process, we all shared in the gaiety.

All was hope and peace.

The expected child was coming to the family group as a sacred token of reconciliation with life. Peace had apparently arrived for good in the home in Flamengo, as if all the pain they had endured had been filed away forever in the drawers of time. Nonetheless, the past throbbed in that small tract of happiness, like the partially diseased root that lies hidden in the ground, yet supports the flowery stem.

One afternoon, both bank clerks found the young housewife looking terribly despondent.

At first, they attributed the change to her organic condition, but when she got worse, they called the doctor. However, he could find no cause for the sudden worsening.

Marina was losing ground.

About a week later, Claudio found time for a private conversation with her. He longed to see her recovered, strengthened. He feared complications. He urged her to be confident and optimistic. She should pray, have faith. In his Spiritist understanding of the matter, he knew that the baby about to be born needed her to rest and be happy. At one point in the conversation, the girl hung her head with a handkerchief to her eyes. Claudio became even more persuasive, begging Marina to open up to him. She should not hold back. He was her father and he was worried. Except for Gilberto, who had come into his good graces as a son, he did not have anyone else on earth, except her, as a reason to go to work every day.

Marina, touched, got up, went to her bedroom and returned with a piece of paper in her hand. A letter. Claudio read it without trying to hide the amazement and pain on his face.

The letter was from Nemesio. He planned to return to Rio after having spent six months in Europe. He confessed he was bored. He was tired of everything, except her, whom he still loved passionately. He had found out about the marriage, but when he returned he would never accept her as a daughter-in-law. His son was just an idiot, a total loser, whom they should avoid in order to cultivate the happiness that he, Nemesio, had cut short when he had so inconsiderately abandoned her. He was asking for her forgiveness and was waiting for her. He had gotten to know new countries and had contemplated wonders that dazzled his eyes, but his heart was like a wilderness, yoked to her by thought.

In the first half of the letter, Nemesio had written notes of compassion and love, but in the second half, he became disrespectful. He jarred her memory. He asked her about places of doubtful reputation. He said he was maladjusted and that he longed for her. He asked to meet her. He would show her how to get a legal a separation. He had a lot of friends in the courthouse. She should not disappoint him; otherwise, a bullet in his brain would be the solution. He would not hesitate between happiness with her and suicide. She had to choose. He was putting his fate in her hands.

The writer did not make the least reference to Marcia.

Claudio appraised the gravity of the situation, thinking, thinking … He recalled the beating he had suffered at the bank – something he had not mentioned to the couple – and deduced that Nemesio was capable of all sorts of violence. He anticipated the approaching storm, but tried to console his daughter. He unfurled his brow and smiled paternally. This was just an unfortunate incident. She shouldn't let it trouble her. He would go to Nemesio in person and ask him for serenity and consideration. At the same time, he would announce the baby's coming, which would also be for him, Nemesio, a smile from God. It would be impossible for him not to melt at such news. Marina shouldn't worry. Her father-in-law would be like a grandfather-to-be, forgetting the past and reconciling with the family for everyone's happiness.

In Marina's eyes, seduced by the magnetism of those words, hope shone with the peace that her father had brought back to her heart.

The next morning, Claudio discreetly started to act. Via some real estate brokers, some of his close friends informed him that Nemesio and Marcia had returned a few weeks ago. Nemesio had been confronted with unpleasant news and was very angry. His son's absence had adversely affected business, not only because it was a blow to Nemesio's moral credit, but also because it encouraged abuse on the part of subordinates who had not lived up to the level of responsibility they had been given. The long trip during a critical time for the organization due to Gilberto's absence had caused financial disasters that were very difficult to repair. Clients of the firm had quickly withdrawn their investments, canceling the deposits that would ensure its viability. With business threatened, the firm had been shouldered with two large loans. Nemesio had had to pay them off by using two thirds of his own assets. Now, the possibility of ballasting immediate operations and avoiding bankruptcy was very narrow. And either because she saw him bereft of all the properties that had attracted her, or because she had spent all her feelings of affection for him, Marcia had left him and was living with Selma. She was planning to open a restaurant.

Claudio received all this information, apprehensive. Even so, after lunch, overcoming his repugnance with the help of a prayer, Claudio set out for the Torres residence.

He bore an ominous, sad spirit...

Claudio rang the bell at the garden gate. However, Gilberto's father had seen him get off the bus, and from the terrace where he was smoking after having taken a nap, he ordered an employee to tell Claudio that he was not welcome there now or ever.

Claudio left, understanding the situation.

Such an attempt was useless.

He went back to work and asked for a private meeting with his boss, who had become a close friend. He showed him the letter his assailant had written to Marina and pointed out the need to protect her in such a way that Gilberto would not know he was defending her from his father.

The director, helpful and humane, felt apprehensive too and suggested a six-month leave of absence. There would not be a problem with it. Claudio had worked there a long time and had an excellent record. That way, he could support the girl and protect her, starting with the mail box, keeping any more letters from reaching her hands, and including continuous assistance at home by the hour in order to ensure her peace-of-mind while pregnant. The manager would inform Gilberto and his colleagues that some doctor friends recommended that Claudio take some time off for an indeterminate amount of time. He, himself, would talk to the doctors and they would not deny the request. Claudio should rest and look after his daughter.

Claudio thanked him, relieved.

That night, he had a conversation with Marina, reassuring her. He said he had reason to believe Nemesio would not be bothering her again. He told her he had been to the Torreses, but did not inform her of any of the details, giving her the impression that the problem had been "nipped in the bud." And interested in erasing the past, father and daughter talked about his leave of absence. Marina was overjoyed. They would use the time doing different kinds of work. They would build a cradle together. They would rearrange the furniture. They would decorate the place differently. Claudio tried to be humorous. He said that he and Gilberto had made a bet. Gilberto was expecting a prince; Claudio was counting on a princess. But whichever, it was time to organize the palace. His heart had told him a granddaughter was on her way ... Consequently, he did agree to rearrange the furniture and paint the walls, but he asked that everything be done with a predominance of pink. They laughed about that. Approving his plans, Marina asked him to help her organize an album for the baby while they waited for Gilberto, who was continuing with night school, aiming at a better salary.

When he finally went to bed, Claudio touched our hearts with wise reflections expressed in ardent prayers. Feeling worried, he could foresee that he would have to accept new responsibilities henceforth. He would protect Marina and, consequently, Marita, whose reincarnation he was awaiting. Nemesio's letter, oozing rebelliousness, and the rudeness with which he had refused Claudio at the gate, left no room for doubt. He would be facing conflict and offenses; even so, there was no reason to be discouraged. He prayed, begging for resources from spirit friends; that he not be left to himself; that he not demonstrate weakness; that he resist any vengeful purpose. He realized he was being tested. He must have harmed Nemesio Torres in other existences. He had to pay. Only in the light of Spiritist logic was he able to unravel the dolorous skein. That man had punished him in both body and soul, and had become the bane of his existence. His conscience ordered him to accept the challenges with humility. If he did not yet feel he was in a position to accommodate himself to virtue, he could at least pay for his debts, even if it cost him his life. That is why he was asking Christ to help him forget himself so that he could follow the road ahead in accordance with the divine laws.

In fact, knowing the approximate time the mail was delivered at the building, Claudio left the next day, saying he was going out to buy some fresh bread. He found another letter from Nemesio to Marina – his handwriting was obvious. He opened it. It was a collection of messages dripping with bile, a mixture of declarations and accusations, allegations of difficulties and crises. He insisted that he needed her in order to restore his finances. He could do it more quickly if she helped him. In spite of his losses, he was still rich enough to make her happy. He demanded an answer. He made threats.

Claudio discreetly burned the letter.

This went on every day for two months.

Detailed or general, a letter arrived every single day. Each text was more inappropriate than the last. At times, Nemesio would report on walks he went on in Flamengo in hopes of seeing Marina. On other occasions, after mellifluous sentences, he would make absurd statements, threatening to blow his brains out and leaving a note for the police, blaming her for it in order to ruin her life. In others, he would forbid her to have children with Gilberto. He would rather kill her or kill himself than receive grandchildren from their home. He referred to his revolver as if it were his constant companion.

Day after day, the businessman seemed more contradictory and less lucid to the patient reader. Every time Claudio delivered the manuscripts to the fire, he could see that the author of such slander was sinking further and further into insanity and obsession. Claudio could do nothing about it, because he was caught between his happy son-in-law and his pregnant daughter. He had to suffer alone, unable to share his thorn of pain with anyone. And to keep Marina from discovering the reason for such solicitude, Claudio became her constant servant.

During the last appointment, the doctor had recommended light physical exercise: no gym; something easy. Short walks would do. She could walk to the beach every day at sunset while it was still possible for her. Nothing more than that. The mother-to-be obeyed, and, as expected, Claudio acted as her bodyguard, enduring a heart filled with ill foreboding. He found no way to create obstacles to the prescription. As far as Marina was concerned, Nemesio's first letter had been swept from her mind.

Marina left the building every day, arm in arm with her father, for a short walk to the seashore, where she would sit with him for not more than half an hour. They talked about domestic matters, when not discussing things of the spirit.

Six days after beginning these trips, the tone of Nemesio's letters changed.

Accompanying Claudio, we analyzed the difference. The modified handwriting, expressing insults, revealed hyper-excitation bordering on insanity. He informed Gilberto's wife that, at last, he had seen her on the beach with that father, whom he covered with pejoratives and offenses, and that he had seen that, against his orders, she had gotten pregnant. He considered himself the most demoralized of all demoralized men. He loathed the passion he had held for her and preferred to die. He confessed he was bankrupt; he had nothing left. When the money ran out, his friends deserted him. He had been able to save only the house, but even it was mortgaged. He had waited for her, waited for her decision. If they were together, he knew he could get back on his feet. However, her pregnancy had dashed his hopes. He would plant a bullet in his head. He was saying goodbye to her and the world feeling total repugnance. She should see the many ink blots on that paper as stains from the tears he was shedding. Tears of revolt, spite, repulsion. He finished with a string of obscenities and said he was signing his name for the last time.

Frightened, Claudio read and re-read the document, and, reducing it to ashes, he went to his room and prayed for that man who was drowning in despair. He pitied him, but it was not feasible to advise his son-in-law of the situation. Nemesio was delirious. It would be best for Gilberto to get the news about his insane father from other sources. Nevertheless, he was so concerned about the message that, after lunch, he went discreetly to a few police stations and hospitals to see if they had heard about a suicide. They had not – not a word. After his walk with his daughter, he went to bed earlier than usual. He was eager for a longer period of meditation. Concentrating on thoughts of benevolence and faith, he prayed to Jesus for his adversary; for Christ's messengers to take pity on Nemesio and assist him; if still in the physical body, for them to extend to him the help he needed for him not to go through with the desertion; that if he had already thoughtlessly forced his way to the gates of the spirit world, for him to be warmed with the assistance of Divine Emissaries.

As Moreira and I were listening to his plea, Percilia came in.

She waited for the right moment and informed us that she had come on behalf of Felix to collaborate with us. Claudio's day-long appeals, transmitted to Almas Irmãs, had compelled several friends to also pray for him. Percilia had come because she wanted to be useful. And we, who admired her silent kindness, were moved at seeing the devotion with which she set to work in the room, like a nurse lovingly devoted to a beloved patient.

Four more days passed without anything of special note, except for Percilia's extreme dedication, which, when it came to Claudio, was analogous to Claudio's love for his daughter.

Between 7:00 and 8:00 p.m., we set out for the usual place.

The Nogueiras talked peacefully about trivial matters in front of the water, which was so calm that it reflected silvery beams from the starlit firmament.

A gentle breeze relieved the tensions of the day.

November was still warm. Here and there, incarnate and discarnate passers-by were part of the landscape; nothing new called to our attention...

After the rest, the walk back.

Father and daughter stood on the sidewalk, waiting to cross the street and watching the string of cars speeding by.

Marina moved heavily and, for that reason, when the light turned green, they began the crossing slowly; however, the unforeseen happened.

A car that had been going slowly suddenly acquired a strange movement, as if it were completely out of control, and, breaking all the traffic rules, sped towards father and daughter at high speed. Claudio had exactly one second to push Marina out of the way before being hit and thrown a good distance.

Percilia, Moreira and I, stunned, saw Nemesio at the wheel with a crazed look on his face, driving the car like an airplane about to take off and escaping guards and witnesses who tried in vain to get him to stop.

Marina screamed and was immediately assisted by some women. Pandemonium ensued. Motorcyclists sped off after the assailant. Telephones near the scene were dialed for an ambulance. The crowd increased around Claudio, who was lying on his stomach. People cried out against soulless drivers, against unconscionable youths...

Claudio, dizzy at first, came to his senses and somehow managed to turn over. Overcoming the resistance of his now stiff body, he was able to sit up, supporting himself on his straining arms.

His daughter! ... He had to know she was still alive, that she was safe! Blood dribbled from his mouth, but ignoring people's concern, he asked about her. Marina, supported by anonymous benefactors, crawled over to him. She had not suffered a single scratch; however, she was dazed and confused. She was afraid she would faint. Nevertheless, seeing her father controlling himself to fill her with confidence, she regained her strength. Claudio attempted an almost happy smile, which the blood saddened, and asked her to calm down. He was wounded, but not badly; it was nothing, really, he explained. A simple problem that a few hours in the hospital would take care of. He was worried only about her. He begged her to remain calm. She should trust God. Everything would be all right. He asked for Gilberto, and one of the men rushed off to fetch him at an address in Gloria, which Claudio himself had given him. He tried to keep on talking in order to comfort Marina, but he noticed his strength was waning...

Percilia was sitting on the asphalt, embracing him in tears. Discarnate friends in the neighborhood had come in answer to our appeal and were busy assisting the mother-to-be. Moreira and I worked hard to strengthen Claudio with our combined magnetic resources.

All around, bedlam...

The wounded man, however, isolated himself in thought.

November ... he remembered that two years had passed since the tragedy in which he thought Marita had sought her own death. She, too, had fallen close to the sea ... Both of them had been hit by a car. He looked up at the sky and remembered that Marita had fallen as the stars were disappearing, whereas he had fallen as the stars were coming out. He looked at Marina, who was crying softly, and noticed that his own tears were stuck in his throat. He wanted so much to live for that daughter; he was waiting with such tenderness for the baby to be born! He felt that his mind was reconstructing the vision in which he realized he had been visited by Marita, and the words of the prayer he had formulated came back to him, one by one: "O Lord, you know that all her childhood dreams were dashed because of me ... If it is possible, dear Jesus, allow me now to give her my life! ... Lord, let me offer everything I have to the daughter of my soul!" When these passages of the prayer came back to him, he smiled and understood. Yes – he thought – he should rejoice. He believed that Marina and Marita were together now ... together! ... So, why not gladly offer his life so that his daughter, prematurely discarnate because of him, could start her life over? Why not thank the Lord for the blessed instant in which he had been able to protect Marina against that homicidal car? Mightn't that moment have been for him, a heavily indebted spirit, a major manifestation of God's goodness? He had impelled his daughter towards death; he had incriminated himself, but human justice had not punished him for it. During his daily prayers, he had asked spirit friends to help him pay for the wrong he had committed. If he could start paying his debt in future reincarnations, why not start doing so right now amidst all those unknown faces, which Marita, too, had had to face?

His spirit was filled with supreme tranquility.

When the ambulance arrived, he asked to be taken to the same hospital where Marita had been taken. He would be grateful to the police for that. Borne by kindly arms, he said goodbye to Marina, urging her to be calm and optimistic. She should wait for Gilberto and tell him what had happened without a lot of details. No cause for alarm. If need be, she could get updates by telephone. She should not be hounded by anxiety.

In the vehicle, as Claudio pondered Marita being taken to the hospital in a similar vehicle under the same circumstances, Percilia, who positioned him in her lap, wept convulsively. Noticing that Moreira and I were troubled at seeing her like that, that normally quiet creature explained submissively:

"Brothers, please forgive my excessive display of emotion! ... Claudio is my son ... I am not weeping with sorrow for his fallen body; I am weeping with joy for his risen spirit! ... I am weeping, my brothers, because I realize that I, a former prostitute, working on my regeneration after enduring arduous trials, can now be near the son God entrusted to me so that I can ask his forgiveness for my having been such a bad example."

Before that testimony of humility, Moreira and I bowed our heads, ashamed of ourselves.

Who should be sorry for having been such a bad example if not I, myself? How much this brave woman – whose family ties to Claudio I had not known before now – must have suffered in order to express herself like this? What bitter torments must she have suffered on earth and after discarnation to acquire the serenity she displayed; she, whom I had learned to venerate, as if she were my own mother during our two years of constant hard work; she, who was invariably interested in understanding and serving? I could not tell what Moreira was feeling. Emotion overwhelmed me. I only know that he and I, in an instinctive movement of respectful affection, bent our heads at the same time over the hand that caressed the wounded man, and kissed it reverently...

A few more minutes of expectation and we arrived at the now-familiar hospital.

The same doctor that had been responsible for most of the assistance given to Marita was called by phone at Claudio's request. He came right away.

We sent a message to Felix; however, we had not yet finished, when our benefactor appeared right in front of us, as if he already knew everything.

He informed us that he had arrived in Rio a few minutes ago, but knowing that Nemesio was relegated to his own misfortune, he had decided to examine him immediately to find out what kind of assistance he was capable of receiving.

I wanted to ask if Nemesio had gone crazy; however, the look on the instructor's face did not encourage any questions for the time being.

Assistance from our plane was set in motion in collaboration with earthly medicine. Even so, Felix informed us that Claudio was about to discarnate. No human measure was capable of stopping the internal, rapidly increasing hemorrhaging. The dedicated doctor improvised measures to save him, but all to no avail.

Claudio was dying. He tried to visualize Marita's face and recognize places, but his head was spinning. He focused his attention on his imbalance, and became conscious enough to ask the doctor if it might not be best to call the family. The doctor agreed, and by the profound look in his eyes, Claudio knew that the end of his bodily activity was near ... He recalled the sleepless nights when he had received the support of Salomao and Agostinho. He mentioned that and added that Agostinho had left for the spirit world a few weeks earlier, but if possible, he would like to see his friend from Copacabana...

The doctor understood and communicated with Gilberto and Salomao by phone. They should come at once.

It was a moving scene. Claudio prayed for strength. He wanted to ask Gilberto and Marina to be benevolent towards Marcia and Nemesio.

Felix doubled his efforts to stop the hemorrhagic flow, even if for only a few minutes, and collaborating intensively with the doctor, he succeeded.

The patient improved suddenly. He could think more clearly and had more self-control.

Now lucid, he saw when Gilberto and Marina entered, grief-stricken. Shortly thereafter, Salomao arrived. Claudio said that he felt much better, impressing his words with all the serenity he could muster. He looked lovingly at his anxious daughter, and with a forced smile, advised her that he might have to go on a long trip for broader treatment.

Marina grasped the meaning of the joke and burst into tears. Her father, however, reprimanded her sweetly. Where was the faith they both cultivated? How could they not trust in God, who renews the sun every morning so that life continues, triumphant? He wanted to speak to them about a serious matter...

His eyes were wet with tears and, in a pleading tone, he asked for their kindness and understanding towards Nemesio and Marcia. He did not know where either of them was; nevertheless, when the opportunity arose, he asked that their home in Flamengo be replete with as much love for them as it had been for him, who was taking advantage of the moment to thank them for their incessant selflessness ... He confessed that Marcia had been an excellent wife and that he, alone, was to blame for their separation ... He stressed the fact that he had no reason to dislike Nemesio; that he considered him to be a brother, part of the family, with the credentials to be understood in any circumstance.

Meanwhile, he had begun to breathe with difficulty.

"But Dad," mumbled Gilberto, holding back the tears, "how can you leave us like this?"

Pressing his fist against his chest as if to control himself, Gilberto added:

"And your grandchild?"

The dying man made an expression that almost suggested a smile and answered:

"My granddaughter..."

And he added, hesitatingly:

"A Spiritist doesn't bet ... but ... if I'm right ... I would ask you to do something ... If it's a girl ... she is to be called Marita ... Promise me."

He was now paler and more exhausted...

The effects of the concentrated magnetic energies were finally waning. Claudio still managed to ask his friend for a prayer and a few passes ... The pharmacist prayed and, with trembling hands, administered the passes. Immediately thereafter, the dying man recalled Marita's goodbye and had the impression that someone was touching his fingers. It was Percilia pressing them maternally. He held out his right hand to Marina, setting his final look on her. Guided by Felix, Marina held out her small hand, which Claudio clutched firmly until he relaxed it, letting us know that he was beginning his rest.

He went into a coma, as if he were sleeping; his vigorous heart beat in his lifeless chest for four more hours, no matter how hard we tried to free him.

Very early in the morning, always assisted by the children, Salomao and us, Felix prayed, and with help from friends from Higher Spheres, he finally succeeded in removing Claudio from his spent vehicle, placing his head in Percilia's arms for the journey ahead of us.

The sun was shining in the sky, and contemplating its rays, crowning that loving mother bearing her son in her lap, I had the impression that the Father of Unbounded Goodness, on seeing their renewal, wanted to bring them from earth to heaven in a golden chariot.

13

The discarnate Claudio was recovering in the assistance organization connected with our work in the environs of Rio.

Felix, who did not rest until he was sure Claudio had fully recovered his balance, handed him into our care without returning to see him.

Now that Claudio was awake, he felt embarrassed and confused as he received our demonstrations of friendship and praise ... From time to time he would criticize himself, showing he was highly attached to guilt complexes.

We used every means we could to dissuade him.

We said we should see our errors as lessons, writing them down in the notebook of the past to be consulted at the appropriate time. Trees may drop their dead leaves but they serve as fertilizer for their roots. The Divine Laws preach forgetfulness of evil so that the good may be incorporated to our individualities, enabling us to evolve. We, too, had been through similar crises; however, we had ended up finding serving others to be medicine for infirmities of the sentiment. All of us must guard ourselves against constantly stirring up the sediment of vices and transgressions from the past in the vase of the soul, or risk frustrating the possibilities of the present for a better future, although life tells us never to forget our smallness. Indebted consciences that we are and will be for a long time to come, we will have to carry in our spirit the remains of old imperfections wherever we go.

We added that we should cultivate patience, for no one can grow spiritually without it. He could rely on friends at Almas Irmãs, whence he had descended to the endeavors of reincarnation. Under the natural effect of the experiences to which he had been conditioned on the physical plane, he was undergoing temporary forgottenness; however, he would, at the right time, recover more of his memory and would rejoice at blessed reunions. We were referring to brother Felix, who had always shown him his special devotion; that is, if we could find any special inclinations in that spirit open to all the appeals of sublime fraternity.

Our friend felt comforted, hopeful.

On the fourth day after his passing, Claudio touched us with a request. He realized he had been supported by many benefactors because, only at the cost of many favors – he argued humbly – had he awakened before death to the realities of the soul … However, he was ashamed to approach such friends immediately, although he longed to deserve to meet them in the future. He considered himself to be a beggar for the light, and if through such devoted friends Divine Providence might grant new opportunities to him, he would ask for permission to continue working, even while discarnate, amidst his family in Rio. He loved his children; he considered them as still young and inexperienced; he wanted to become their servant. But that was not all … He had left two people behind, Nemesio and Marcia, and he regarded himself as their debtor. He had no intention of leaving the earthly workshop without having paid his debts. Besides longing to redeem himself before his creditors, he dreamed of helping and loving them. Wasn't it his responsibility to devote himself to the good of others, especially to those two associated with his destiny, practicing the Christian-Spiritist teachings he had learned in theory?

Of course, due to discreetness and respect as he contemplated the past, Claudio made no mention of Marita, whose image could be seen on his mental screen.

He added that if his request was granted, he would faithfully follow all the plans of action that might be traced out for him, that he had no other ambition but to learn, evolve, understand and be useful...

We were touched by his request but we had no authority to make a decision.

Authorities from the institute viewed the matter sympathetically and offered a basic measure for solving the impasse. Provided Claudio was given permission, he would live at the institute, although he could still work on behalf of his family members.

We thanked them warmly, and Percilia left almost immediately as messenger. She would advocate Claudio's cause at Almas Irmãs, convinced that Felix would lend her his prestige and sponsorship.

In fact, Percilia returned the next day with the necessary authorization.

Claudio would be allowed to watch over his family for ten years, before moving up to the next circles of the Spirit World to be evaluated with regard to his latest existence. Casa da Providencia reserved for itself the right to amend the concession, whether by extending the time, if Claudio was doing well at fulfilling his promises, or by canceling the license if he proved to be unworthy of it.

The petitioner was satisfied, exuberant. Encouraged by the support he was receiving, he asked for collaboration in returning to Flamengo. He felt weak, hesitant … A fledgling bird longing to leave the nest … Even so, he longed to forget his own problems and get to work, work…

Measures were taken.

Moreira, who was still working alongside Marina, would help him.

Speechless, I admired the mechanism of the love of Divine Goodness. Moreira, who had been his partner in disequilibrium, would be his support in the endeavors of readjustment.

Six days had passed since the accident that had taken Claudio to discarnation. Dawn was breaking when we stepped onto the sands of Flamengo beach, bringing Claudio back home.

We made sure that our friend was confident enough to start over. We intentionally crossed the street with him where he had been struck, but he did not make one remark regarding the tragedy. Leaning on Percilia, with me close-by, he entered the apartment and was greeted by Moreira, who had cautiously arrived earlier. Claudio headed for his old room and saw that his children had left everything intact. He sat down on the bed to reflect.

The alarm clock went off at 6:00 a.m. and Marina got up. She isolated herself in the bathroom and got ready before talking to Justa about Gilberto's breakfast. Then, she entered the room where we were and addressed Jesus in thought, asking him to bless her deceased father, wherever he might be. Delighted, we listened to her every word in an atmosphere of harmonious thoughts while the young mother-to-be silently asked the Lord for assistance.

Claudio stood up and approached her. When he touched her, full of joy, he perceived that his daughter bore in body and soul the sweet presence of the unborn Marita ... He stepped back and looked frightened. He was afraid of tainting the sanctity of that sublime picture. To him, Marina was like a luminous plant made of flesh, containing a bud about to blossom.

Claudio's thought glittered in prayer. He asked God to help him put his obligations above his desires ... He approached her again, embraced her lightly and pled:

"O my daughter! ... My child! What has become of Nemesio? Let's go look for Nemesio! We must assist him! ... Help him!"

The girl, expectant, did not register the plea with her physical senses, but without being able to understand why, she remembered her father's request just before he died.

Nemesio, yes – she concluded mentally. She and her husband had received news by phone, especially from Olimpia, the family doctor, who had visited Gilberto at the bank. The news he brought was alarming; however, she and Gilberto were hesitant ... She felt especially anxious whenever she imagined herself meeting him again. The rumor was that her father-in-law lay ill in serious condition ... She rearticulated in her memory Claudio's plea before he discarnated and she made a decision in spirit: she would forget the past and would help the sick man as best she could. She would urge Gilberto to reconcile with his father. They would not postpone the visit any longer.

Domestic duties, however, occupied her mind and she left the room. Still, she retained Claudio's request in the form of a solid intention.

During breakfast, she suggested to her husband the first measures regarding the matter. Claudio, who was watching attentively, got right to work. He nourished the couple's favorable disposition. They should not retreat; they should move forward. Nemesio was also a father. Marina proposed; Gilberto counter-argued, but in the end, he agreed. He would phone the doctor from the bank to sound him out. If Nemesio's illness really was serious, then despite Marina's constraints due to advanced pregnancy, they would take a taxi that evening to visit him.

I left Percilia, Claudio and Moreira busy at work, and went to Nemesio's place. I had not seen him since the tragic incident involving the out-of-control car.

I went in.

Empty silence in the main rooms.

I was surprised by this and went to his spacious bedroom, where I had met Beatriz for the first time. He lay hemiplegic and aphasic in bed, accompanied only by Amaro, the faithful spirit friend that had watched over Beatriz.

I summoned all my understanding and resistance so as not to be overly sensitized, thereby harming instead of helping.

Perplexed, I listened as Amaro gave a summary of the tragedy that had hit that man who used to be so well thought of and so wealthy. Giving in to passion, which consumed his senses, and induced by his obsessors, who abandoned him as soon as they saw his useless, ruined body, Nemesio had decided to murder Marina and then commit suicide. But when he committed the crime, he saw that he had struck Claudio and not Marina. Consequently, he went into despair, which increased in his spirit to such a degree that his sick body could not endure it. He had suffered a stroke. Informed by friends, he – Amaro – had found him still in the car, semi-paralyzed and unable to speak, in a spot far from where the crime had happened. He seemed ready to discarnate, but Felix appeared suddenly, asked for help from all the spirit world institutions offering assistance in the area, and received it. He had prayed, asking the Divine Powers not to permit his exit from the physical plane without having benefited from the infirmity in his physical vehicle, which had been completely demolished with no possibility of repair. The director of Almas Irmãs had recommended the advantages of pain, which he considered holy, and the discarnation process had been immediately stopped. So, who was he, Amaro, to dispute brother Felix's decisions? – confided our friend. Nevertheless, he did wonder whether it was really worth it to save an active and intelligent man like Nemesio if he would be tied to such a damaged body ... Since Felix's intercession, the older Torres was exactly what I could see for myself: a bedridden human wreck. The place had been plundered by Nemesio's creditors, and dishonest housekeepers had carried off an enormous booty: silverware, crystal, china, clothes, paintings – a small fortune that had belonged to the ancestors of the Neves and Torres families. Even Beatriz's piano and jewelry were lost in the vortex. Only Olimpia, an old friend, came twice a day to give a bit of assistance to the sick man, who, though perfectly lucid, could not utter a single word due to the changes in his nerve centers. And all that – the discouraged informant finished – in less than a week.

I stayed there, filled with pity, waiting for nightfall.

Gilberto and Marina entered, followed by Percilia, Moreira and Claudio. They were taken with dolorous surprise.

Believing they were alone, the young bank clerk and his wife could not contain their astonishment, and when they approached the bed, whose solitude seemed exaggerated by the stark lighting, they fell on their knees in tears. Nemesio recognized them. He tried to raise his afflicted carcass of a body but failed. He wanted to speak but could not, despite all his supreme efforts.

"So this is how we find you, Dad?" gasped Gilberto, heartbroken.

His head trembling, Nemesio could only mutter:

"Ah ah ah ah ah..."

But we, who could hear his thoughts, noticed, filled with pity, that, having regained a sound mind, he was begging for his children's compassion and benevolence...

He gazed at his daughter-in-law through a veil of tears and said in the unarticulated language of his mind:

"Marina! ... Marina! ... I am a wretch ... Forgive me, for God's sake! ... Forgive me for those insulting letters; forgive me for my crime! ... I was completely out of my mind when I rammed my car into your father's body! ... Please, tell me if he died ... Forgive me! Forgive me!" But his twisted mouth could only repeat:

"Ah ah ah ah ah ..."

To the two witnesses, Nemesio's dreadful confession was simply a long series of meaningless interjections.

We realized that Claudio really was advancing towards the good that he had promised to dignify. It was only at that moment that Claudio discovered the identity of the author of the attack that had pushed him to his death ... But rather than asking for our guidance or advice, he instinctively remembered another night besides the one when he had lost his life: that night at Crescina's place, whose darkness had hidden his insult to his daughter, compelling her to the fatal tragedy ... He looked at Marina on her knees, and obeying orders from his soul, he, too, went to his knees and embraced her, and as if he were occupying the young woman's inner being, afflicted with mental suffering, he made her grasp Nemesio's hand and kiss it with the reverence that children owe their parents.

The patient, touched in his heart by such a gesture of respectful tenderness, stuttered unintelligible sounds, begging mentally: "Forgive me ! ... Forgive me !"

Claudio, demonstrating brave humility, suddenly stood up, and gazing towards heaven, he clamored in tears:

"God of Infinite Goodness, forgive me, too!

That same night an ambulance came to take Nemesio to the hospital. After a few days of treatment, always attended to by his son and daughter-in-law, he went by wheelchair to their Flamengo apartment, where he began to live, mute and paralyzed, looked after by Marina and constantly assisted by Claudio in the very room that had belonged to the one he had persecuted as a rival, and who was now acting as his dedicated guardian.

Claudio's moral successes were commented on with admiration by some friends in Almas Irmãs, but for Felix they created a serious problem, although without any importance outwardly. Beatriz was aware of the fact that Marina's discarnate father had received permission to stay near his family on a mission of assistance, so she too wanted to at least see her husband and son again. She had been informed superficially about the unpleasant events involving her loved ones, but far from grasping their full extent, she used them to reinforce her request. As an important piece in the domestic machine, she argued that she should be present too. If Marina had married Gilberto, she accepted her as her daughter, and if her parents had problems – although she did not know all the details – it seemed only fair to share in them, working as a mediator.

Felix did not approve.

Beatriz resorted to Pedro, gained Sara and Pricilla's support, and tried again. However, the director remained adamant. Even so, Pedro, who was not yet completely healed of his impulsivity, emphasized the apparent reasonableness of the request. He made use of so many relations and commitments that the instructor had no choice but give in. Although he was very concerned, Felix took all the measures needed to organize the trip. When Beatriz asked him to add prestige with his presence, he refused politely and conferred broad freedom of action and time on Pedro. He asked me in particular to accompany the two travelers – father and daughter. I was to collaborate with Pedro to solve any emergency. He foresaw obstacles and feared risks.

Beatriz was enthusiastic thinking about Rio, despite the fact that she knew that Nemesio was now living with his son. She was eager not only to embrace her husband again, but also to visit her old home. She wanted to breathe the fragrance of the happiness she had enjoyed – she said happily. And her happy father encouraged all her plans. I followed the couple but did not allow myself to interfere.

I proceeded to Flamengo, listening to Beatriz and admiring the reserves of sensibility and tenderness that vibrated in her soul. She exhibited the joy of a bird that has just been freed from its cage. However, immediately after being greeted by Moreira and Claudio, and seeing her husband paralyzed, she paled and bent over his wheelchair. She embraced him, although he did not register it, and she bombarded him with pitiful questions: Why had he changed so much in only two years? What tragedy could have relegated him to such physical ruin? What had he done? Why? Why?! ...

Hearing only the noise made by Marina and Justa as they went about their daily chores, Nemesio was touched by profound reminiscences. He could not explain the ideas boiling around in his head, but he thought of Beatriz. He reconstructed her image in his inner being. My wife! ... Ah! – reflected the patient, in whose spirit the aphasia had refined the inner life. If the dead could help the living – as so many people believed

– his former companion would surely have compassion on him and would extend her hands to him! ... He remembered her silent understanding, her irreprehensible dignity, her kindness, her tolerance!

Unaware of the fact that he was automatically answering all the questions of his anguish-torn wife, who was actually embracing him then and there, he reviewed all the events that had happened since her discarnation, as if to disclose everything in detail to her. Gilberto, Marina, Marcia and Claudio were the main characters in those scenes, which his perfectly lucid memory displayed on the bright frames of his aura, exhibiting them to his wife and to us as a dramatic, true story up to the moment he had fallen into wrongdoing. If only Beatriz had still been alive – he concluded – he would have avoided afflictions and temptations. By her side, he would have received protection, guidance. Profound longings pierced his soul. He recomposed the dreams of his youth, his marriage, and his plans for happiness, focused on little Gilberto ... With enormous difficulty, he moved his left hand to wipe away the tears that wet his face, unaware of the fact that his sobbing wife was helping him.

Pedro, apprehensive, tried to pick his daughter up off the floor, where she was stretched out like a tormented mother who refused to let go of her half dead son. In vain, he spoke words of encouragement, exhortations to patience, evangelical concepts, and promises of a brighter future ... His hurt daughter responded that she loved Nemesio, and that she would rather be tied to a cot beside him than be separated from him again. She was grateful for the love she had received at Almas Irmãs; still, she was asking for permission, considering that her husband was suffering. How could she rest, mindful of his torment? Jesus, too – she argued tearfully – had borne the cross out of love for humankind ... How could she help but bear earth's little vexations, mitigating the pain of the man she loved? Christian doctrine had taught her that God was a compassionate father, and a compassionate father would not approve of ingratitude and abandonment.

Her father had not foreseen this resistance. He took me aside and told me that Nemesio Torres had done nothing to deserve such selflessness, and that he, Pedro, was about to lose control; however, I suggested that he calm down. Accusations would only make things worse.

I stepped in.

I pointed out to Mrs. Torres that her son was about to give her a granddaughter, that her resignation with regard to her husband's trials would be a great help to us.

Accepting my suggestion, she stood up, constrained, and went with me over to Marina, whose true story in the Torres family Beatriz had only become aware of through her husband's reminiscences ... But a kindly soul, she understood the connections that had existed, and looking at Claudio, who had forgiven her husband for so many injuries, she kissed his daughter with motherly tenderness. She embraced Justa with sympathy and then went with us back to Nemesio's room, where she shared in the prayer and magnetic assistance. Beatriz seemed greatly comforted when she saw Gilberto arrive home for dinner. She was delighted to see her son go get his father for the meal after patting his shoulder, accompanying the gesture with expressions of encouragement and love. However, when Pedro said it was time to go, the dedicated woman curled around Nemesio, and almost forcefully separated by us, she displayed the early signs of a mental breakdown.

Beatriz left the building, depressed, speechless. In a praiseworthy attempt to warm her heart, Pedro, who had only heard rumors of Nemesio's bankruptcy, proposed a quick visit to their old home. His apathetic daughter did not refuse. She obeyed automatically.

It was well after nightfall when we approached the place, which had been reduced to a big, dark house. The full moon was like a huge lamp that knowingly kept its distance because it was ashamed of presenting such a gloomy vision to the former lady of the place.

Pedro regretted his unfortunate suggestion and tried to retreat but failed ... Painfully magnetized by her own memories, Beatriz went in quickly to search for her domestic treasures; however, she found nothing but dust and darkness in the family oasis she had built ... And worse yet, the elegant house, condemned to being auctioned off, had become a den for discarnate criminals, whom Pedro knew he did not have the strength to throw out. The desperate creature ran from room to room, from fright to fright, from scream to scream, until she threw herself to the hardwood floor of her favorite room, muttering incoherent phrases.

Beatriz had gone insane.

I rushed to her side to calm her down, while Pedro, heartbroken, resorted to nearby first-aid services connected with Almas Irmãs.

Help came immediately.

The next day, specialized healthcare givers collaborated with us as ordered by Felix, but it was only after four days that we managed to return to the institute with the insane Beatriz.

Two weeks of hard work and constant attention passed unprofitably at Felix's home, until one of the instructors of the medical team suggested putting her in an adequate hospital in order for her to undergo sleep therapy and narcoanalysis[35] so that they might possibly unearth some memories of her previous

---

35 Psychotherapy that is performed under sedation for the recovery of repressed memories together with the emotion accompanying the experience and that is designed to facilitate an acceptable integration of the experience in the patient's personality. http://www.merriam-webster.com/medical/narcoanalysis – Tr.

existence with due caution in order not to hasten immersing her memory in lifetimes prior to her previous one.

The suggestion was embraced.

Felix invited Pedro and me to go with him and brother Regis to the room where the research would be conducted.

At the indicated time, at the foot of Beatriz's bed, as she slept with her head on a pillow saturated with special electromagnetic resources, Felix and Regis – the distinguished psychiatrist who had suggested the procedure – accompanied by two assistants, the file supervisor from Almas Irmãs, Pedro and myself – eight of us in all – observed the patient. I must explain that every authority in that room made use of a perfected system of communication for instant consultation with other parties with whom they were in contact.

Felix, circumspect; Pedro, nervous; the doctors, busy; the rest of us, expectant...

The experiment began and Beatriz, with voice and manners different than normal, showed herself to be at an indeterminate point in a previous existence, complaining about a certain Brites Castanheira, a woman she blamed for the misfortunes devastating her soul ... Judging from the bitter statements, we could see that the analyst had exposed an important trouble spot, making it easier for him to enter the recondite realms of her mind. Taking advantage of this, the doctor asked Beatriz where, when and under what circumstances she had met Brites. Beatriz, always in induced sleep, replied that in order to answer that, she would have to recall her youth. Duly stimulated to do so, she told us she had been born in Rio, in 1792, and was called Leonor da Fonseca Teles, a surname that belonged to the man she had married as her second husband. She said that she had been born on Matacavalos Street in a simple house where she had lived a carefree childhood. In 1810, however, her destiny changed. She married a young Portuguese man named Domingos de Aguiar e Silva, who was living in Brazil and working for the Duke of Cadaval in the Court of Dom Joao VI. From that marriage, she had a son named Alvaro in 1812. Her husband, however, died prematurely on Boqueirão Way in Gloria while he was in charge of delivering unbroken foals to the royal stables. She referred gratefully to the demonstrations of love she had received from influential persons of the time and the promises made regarding the little one, who was now fatherless. A widow at only twenty-two years of age, she was courted by a rich jeweler, who had a shop on Direita Street. His name was Justiniano da Fonseca Teles, a young man only three years older than she. She accepted his marriage proposal and was pleased to see that both stepson and stepfather got along very well.

Alvaro grew up affectionate and intelligent, and since she did not have any children from her second marriage, he stood between her and her husband as a bond of light and love. When he was fifteen, in 1827, the boy sailed for Europe under the sponsorship of some of his father's friends. He achieved excellent results in his studies in Lisbon and Paris…

The magnetized patient talked about circumstances of the time, expressing her impressions about people, things, accomplishments and events as if her imagination was a deposit of living chronicles. She told us her son had returned to Brazil in 1834. For Justiniano and her, their home was once again a sea of roses – until one night…

Noticing her reticence, Felix, visibly moved, asked the analyst to focus on the possible memories of that particular night.

The analyst did so.

Beatriz grimaced, displaying the suffering of someone that has just discovered a wound on her body without the means to extirpate it. She replied unhappily:

"I must explain that Brites was married to Teodoro Castanheira, a rich merchant who lived on Valinha Street. They were both quite young and had an only daughter, Virginia, age eleven ... Although I was over forty and Brites was not yet thirty, we loved each other dearly. Our husbands felt the same way about each other, despite the differences in their ages ... They were united by business interests; we, by family dreams."

She continued:

"On the night I referred to earlier, my husband and I were introducing Alvaro to our social environment at a soiree put on by Commander Joao Batista Moreira on Pedreira da Gloria Street ... I had a horrible premonition when Alvaro and Brites were introduced, ecstatically gazing into each other's eyes while listening to the sonatas ... I tried in vain to come up with reasons for us to leave early ... We went home late, with the boy fantasizing. He thought it was just impossible that she was married and the mother of a daughter ... By the way she was dressed and made up, she looked like a regular girl in the ballroom. I did all I could to prevent disaster, but fate ... Both Brites and Alvaro were taken with mutual passion and started seeing each other. Walking along Mangrulho and playing on the beach in Botafogo, trips by carriage to Fazenda do Capão[36] and rides beyond Muda da Tijuca ... All this occurred peacefully until Teodoro found them together in a room at the Pharoux Hotel. Scandalized, Brites' husband lost all interest in her, although he did not leave home, because of his love for his daughter ... But even in that position, he courted Mariana de Castro, whom we called Naninha, a young woman of respectable habits who lived with her parents on Cano Street ... Rather than being bitter, Brites encouraged Teodoro and Naninha's affair as much as possible so that she could be free of him ... Naninha ended up

---

36 Capão Plantation – Tr.

giving in secretly, but she rejected two babies she had by the merchant, abandoning them at the Portas da Misericordia[37], as everybody calls it.

Beatriz Torres burst into tears but continued, saying that after four years, Alvaro became bored with Brites and only then did he inform his family that he had left a fiancée in Lisbon ... He longed to go back but was afraid his lover would commit suicide. After several unsuccessful attempts to end his affair, he devised a Machiavellian plan, the consequences of which brought her, a loving mother, irremediable unhappiness. Little by little he had noticed Brites' weakness for jewels, so he insinuated to his stepfather that she was in love with him, falsifying messages and setting traps. Justiniano yielded to his stepson's suggestions and managed to impress Brites with rare gifts, until, during their first meeting – arranged by Alvaro, himself – the young man burst in on them, playing the role of the outraged partner. At long last, he withdrew to Portugal, leaving several tragedies in his wake.

The scam changed Mrs. Castanheira's personality. She became a horrible, calculating, cruel woman. Never again was she seen making a compassionate gesture. Moreover, she transformed Justiniano into a man of corrupted sexuality, extorting more and more money from him, even going to the extreme of giving him her own daughter, Virginia, who had just turned fifteen, selling her to her lover, an old man, in order to control his lands and personal assets. Even so, not satisfied with her own follies, she lured girls from noble families and seduced them into prostitution. She also encouraged adultery, vices, crimes, abortions...

Virginia, with whom Justiniano was now living permanently after having abandoned his wife, became a cause of discord between Fonseca Teles and Teodoro Castanheira, who

37 Gates of Mercy – Tr.

tormented each other for eleven years of pointless conflict, until Mrs. Brites' husband, who had been living with Naninha de Castro as husband and wife for a long time, turned up stabbed to death on Cadeia Street. The homicide was blamed on runaway slaves. Naninha, however, had no doubt that Justiniano had ordered it and she plotted her revenge. She found another man, whose spirit she infused with spite and hate against the jeweler, and the two of them, now living in a corner of Botafogo, made plans to murder him in a fake accident. Justiniano, already sickly and aged, had gotten in the habit of making a Sunday visit to Bica da Rainha in Cosme Velho[38]. One night, when he was returning from one of these outings, driving his own carriage, Naninha and her partner, hidden in the shadows after having chosen the best stretch of road for the tragedy, pelted the horse with sharp stones ... The animal flew completely out of control and galloped down the hill, shattering the breaks and throwing the old man out over the top of a ravine, where he landed on a pile of bricks. He died almost instantly.

Beatriz finished regretfully:

"Oh! My God! It was all for nothing because Alvaro, on arriving in Portugal, discovered that his fiancée's parents had forced her to marry another man. Later on, he returned to Brazil, where he finished up his life as an unmarried teacher ... Ah! My son, my son! Why did you have to cause such calamities?!"

At that point, Felix asked the scientists to stop so he could give some explanations before leaving.

The patient was induced back to sleep and the instructor asked the file supervisor for Beatriz's reincarnation certificate; after all, she had left that very place nearly fifty years ago to

---

38 Cosme Velho is a traditional neighborhood in Rio de Janeiro. Bica da Rainha was the first fountain of ferruginous water in Brazil. – Tr.

reincarnate in Rio. In preparation for the case, the file supervisor had brought Beatriz Neves Torres' file.

Yes, her present name was preceded by the name Leonor da Fonseca Teles. She had discarnated in Rio and had lived in the lower regions of the Spirit World for some time before spending twenty eight years in a spirit re-educational colony nearby. Then, she had spent only two months at Almas Irmãs in 1906 at the request of Felix himself, who had sponsored her rebirth in the home of Pedro Neves.

Felix, however, requested more information, if possible, about the individuals mentioned by Beatriz, and who had connections with the Institute.

Devices were switched on and the central file responded quickly. Justiniano da Fonseca Teles, Teodoro Castanheira, Virginia Castanheira and Naninha de Castro had reincarnated in Rio, and all of them had a reincarnation certificate from Almas Irmãs. Justiniano was Nemesio Torres, a businessman with increased debts; Teodoro Castanheira had been known as Claudio Nogueira, now discarnate but at work on the physical plane, displaying significant spiritual growth; Virginia Castanheira was now Marina Claudio Torres, who also displayed promising indications of inner reform; Naninha de Castro had been Marita Nogueira and had recently lived as a discarnate in one of the organization's rest parks, before currently undergoing rebirth at the direct request of the Institute's director himself; and Brites Castanheira was known as Marcia Nogeira, whose file was truly heartbreaking. Her record contained a long list of abortions and desertions from duty, not to mention several indirect responsibilities for broken homes and sacrificed lives. Hers was one of the institution's worst files ever.

One of the doctors present, perhaps impressed by Beatriz's testimony, asked about Alvaro. The File explained that Alvaro de

Aguiar e Silva did not have a reincarnation certificate from Almas Irmãs. He was registered only in the Complaints Department.

Before they had gone back to earth for another incarnation, Leonor, his mother, Justiniano, his stepfather, and even Brites Castanheira, herself, had written severe complaints against him, although the last two had lived at the institute for only a short time after having left a penal colony.

Brother Felix asked if Marcia's file contained any noble gestures at all, for which we might try to help her effectively. Yes, she did – the appropriate department confirmed – on the day she had used her best motherly impulses to ensure a dignified marriage for her sick daughter.

Then, in a mixture of dignity and modesty, the instructor stood up, and with his typical humility, he informed us that Alvaro de Aguiar e Silva and he, Felix, were one and the same spirit, who was now standing before God and us, the defendant in a trial in which his conscience required him to willingly plead for an opportunity to reincarnate in order to be near Brites, now living as the widow Marcia Nogueira ... He promised that he would work hard on his own regeneration and would give her life back to her since he realized he was the tormenter and she was the victim.

A bolt of lightning could not have struck us with such force.

The doctors bowed their heads; Regis had tears in his eyes; Pedro had gone pale, and I could hardly breathe...

Felix courageously continued explaining that, as the spirit becomes more and more enlightened, Divine Mercy gives the tribunal of the conscience the duty of correcting and harmonizing itself with the Laws of Eternal Balance, without having to appeal to compulsory dispositions. Consequently, from that time on, he was making public his decision to submit himself to preparatory endeavors for rebirth in the physical arena.

He confessed that sexual delinquency had created for him responsibilities similar to those of a wrongdoer who had blown up a building or city by using a chain of explosions. By harming the sentiments of Brites Castanheira – a respectable woman until he destroyed her heart and mind – he declared himself, according to the principles of cause and effect, guilty to a certain extent for all the emotional crimes she had committed since, after having abandoned her, he deliberately pushed her into disloyalty and licentiousness, comparing her to a bomb that he himself had prepared for all the people the poor thing had hurt, as if she wanted to take revenge on the next person for all the misfortune she had suffered.

He, who had brought us so much happiness, was now pleading for our fraternal support so that he could find a place as a son in Gilberto's home as soon as Marina's womb recovered from Marita's birth. He had made plans to meet Marcia in the tenderness of a grandson ... He would be her companion in the barren years of old age; he would receive her pure love; they would suffer together; and he would give her his heart. He could not remain indifferent, because he was sure that God's Infinite Goodness would make the rest of Marcia's life extremely worthwhile ... If the Lord did grant his request, he was asking us to help him be faithful to his commitments from early childhood onwards; that we help him on days of temptation and weakness; that we forgive his rebelliousness and wrongdoings; and that, out of love for the trust that had brought us together, we should never, ever support him in any delving into noxious circumstances in the name of friendship.

Austere but sweet, he addressed brother Regis in particular, informing him that both sisters, Priscilla and Sara, were being prepared for the return to earth; that they would depart before he did; that he hoped to be able to leave his duties as director of the Institute in about six months in order to prepare for his own return; and that he longed for nothing else but to see Regis, with his experience and happiness, as the head of the institution.

None of us felt like breaking the silence. The doctors requested replacements to guarantee Beatriz's recovery. Speechless, Regis left with the supervisor of the File Department. Pedro approached his inert daughter, giving us the impression that he longed to isolate himself in order to meditate on the lesson. I found myself alone with the instructor. Looking at him as I had done the first time we met at Nemesio's house, I made an effort to compose myself while gazing at his imperturbable face. He was the same man, whom I did not know whether to love as a father or as a brother. He perceived my state of mind and embraced me. His firm and piercing look told me that he did not want me to be impressed, so I tried to control myself. Nevertheless, incapable of complete control, I lay my head on that shoulder that I had learned to venerate, but before I began to weep, I felt his right hand patting me on the shoulder, while at the same time, he asked me about my fluid-therapy class, which I should not skip.

We left together.

Outside, observing him walking erect and calm, I had the impression that the sun blazing in the sky was a message from Divine Wisdom encouraging us always to be loyal on our ongoing march towards the Light.

14

Having received an extension of my term at Almas Irmãs in order to further my studies, I stayed with Felix until he resigned as its director to start preparing for his new endeavors.

The instructor had chosen Casa da Providência to say farewell to the community.

When that day arrived, the doors of the building were opened early in the morning to everyone who wanted to say goodbye to their beloved instructor, who was considered a hero by all the residents at the Institute. Ministers from the city, admirers from neighboring places, representatives from several service organizations, all the authorities from the organization, friends, disciples, beneficiaries, and other colleagues coming from farther away – all gathered together there as brothers and sisters in a single vibration of gratitude and love.

Regis had been informed that the instructor would like to see the patients once more during his final hours of administrative activity, but realizing it would not be possible because of time constraints, he asked us to go to the patient wards and select those who were capable of attending the transference of powers without upsetting the endeavors at hand.

We chose two hundred who would not cause problems, and longing to highlight Felix's incessant dedication to these less fortunate brothers and sisters, Regis ordered that they should be seated in the first row of the auditorium as a silent homage to the man who loved them so dearly ... Nearly all of them were weak and trembling, symbolizing the vanguard of longing and suffering in that assembly and holding bouquets of flowers in their hands ... I was contemplating them tenderly when Felix finally arrived, exhibiting the firmness and serenity that marked his character. He sat down, serene, between the Minister of Regeneration, who represented the Governor, and brother Regis, who would replace him. However, as he looked around at the thousands of faces that filled entryways, halls, stairways and galleries, with the sickly sitting in front, Felix's own face displayed unfathomable emotion.

A choir of five hundred children's voices, prepared beforehand by grateful sisters, sang two hymns that transported us to the heights of sentiment. The first was entitled "God Bless You" and was sung as an offering from his older acquaintances. The second was "Come Back Soon, Beloved Friend!" and was a homage of reverence from his younger acquaintances. When the last chords of the orchestra – which had added extra beauty to the hymns – died away, two hundred patients paraded by Felix in the name of Almas Irmãs, giving his less fortunate brothers and sisters the joy of shaking his hand and offering him flowers.

The transfer of authority was very simple, with an exposition and reading of a text related to the change. With the transfer completed, the Minister of Regeneration, on the

Governor's behalf, embraced the brother who was leaving and invested Regis, who was staying.

The new director, in a voice of someone who was weeping inwardly, made a short speech, asking the Lord to bless the colleague about to reincarnate, while simultaneously wishing Felix vows of triumph in the endeavors he would undertake. Hesitant and humble, he ended by inviting Felix not only to speak, but also to continue as head of that Place, a right that he, Regis, deemed incapable of being transferred.

Extremely moved, the instructor stood up and, as if he did not have anything else to say to the institution that had benefited from more than fifty years of his work, he lifted his voice in prayer:

"O Lord Jesus, what more could I ask of you, when you have already given me everything, expressed in the devotion of my friends, who have surrounded me in the undeserved light of their love? Nevertheless, O Master, in placing myself under your blessing, I still have something to ask of you in faith! ... Now that new endeavors are calling me back to earth, please help me, in your mercy, so that I may be worthy of the trust and devotion of this place, where, for more than half a century, I have received the magnanimity and tolerance of all! ... Faced with this opportunity of taking on a new body on the physical plane in order to redeem my debts and to heal the old, internal wounds that I bear as a dreadful vestige of my transgressions, mercifully induce these friends listening to me now to help me with the benevolence with which they have always surrounded me so that I may not slide into new failures ... O Lord, bless us, and may you be glorified forever!"

Felix pronounced the last words, having difficulty overcoming the emotions he had tried to hide, but as if the firmament were immediately answering his prayer, friends from the higher realms, who were present for the occasion but invisible to us, made use of the spiritual energies of the entire audience and focused them on one purpose. An outpouring of luminous petals materialized, descending from the ceiling in waves of unforgettable fragrance and vanishing as soon as they touched our heads.

Expectations were continuing in moments of joyful silence, when a vehicle stopped at the entrance door. A woman dressed in light entered the auditorium.

Immediately, the entire audience stood up, including the Minister of Regeneration, who enveloped her in a look of profound reverence.

I hesitated, but just for a moment. Jubilant, I recognized her at once. She was Sister Damiana, a member of Nosso Lar's team of champions of charity in the darkness. Felix had kept a portrait of her in his home and was tied to her with strong bonds of affection ... The extremely modest benefactress had dressed herself in splendor – a splendor that had cost her many, many sacrifices – just to show the delight with which she had come there to receive and prepare that man, whom she loved as a son of her heart, for reincarnation.

....

Four years passed very quickly
Years of hope, effort, work, renewal...
Although I never forgot Felix, a number of instructors had requested that we keep away from his new mission for a while so that we would not be tempted to harm him with excessive pampering. Nevertheless, when I was least expecting it, brother Regis sent me a fraternal message informing me that the request had been lifted. Felix had overcome all the struggles of adjusting

to his new physical vessel. A few days later, Claudio, Percilia and Moreira, at work in Rio, kindly invited me, by means of a loving message, to come visit my unforgettable friend, whom everyone in Almas Irmãs surrounds with untiring affection even today.

Reliving moving memories, I went back to Flamengo; however, time had changed everything. A different family was now living in the old apartment. A discarnate friend, asked by Moreira, whom I had notified about my impending visit, kindly gave me the family's new address, explaining that Gilberto and Marina had had to sell the apartment a few months after Claudio's discarnation in order to meet legal matters related to his will. The family was living in Botafogo. I eagerly went there.

There are no words in human language to describe the happiness of that reunion. Claudio and Percilia were there. Moreira was out, working, and would arrive later. Thrilled by the balsamic vibrations I received from my spiritual hosts, I saw the couple talking to Justa, just as before, and I saw Marita once again, this time in the form of a cute little crybaby... Deeply moved I contemplated Felix, now called Sergio Claudio, in the rosy tenderness of a four-year-old. He had a temperament completely different from his sister's, and already demonstrated serenity and lucidity in his words and thoughts. I was completely speechless and did not know how to express my joy ... It really was him! ... Delighted, I discerned once again the flame in those unforgettable eyes, although it now shone in the body of a carefree child.

Claudio and Percilia informed me that Nemesio had returned to the spirit plane one year ago after horrible suffering. They said that veritable gangs of obsessors had been threatening the Botafogo apartment when the poor man was about to discarnate. Percilia, however, had joined the intercessory activity on his behalf in Almas Irmãs. Devoted friends had written petitions asking for compassion and mercy when they were informed that the Institute's Justice Department considered him subject to being banned for good. Former companions ardently mentioned the gestures of beneficence he had practiced while married to Beatriz, and also the three years of disease and paralysis that he had resignedly endured. In light of all these many efforts – which even brother Regis took part in after taking over from Felix, subordinating power to benevolence – the judges allowed the case to be reopened for further debate. Consequently, Casa da Providencia had sent two notaries to Botafogo to verify the accumulating petitions. However, they had arrived at the exact moment when Nemesio, partly discarnate, went mad when he saw his house surrounded by the unfortunate creatures that he had thoughtlessly nourished. Due to this unexpected twist, the judges, in a spirit of equity, ordered that he should remain insane for his own good. Moreover, their decision had been approved by Regis because it was the only way he could be protected against the fury of the discarnate evildoers, who were eager to conscript his vile concourse as soon as he vacated his dilapidated body. In light of this blessing, he had been admitted to a reputable asylum administrated by Almas Irmãs in a purgatorial region dedicated to works of renewal, and where he remained undergoing lengthy treatment, thus making it impossible for him to make any commitments to the Intelligences of darkness.

As for Marcia, she was sickly, but remained distant. She had never gone back to her family, despite Gilberto and Marina's tireless interest in regaining her trust. She would say she hated relatives. In spite of her illness, she drank and gambled in excess. Claudio emphasized the fact, however, that her children were waiting for the right time to introduce her to her grandchildren. And Percilia added that I had arrived exactly on the day before that promised attempt. On that Saturday morning, the couple had found out that, following doctor's orders, she went to Copacabana every day to lie on the sand and breathe the pure sea air. The very next day, Sunday, Gilberto and his wife had plenty of time for a new attempt at the hoped-for reconciliation. Claudio was invited to take part. He should rest there with them. He should wait.

We entertained ourselves for a long time discussing the wonders of life. Percilia compared the earthly existence to a priceless tapestry, of which the reincarnate spirit – the weaver of its own destiny – knows only the underside.

Later that night, Moreira arrived and added to our pleasant cordiality.

I yearned to approach Sergio Claudio in order to discern his state as a spirit during that phase of childhood. But I suppressed the impulse. While at Almas Irmãs, I had promised to do nothing in the name of love that might risk his tranquil evolution.

I used the peaceful moments to study, reflect, remember…

Early in the morning, we were at our work stations.

Marina, an early bird, got up at 6:00, and at 8:00, under Justa's supervision, the family gathered around the table for a light breakfast in preparation for some fun at the beach. Marita wanted to wear her green bathing suit and carry the cake tin. Sergio Claudio preferred ice cream.

Before going out, Marina, in a display of admirable maturity, considered the mission they had chosen. Sensing Claudio's spiritual assistance, she asked the two children to pray with her.

The little one stood up straight in the middle of the living room and recited the Lord's Prayer, accompanied by his sister, who, despite being older, only managed to stammer a word here and there.

Marina said to the boy:

"Son, recite the prayer I taught you yesterday."

"I don't remember it, mommy."

"Well, let's do it together again."

And looking up towards heaven, in that reverent posture we knew so well, he repeated each one of the words he heard from his mother's lips:

"Dear Jesus … we would ask you to bring Grandma … to come and live … with us…"

The small group, accompanied by us, got off the bus near the beach at 9:00 a.m. Splendid sunshine. Four discarnates, four incarnates.

So that Marcia would not prejudge their intentions, Gilberto and Marina decided to join the kids for a swim. Around them, hundreds of laughing bathers shared the permanent festival of nature. The bank clerk and his wife looked at each other knowingly, and then began searching here and there … They kept searching until they spotted Marcia in a bathing suit, lying under an umbrella. She looked sad and tired, although she managed to smile at her fun-loving band of friends.

Claudio, deeply moved, suggested that we envelop her in edifying memories of the past.

We approached her while Gilberto, Marina and the children walked towards her displaying a carefree attitude.

Under our influence, Claudio's widow inexplicably started to think of her daughter … Marina! Where might Marina be? How she missed her! … How painful their separation felt right now! How difficult her pathway had been since then! … Downcast, she remembered her home as it used to be … Claudio, Aracelia, her two daughters and Nemesio reappeared in her imagination as pictures of love and pain that she could never forget! … Was life really this bitter? And she asked her troubled soul if it had been worth it to live to old age in such loneliness…

Just then, she sensed the group approaching her; she stood up, startled, and recognized them. She looked at Marina, Gilberto and Marita in astonishment; however, the moment her eyes met Sergio Claudio's, she was enraptured. "Oh, my God! What a remarkable, beautiful child!" she exclaimed to herself.

The boy's mother whispered something in his ear. He let go of her hand and ran towards Marcia, shouting happily:

"Grandma, Grandma! … Grandma!"

Marcia automatically opened her arms to receive the small one that embraced her in a hug … The tiny heart beating against hers seemed like that of a bird of light that had descended from the skies to land on her sorrowful chest. She made a gesture as if she was about to kiss the child, but recondite impressions of happiness and anguish infused her with feelings of love and fear. Why did her grandson awaken such conflicting thoughts in her mind? However, before she could decide whether to continue embracing him or not, Sergio Claudio lifted his head from Marcia's bare shoulder and covered her face with kisses … There was not a strand of hair that he did not smooth with his tender fingers, nor a wrinkle he did not smother with his loving lips. Overwhelmed, Marcia greeted Gilberto and Marina, hugged the girl she was also meeting for the first time, and commented on her own health. When she remarked on how vivacious the children were, Marina asked her son to recite the "Grandma Prayer" he had repeated at home before going out.

Sergio, with the innate sense of the reverent attitude with which one should pray, got off Marcia's lap and stood up straight in front of her, planting his chubby little feet on the sand … And, closing his eyes to offer that manifestation of love, he repeated firmly:

"Dear Jesus, we would ask you to bring Grandma to come and live with us…"

Marcia burst into a flood of tears while the little one again looked for her arms that trembled with joy...

"What's this, Mom? You're crying?" Marina asked gently.

"Ah! Marina! ..." answered Marcia, holding her grandson against her chest, "I'm growing old!"

A little while later, she said goodbye to her beach friends, announcing that this Sunday she would be having lunch in Botafogo; however, inwardly she was certain she would never ever leave her daughter's residence again.

The boy had captured her heart.

I accompanied the group to the street. Gilberto, very happy, hailed a taxi. Claudio, Percilia and Moreira, who would be going with them, embraced me in celebration! I watched the car as it slid off in the direction of Lido and beyond...

Alone in spirit and facing the Sunday crowd, I allowed tears of tenderness and joy to roll down my face. I yearned to embrace those spontaneous, kindly people as they swam in the sea and played shuttlecock on the sand, practicing fraternity as part of the family of God...

Filled with profound emotion, I went back to the place where Marcia and her grandson had enjoyed their sublime reunion. To me, they symbolized the past and the present, weaving the future in the light of love that never dies. I kissed the ground where they had stood, and I prayed, asking the Lord to bless them for the lessons with which they had enriched me ... Of all those thousands of laughing reincarnate brothers and sisters, not one had the slightest notion of my worship of gratitude and hope. The sea, however, as if it had witnessed my feeble gesture, launched a broad veil of foam onto the patch of sand that I had kissed, as if it wanted to hold my gratitude and reverence forever in its waves, incorporating them into the powerful symphony that never ceases its endless praise and beauty.

Made in the USA
Middletown, DE
21 December 2019